NOT QUITE THE GENTLEMAN

by

Dale le Vack

Featuring the life and diaries of
Frank W Clarke
A fisherman at war

ORIGINAL WRITING

IN ASSOCIATION WITH CONFLICT BOOKS

978-1-907179-28-0

Book Cover Design by Andy Saxby, Stratford-upon-Avon
The Action at Elouges
Reproduced by kind permission of David Rowlands
Photographs reproduced by kind permission of
Royal Norfolk Regiment Museum, Norwich
Photographic reproduction by Elvin Derrick

Published by Original Writing Ltd., Dublin, 2009.

Printed in Great Britain by the MPG Books Group, Bodmin and King's Lynn

Dedicated to

The Norfolk & Cheshire Regiments

The 9th Lancers & 4th Dragoons

Heroes of

The Action at Elouges

24th August 1914

'We'll do it. What is it? (BEF)

Acknowledgments

While living on the Norfolk Broads with his wife Maud and three children Phyllis, Arthur and George in the early 1930s, my grandfather Frank Clarke, an ardent diarist, wrote nearly two hundred pages in his neat hand-writing describing his early life, war experiences and captivity. He sought a publisher, failed to find one and put them away in a drawer on the ground-floor of the house. In the following winter the house was flooded and the manuscript, personal letters and diaries were destroyed.

I learned enough from the old man while I was still a boy to write a reasonably accurate book in novel form about his life up to the end of the First World War. I have recreated his lost diaries and letters and retold his dreams about fishing which he was able to use to maintain his sanity while in solitary confinement in a prisoner of war camp. The result is an unusual and heroic war story, indeed a wartime romance and a series of adventures that take my grandfather to the depths of despair, including an unsuccessful suicide attempt and, I am happy to say, a fulfilling conclusion.

In 2007 my cousin Dale Clarke and his wife Cathy persuaded me - while I stayed with them and Georgie (Frank's great grandson) in St Erth, Cornwall - to use my imagination to recreate what had been lost so many years before. It was an inspired idea and I have had the pleasure over the past two years in carrying out research into the history of my own family.

Help and encouragement also came from Auntie Mary, cousins Douglas, Ally, Greg, Lorraine and April Clarke and my sister Annette Carr, who all provided family photographs and documents. My children Dominique, Zoe and James were of assistance in encouraging me through the process of writing a long book. Tutie, my wife, always showed great patience as I burned the midnight oil.

Thanks also to Bernie Devine for allowing me to stay at the Duke of Wellington in Norwich during my Norfolk research. Douglas and Bernie's pub is to be recommended to lovers of real ale and good company. Some of the customers at The Duke, notably Dick Barham, gave me valuable information about the history of Norwich and its market at the turn of the last century. I am grateful to Kelvin Browne a member of the historic City Club for my kind invitations to dine there.

An old friend and fellow writer Major Patrick Coulter, who saw service in Northern Ireland, kept me on a steady track with correct military terminology, protocols and the battlefield environment. I hope I haven't let him down too badly. Captain Mark Harrison, a serving officer in the British Army, was also generous in his time and assistance in providing pictures and information about Sennelager Camp where Frank was a prisoner in 1915 and 1916.

Frank Clarke's severe wound at Mons, in the age before antibiotics and modern treatment, presented me with a dilemma. Dr Simon Reid and Dr Rory Nicol - both long-time friends from Claverdon Rugby Football Club in Warwickshire agreed most kindly to read my draft manuscript and offer advice on how to avoid howlers.

Professional researcher Sarah Minney worked for me at the National Records Office in Kew, providing a stream of valuable information. The Regimental Museums of the Cheshires and the Norfolks provided a source of accurate historic information from regimental histories and diaries.

I should like to thank Kate Thaxton particularly of the Norfolk Regimental Museum in Norwich and Geoffrey J Crump of the Cheshire Military Museum in Chester for responding to my endless requests for information. Elvin Derrick, a colleague from Westward TV days who lives in Norfolk, helped with advice on the text and with taking wonderful photographs. He then did hours of painstaking work scanning and reproducing old prints which have enriched the book. Victoria Parnall-Vaughan kindly took the excellent photograph of Frank's childhood home in Islington and another professional photographer Tony Flanagan supplied the cover shot of me.

I was always grateful for the wise thoughts of Gordon Lang, another former colleague from newspaper days now living in Scotland, Robert Crick of Sidmouth and Andrew Webb of Sidbury, Devon, who give shrewd counsel.

My good Warwickshire friends Danny Keaney and Richard Hoyland helped me with fishing stories that filled blanks in my memory of the conversations I had with my grandfather as a child.

Designer Andy Saxby of Stratford-upon-Avon has done a stylish job with the dust jacket. I should also like to thank the war artist David Rowlands for generously allowing me to use the image of his painting of the Action at Elouges as an element of the dust jacket for the book.

I spent weeks trying to pin down exactly what rugby club in Ireland Frank Clarke had played for as a young man. A 1904/05 season representative cap has been in the family for more than 100 years. We turned our attention to Leinster and discovered that the cap belonged to one of Ireland's most historic clubs - Monkstown Football Club - based in what was then called Kingstown, the old ferry port, now DunLaoghaire. I am indebted to Tony Cody, the secretary of Monkstown Football Club, for all his help, especially in producing the team photograph which features in the book.

The book could not have been written without my drawing heavily upon two online publications, WithinFourWalls by Major M.C.C. Harrison and Captain H.A. Cartwright published by Ripping Yarns.com and Sixteen Months in Four German Prisons by Henry Charles Mahoney published by The Project Gutenberg.

They gave me a clear insight into conditions in WWI camps and the opportunities for escape. I have had to borrow from both for some of the story guidelines in my book which is now, I believe, the better for them.

Other books which were immensely valuable for reference and also inspiration were True World War I Stories (Robinson), MONS Retreat To Victory by John Terraine (Wordsworth Military Libtary), Mons 1914 by David Lomas (Osprey), Doings of the 15th Infantry Brigade by Brigadier General Count Edward Gleichen, The Fifth Division in the Great War by Brigadier-General A H Hussey and Major D S Inman (The Naval and Military Press), Military Operations France and Belgium 1914 (Imperial War Museum), Silent In An Evil Time by Jack Batten (Tundra Books), Edith Cavell, Pioneer and Patriot A E Clark Kennedy (Faber), Prisoners of the Kaiser by Richard Van Emden (Pen and Sword), The Cheshire Regiment In The Great War by Colonel Arthur Crookenden (N & M Press), The Royal Norfolk Regiment by Tim Carew (Royal Norfolk Regiment Association). Thanks to Osprey Publishing for licence to use photographic and an artist's work in this book.

There are so many other people that I should thank, including my literary agent Robert Dudley, and I can only ask you for your forgiveness if you have not been included in these acknowledgements.

This horrific collection of bayonet charges and hand-to-hand fighting in the early weeks of the War may owe more to the imagination of the artist than to reality. The scenes may have been inspired by the Government's agenda to inculcate a sense of patriotism among the British people.

However, it is widely believed that British infantry regiments of the BEF - all highly trained regular soldiers - did strike fear into the heart of the enemy by the elan displayed in their bayonet charges and skill at arms in hand-to-hand fighting in 1914, along with a superb level of marksmanship.

They were professional soldiers who were serving in the Army because they wanted to be.

CONTENTS

Frank W Clarke

SCENE SETTER

Dear Mother,

I do hope my dear thing you have forgiven me for taking this step and for embarrassing you socially in Norfolk, but joining the Army as a common soldier satisfies your youngest boy and I do not crave to be an officer like James. I am not disappointed about failing the Commission Board. Perhaps I am none too ambitious and would ask forgiveness for that. Maybe I shall tire of soldiering after a few years and return to civilian life.

Besides, I am having many adventures. As you know The Royal Family has a close association with the Norfolks because of the estate at Sandringham. In February 1907, before I joined up, the London Gazette published a notice announcing that the King was going to become the Colonel-in-Chief of the Regiment but after that it all went quiet.

We were told on parade by our colonel that the 1st Battalion had been detailed to furnish a detachment for duty at the Tower of London. I was ordered to be part of that detachment along with other private soldiers and junior NCOs who stood around six feet in height.

By coincidence it was arranged that the King would present his colours to the Battalion in the grounds of Buckingham Palace on Friday June 4th but the presentation was postponed till the next day because of bad weather.

As the ground was still soft and wet on the Saturday, the King decided to make the presentation in the state ball-room of the Palace. We were paraded at the Tower - around 500 of us, about half the battalion; three companies from Gravesend and headquarters' company from Warley. We marched to Wellington Barracks leaving our rifles there, as the ceremony was to be indoors.

It was an incredible experience to be in Buckingham Palace. We formed up on three sides of the ball-room with the regimental band occupying the gallery. Half an hour later at noon the King and

Queen Alexandra entered the ball-room, followed by the Prince of Wales, Princess Victoria and the Duke of Connaught. Then the old King mounted a dais to address the Battalion and of course it was the first time any of us had ever heard his voice.

What astonished us was that he did not have an English accent but sounded quite German. I think that rather shook many of us and when during the inspection we heard the voices of some of the other members of the Royal Family it seemed that many of them spoke in a similar way to the King. It wasn't the clipped tone of the British upper classes. They spoke English with a rolling tongue that sounded foreign.

It was a day of pomp and ceremony - but my over-riding memory of it was when Queen Alexandra walked past us. I noticed that her white collar, which was loose, needed a good scrub – it really was quite grubby. Of course, I couldn't move my head and follow her as she went by, but as luck would have it she paused for a few moments right in front of me to exchange a few words with the escorting officer.

She certainly wouldn't have passed muster. I think her dresser should have been charged with negligence or some offence like it. I was told later by some well connected friends in Dublin that the Queen is self-conscious about a scar on her neck that she's had since childhood and she hides it by wearing high choker necklaces and dresses with high necklines.

Last week we also saw the Prince of Wales at Aldershot when we furnished the Guard of Honour on the King's arrival and he walked by during the inspection only a few feet away from me in the front rank.

I remember thinking that he was just a nipper in height compared to many of us, but he looked extremely distinguished with his black moustache and naval officer's bearing. So you see life is never boring here Mother.

You may be pleased to know I am now playing cricket for the Battalion – I am also in the athletics team - for which I get extra time off and the chance to socialise with many different types.

Your loving son

Frank W Clarke

"Go ask Miss Gracewood for a cup of tea boy," he said directing the lad to the lock-keeper's cottage one hot day in the summer of 1953. She was an eccentric old woman with grey hair that fell uncombed and dirty below her shoulders. The village boys played pranks upon her. As a result she was defensive and suspicious with strangers, but his charm, when he had visited the lock every day in the previous week to bait the swim in his quest for a specimen fish, had won her round. She reasoned, somewhere in her fog of confusion, that Mr Clarke was a gentleman with his mellifluous voice and winning smile, especially when he doffed his trilby in greeting as she stood outside her cottage.

The tall man with his commanding voice reminded her of the leading actors of her day. She had performed with most of them on stage at the Shakespeare Memorial Theatre in the early years of the century, including Sir Frank Benson. Dear Frank had never recovered from losing his beloved son on the Somme in 1916.

In this new and youthful Elizabethan post-war age, Miss Gracewood was a forgotten thespian, a once striking woman with a dark countenance and resonant voice that had gripped audiences. Her Ophelia had been reviewed in the London Times in 1926. She had also been a stage actress in Australia in the 1930s.

Now she filled a chipped cup for the apprehensive boy from the kettle on her coal range - which she kept alight all year. She offered him a ginger biscuit but he recoiled in disgust. The room smelled of piss. Through the open bedroom door he could see several cats lying on the old woman's bed. It did not look as though the bed had been made for many weeks, or its sheets washed.

Miss Gracewood was lonely and reduced to the role of playing a demented hag to the village boys. They talked of how the old woman smelt of urine, sometimes shouted without reason at passing fishermen, and shrieked at the cowman when he directed his herd of Friesians along the towpath to the meadow above the cottage. There were those in the village who muttered the old woman was probably dabbling in witchcraft, a rumour heightened by sightings of her inside her cottage completely naked reciting the prayers of the devil.

The truth was more mundane. Once a month Miss Gracewood would fetch water from the well 200 yards from the cottage, pour the contents of the bucket into a copper saucepan and place it over the coal range. She would then remove all her clothes and put them in the boiling water. Miss Gracewood felt uninhibited walking around her home naked, alone with her thoughts and memories of stage triumphs at Stratford-upon-Avon and many other theatres across the Empire. The prayers of the devil were lines from Shakespeare.

When, on the third day of his visit to the lock to bait the swim by the cottage at Yarningale Common on the Stratford-upon-Avon canal, the well spoken man was offered a cup of lukewarm brown liquid in a filthy china cup, he consumed it with gratitude. Years in a prisoner-of-war camp had broadened the old soldier's outlook upon what was consumable and what was not.

In the decades after the Second World War the Stratford-upon-Avon Canal was not navigable. The lock-keepers' cottages had been sold off, the lock-gates were crumbling, the reedy banks untended, and the waterway itself was choked with indigenous weeds, especially lilies, which in summer created an insect buzzing vista, magically enhanced by darting kingfishers which thrived there. The canal was a prolific fishery harbouring tench, bream, roach and perch. During the winter months it provided excellent sport for pike. Anglers cherished the fishery, which provided a sheltered environment for specimen fish, away from the boat traffic that had diminished sport on local rivers like the Warwickshire Avon.

The boy handed his grandfather the cup of tea and stood beside him.

"What will you catch?" he asked as the old man threaded a large lob worm onto a nylon cast with a size 14 hook three and a half feet below a red quill float. He pulled sufficient line off the wooden star-back centre pin, and flicked the 12-foot cane rod forward towards the end of the lock gate. Water gushed through a fracture in the timbers causing a perceptible current which flowed towards the bank where tall reeds stood sentinel. The float landed at the side of the lock gate and settled there until the current carried it forward laboriously towards the far bank, with the worm just trailing above the mud bed of the canal.

"I think we might find a big perch if we are patient and quiet," he murmured. The minutes ticked past. As they watched the float together, the old man's mind moved to other times in his life and he recalled another canal thirty nine years before, when he had been a regular soldier.

Senior officers realised by the early morning of 23rd August 1914 that the coming battle at Mons was not going to be what the allied strategists had planned for. One way or another, the British Expeditionary Force was likely to pay a high price for being in the wrong place at the wrong time. However, this bleak prospect hardly dimmed the euphoria among the rank and file of soldiery, as the 15th Infantry Brigade of 5th Division, II Corps moved into their positions in the hot sun.

Belgian miners had dug shallow trenches, or shell scrapes, each large enough to hold four men. The deep trenches that symbolised the four years of the First World War on the Western Front would be dug in later weeks during the autumn of 1914 when the armies reached a state of stalemate.

In the opening weeks it was all mobile warfare. The Brigade's part of the line, stretching nearly three miles, ran along a railway embankment and was about a mile and a half behind the forward positions, held by other infantry regiments along the Mons-Conde canal. This reserve line was held by soldiers of the 1st Battalions of the Norfolk, Cheshire, Bedford and Dorset Regiments.

Frank recalled - as he ate bully beef and biscuits with the men of his platoon soon after they arrived in the line - that the soldiers at Holywood Barracks in Belfast had been in high spirits throughout July 1914, as the war rumours circulated. He reckoned now they would certainly get what they had been craving for and what they were paid to do.

You couldn't blame them for that, but he had joined the Army for the benefits of peacetime soldiering, and although he always accepted that real fighting might be around the corner, he did not relish killing. The men had been bored with policing Irish unrest. They were mainly English country boys and did not give a fig for Irish nationalism or the political complexities surrounding the issue of Home Rule.

The rank and file of the Norfolks hankered after soldiering in the traditional sense. The older regulars were hard men, in top physical condition, well trained and for the most part fine marksmen. Off-duty many were hardened drinkers often in trouble with the military police in Belfast. They were also fiercely loyal to their "muckers" and ready to fight anyone, confident they would get the better of the Germans if the odds were anything like even. When the reservists began drifting back, the rumours of a coming war were deemed to be true.

These reservists were much older soldiers – some with service in the Boer War - who still had an obligation to serve in times of emergency. The reservists constituted as many as 400 men out of the battalion strength of just over 1,000. In many infantry battalions the ratio was even higher. Experience counted in their favour but few of these much older men were physically fit – many more were unfamiliar with the Lee Enfield rifle which they would be required to fire accurately at up to 15 rounds a minute.

During the summer of 1914 recruits and reservists went on arduous route marches, practiced at the butts, were inoculated in preparation for going overseas, and experienced the throbbing arms and aching heads which were the aftermath of anti-typhoid injections. It was a tough assault course upon the body.

They had to be ready to fight in just a few weeks. As it turned out they were better than the Germans man for man when the time came, but few of the 160,000 regular British soldiers of 1914 would survive the four year conflict. It wasn't all over by Christmas - as the politicians and generals had hoped and expected. It turned out to be the most terrible war in human history...and one that destroyed the best young men of an unfortunate generation.

Frank "Nobby" Clarke had originally led a pukka sniper section in E (headquarters) company, and had been a member of the Battalion's skill at arms team in the peacetime years. Shortly before mobilisation he was transferred to a rifle platoon on D Company which had a large preponderance of young soldiers in it.

Perhaps they thought the old fart would be a father figure. He passed on his skills to both the elderly reservists and the teenage rookies who had joined the colours during the early months of 1914. There was not much he could do about fitness in such a short time and he hoped they would not be faced with long forced marches into, or away from combat. However, he could teach them to shoot and use the bayonet.

"I'm going to teach you tossers to use this dagger on the end of your rifle aggressively - like the heathen you really are," he barked at them, a group of raw recruits with nicknames like Tinker, Gaz, Cocker and Baz. They practised the drills for three or four hours a day and at the end of it most complained that the bayonet would be better used for chopping wood, opening cans, and even hanging up clothes. Frank laughed too, because he also recognised the limitations of the bayonet. He explained that in hand to hand fighting they couldn't fire their rifle at random because it was not a good idea to shoot people on their own side.

He taught them that the target areas of the body were the throat, the chest on the upward thrust and downwards to the groin – but conceded that the better option at close quarters would probably be the other end of the rifle; using the butt as a club. Stabbing another soldier in the chest or groin, he warned, could present problems of withdrawal.

"Best way is to put your boot on his chest, fire off a round and pull hard. But in that split second you leave yourself vulnerable to attack from some-where else," he warned. They listened to it all and approached the training in Belfast with enthusiasm. In fact the young soldiers bayoneted and clubbed the stuffed sacks hanging from poles with exaggerated ferocity.

The people of Belfast turned out in their thousands waving handker-chiefs and cheering - as the transports warped out of Belfast docks and moved slowly down the channel. The weather was fine, the sea was calm on the passage and the men slept out in the open on the packed upper decks of their ship.

On the early evening 16th August the Brigade arrived at Le Havre. He stood on the deck of his troopship, the S.S. Massillia, as she sailed into port. He had his kit and his Lee Enfield rifle with him and stood tall among the men of his platoon, many of whom regarded him as a reassuring presence. The youngest recruits had been sent back to depot in Norwich to continue their training and would not reach France until 1915. Reservists made up the gaps in the ranks.

He stroked his waxed moustache with its Kaiser Bill twist as the ship came alongside the quay. They watched in amazement. The crowds were large and wildly enthusiastic. Some people were waving the Tricolor, oth-ers the Union flag. They were even more excited than the Irish crowds in Belfast had been two days before.

"Crikey Sarge, you'd think we've already beaten the Hun to look at that lot!" said Private Ralph Colby, a 19-year-old from North Walsham whose father was the landlord of the Red Lion and a former regular sol-dier in the Norfolk Regiment in the 1890s.

"Enjoy it while you can Colby – these people actually like us. Pretty soon we'll be meeting up with thousands of blighters who want to blow our heads off," he laughed.

The cheering continued as the Battalion, led by its band, marched through the town in the sunshine to rest camp number eight on a steep hill above the town six miles away. They were plied with cups of wine, chocolates and fruit. It had been pouring with rain onshore for two days, so the ground where they were to encamp was waterlogged. The camp was not easy to find in the dark, especially as the sketch-maps with which the officers had been issued were grossly inadequate.

Adding to these difficulties, a motor-lorry broke down on the way up the hill and blocked the rest of the Brigade's transport for the night. Most military planners considered the internal combustion engine far inferior to the horse. The Battalion camps were dotted on the open fields at some distance from each other and pitched in no particular order, so that by the time the troops finally encamped, it was about 2300 hours. There was no baggage, nor anything for the men to sleep on except the bare ground. The officers used their saddle as a pillow. He was woken at 0200 hours by his platoon commander Lieutenant Briard who told him dozens of horses had stampeded.

They had torn up their picketing-pegs from the soft ground and disappeared into the darkness in different directions. Briard had more unwelcome news. It would be the job of his platoon to find them.

"Sarnt Clarke organise a section to join in the hunt for the animals. The CO mentioned you particularly – apparently he buys excellent unbroken horses for his estate off your relatives in London."

He added with a hint of good natured sarcasm: "You should use your inherited family knowledge to find those animals. Select a party to go with you – and make sure they are used to being with horses."

"Of course Mr Briard," he said politely in front of the men. "Leave it to us, Sir."

He didn't mind the jibe because Ernest Briard, a Jerseyman, had been a member of the battalion cricket and hockey teams for several years. They had enjoyed many pints together.

He chose a section and issued them with halters before they set off blindly into the pitch dark swearing profusely at their luck while others were allowed to sleep. They roamed the dark lanes carrying lanterns without success seeing nothing but terrified rabbits and the occasional fox, until a wagon was brought up carrying a light.

Some of the horses were now being rounded up individually and some had strayed collectively to nearby villages. It wasn't until shortly before dawn that Private Arthur "Tinker" Elsiegood, using the searchlight to illuminate a large paddock, discovered most of the Battalion's horses grouped at the far end of it. They had befriended a number of local shire horses who were grazing there.

The sun was rising on the horizon before the section got back to their tent. They soon fell asleep, oblivious to the arduous job now facing others. The CO ordered that the remaining transport should be brought up a steep and narrow road which was the only alternative to the blocked one.

Some of the horses jibbed – they were still excited by their escape - and it took two platoons from each company to bring up supplies by hand from the now abandoned motor vehicles.

The job done by shortly after midday, the Battalion was settled down and expecting to spend another night in Le Havre. The NCOs were hoping to find time for a trip to the town later in the evening. Everyone seemed to be in a party mood there. At 1415 hours that expectation was shattered when the Battalion received orders to move off by train that night.

The French army had already moved into Belgium and was waiting for the BEF with considerable impatience. The Brigade started to move at midnight from three different stations. The first train carrying the Norfolks left its station shortly before dawn and the platoons of D Company were aboard the front cattle trucks which were laid out with clean straw.

The locomotive, pulling two passenger carriages for the officers and 18 livestock trucks for the men, horses and mules, laboured at 15 miles an hour as it rattled through the countryside making slow but steady passage across the flat agricultural expanse of northern France. They would stop at Rouen for coffee, sardines and French bread and then later in the journey, they would halt again at Amiens.

The men of the platoon were comfortable. The sun had not yet risen to give heat to the day, and the soldiers needed warmth to sleep. He closed the sliding door until later in the morning. Gradually the chatter and the singing subsided and they settled down to take rest.

"Come on lads, let's get some kip," he told them.

He laid down his rifle and rested his head upon the kitbag – breathing in the fresh air from the countryside. Then he turned on his stomach and wrote an entry in his diary. He had kept one since he was an adolescent and was meticulous in keeping it up to date. In particular it recorded his adventures and expeditions as an Edwardian fisherman in Ireland, Norfolk and other parts of England from the turn of the century. He finished writing and fell into a disturbed sleep.

Someone tapped on his shoulder an hour later. Half turning he expected it to be Walter the gamekeeper on the Bandon Estate, near Cork, but it was Ralph, the youngest member of his platoon and his unofficial batman offering him a mug of tea and bully beef and biscuits.

It was already dawn, and he realised he was back on the troop train heading towards Belgium and the Kaiser's Imperial army.

"I was in the middle of a dream Colby. A bloody great sea trout on a river in Ireland – but I didn't land it thanks to you!" Ralph held the older man in awe and had become his self-appointed batman.

"Sorry sarge, but I thought you'd better have this. There won't be any more scoff until 1200 hours."

"Yeah, OK thanks," he yawned. The troop train, travelling barely at walking pace, was passing over a steel bridge – a wide and muddy river below the girded steel structure meandered slowly westwards towards the sea. Someone said it was called the Somme.

1914

War broke: and now the winter of the world
With perishing great darkness closes in.
The foul tornado, centred at Berlin,
Is over all the width of Europe whirled,
Rending the sails of progress. Rent or furled
Are all Art's ensigns. Verse wails. Now begin
Famines of thought and feeling. Love's wine's thin.
The grain of human autumn rots down-hurled.
For after Spring had bloomed in early Greece,
And summer blazed her glory out with Rome,
An autumn softly fell, a harvest home,
A slow grand age, and rich with all increase.
But now, for us, wild winter, and the need
Of sowings for new spring, and blood for seed

Wilfrid Owen

He was wakened by the lurching of the train as it slowed on the approach to a station and then came to a shuddering halt where food was taken on board. Once again Ralph stood over him with another mug of tea, and French bread stuffed with sardines.

"It's 1200 hours sarge. Apparently we're resting up here so the rest of Division can catch up, before moving on to Le Cateau. You are due to be at an O Group meeting at 1630 hours in the front carriage. There'll be no more scoff till tonight."

"Thanks Colby. I feel refreshed now – I had a good nap," he said rubbing his eyes. "By the way have you written to your folk in the last few days?"

He added: "Cos if you haven't you should do it now because it's the right thing to do with a battle coming up. You know, take no chances with fate."

The private soldier looked at him and said with a worried look on his face: "What do you make of it Sarge? I couldn't sleep myself."

He noticed the anxious faces of younger men.

"Get a letter or field card off when you can. Don't put if off. You don't want them worried about you eh? One other thing, the Boche won't be waiting for us conveniently up the road near Le Cateau when we get off the train. I'm anticipating a long route march in hot weather before we reach our positions, probably somewhere over the Belgian border.

"Not everyone is as fit as he should be, so do everything to prepare for that march. All spare socks should be darned and blisters treated to harden the skin. Replace dirty bandages and work on those new boots with grease to get the leather as soft as possible. One other thing – make sure you are all carrying sufficient field dressings – they're not for anyone else but you!"

Two hours later Captain Robert Brudenell Bruce, OC of B Company and Captain Eddie Snepp OC of D Company convened the orders general meeting. Bruce looked at the officers and senior NCOs who faced him in the railway carriage at the front of the train. He was a tall slim fair-haired man, six feet in height with a clipped upper class accent that commanded attention from its audience. Assembled around Bruce and Snepp were the officers and senior NCOs who comprised their immediate family in the regimental sense of the word.

These were the men with whom the two officers had lived and trained in Aldershot, the Curragh, and Belfast since the Battalion returned from Blomfontein in South Africa in 1907. The rank and file respected their officers, and this trust was mutual. There would be no doubting an officer's word when the fighting started and the years of training kicked in.

Frank stood next to Lieutenant Ernest Briard, a sandy-haired Jerseyman of 25. Ernest had been with the Norfolks since leaving Sandhurst, and before that at Felsted, a public school in Essex. He was also an old boy of Jersey's Victoria College. Frank admired him for his deep concern for the men, and his ordinariness. The lieutenant and the sergeant shared a similar educational background and off duty enjoyed one another's company, especially as cricketers.

Bruce began his briefing: "Gentlemen, The CO has asked me to tell you that everything we have done as a Battalion since returning from overseas seven years ago will be put to the test in the coming days. Following the surrender of the Liege Forts by the Belgians, the Boche is now deep into their territory and pushing relentlessly towards Brussels.

"The Belgian Army is retreating north west to its forts at Antwerp under the command of King Albert and the national government is also believed to have taken shelter there. Our presumption is that the Belgian High Command will eventually find a way to link up with the Allied armies."

He paused before continuing: "Unfortunately the news from the French is not good either. The fifth French Army at Namur has been pushed back. The BEF has the task of moving into Belgium to meet the German Army – but for the moment we do not know where their forward elements are, or what their specific strategy is going to be."

He now searched the faces around him: "It could turn out that the weight of the German advance will fall upon the British Expeditionary Force. We think, but cannot confirm, that our job in the next few days will be to get into Belgium, dig in and wait for the enemy to engage us. The French need to consolidate their reserves and get themselves into a position where they can mount a sustained counter attack. The logistics of moving two army corps (75,000 men) forward into Belgium along a primitive road and rail network are going to be difficult. The next three days will be spent at Le Cateau in preparation for our march into Belgium over some of the roughest cobbled roads in Northern Europe. Our target will be to reach Mons before noon on August 22nd. We will be covering nearly 40 miles in two stages."

Frank thought to himself "Christ, that'll be tough, the men will be carrying 120lbs in kit, 200 rounds of ammunition plus their rifle and entrenching spade etc...."

Brudenell Bruce continued: "Companies will stop briefly every hour for 10 minutes to take water. The strict ration will be one pint of water per man at these stops, no resting once it has been taken. Rations will be eaten every eighth hour – one hour to cook and brew up. At 2200 hours we will halt at Gommignies and bivouac for five hours. At 0300 hours the march will continue – so Brigade can take advantage of the cooler conditions. Afternoon temperatures are forecast to be in excess of 80 degrees fahrenheit.

"This will be tough. Some of the older reservists may not make it. They will be left where they fall. Military police will deal with exhausted men who cannot continue. The MPs will also provide route indicators to each platoon."

Frank caught the glance of CSM Fred Mather. He was the oldest serving NCO in the Regiment at 39 years of age, who had seen service in both

India and the Boer War. Fred whispered in Frank's ear: "Poor bloody infantry!"

Fred knew that some of the reservists would not be up to the punishing ordeal prescribed by the OC. Nobby could even name one or two of those in his platoon who would not make it all the way to Mons, let alone be in a physical condition to fight a critical battle when they got there.

The troop train arrived at Le Cateau at 1730 hours and de-trained the horses in half an hour. The smell of horseshit from the carriages carrying the animals was overpowering and the grooms were glad to get them off the train, watered, scrubbed and fed. In the army of 1914 the only antidote to the ubiquitous stink of horseshit was the strong and fresh aroma of saddle soap and polished leather.

The Battalion marched off to its billet in Pommereuil, a small village. Under Frank's supervision the men set about preparing their kit, darning socks, and tending to any minor injuries sustained in training. Every rifle was cleaned and checked, and bandoliers filled with 200 rounds of .303 ammunition. Company commanders had agreed to spend two of the days ahead improving the fitness of the older reservists. They would organise route marches for these soldiers and platoon corporals would accompany them. Frank got busy on his diaries and letters home and later fell into a deep sleep in which his whole life seem to roll out before him.

A FECKLESS YOUNG MAN – DIARY APRIL 1905

Henry Jocelyn Clarke sighs and looks with disapproval at me before turning to gaze through the window of the study. He is a Norwich man, son of the landlord of the Grapes Hotel, and has done well. He now runs the New York Insurance Company's interest in Ireland and is well known in Dublin. I am already 22 and have not yet chosen a career. Henry once held high hopes that at least one of his three sons would inherit his own industrious sense of purpose. I am a disappointment to him.

He tells our mother Anna we seem to lack what he calls 'substance.' Henry is an ambitious man yearning to improve his social standing in a hierarchical society.

'Life is all about having means Frank. You are throwing your grandfather's money away recklessly on racecourses as if you have enough to last forever. If you spend your inheritance you will have nothing left.'

'I do realise that father,' I say meekly as I watch Henry make out a cheque for one hundred guineas, wishing it was for twice as much. I have taken a big hit on a fancied horse at the Curragh and won't use that tipster again.

'This is the last occasion I intend to bail you out, so buckle down, get a job and take life more seriously. It's all very well playing rugby football for Monkstown Rugby Club, but it doesn't pay the bills.'

He hands me the cheque. 'Spend less time gambling, less time fishing and less time playing rugby. That goes for cricket too. OK?'

'I promise father. We are in the semi-finals of the Leinster Senior Cup, you know that - and I'm not going to miss out on that game. But I shall retire after the final if we reach it and not play the 1905/6 season.

'As a matter of fact our skipper H J Millar has introduced me to a man who wants me to go out to East Africa and work in his trading company as a manager. I see it as my best chance to acquire some capital and come back here with a future.'

'What kind of trading company?' enquires Henry, his eyes narrowing in suspicion at what he anticipates will be some idiotic scheme cooked up by my rugby-playing friends in a bar in Dublin.

'There are Arab traders in the shanty cities on the Indian Ocean who have exotic spices from the East Indies and there are white farmers growing chilli spices in East Africa.

Others are trying to grow coffee. They won't risk shipping their produce to Europe if they can get a good price locally. So we can buy low there and sell high in London.

'I don't know much more than that, but it seems like a good way to do business and without too much risk providing there is safe passage of the cargo. So we'll need insurance which perhaps is where you can also help us.'

"Mmm," says Henry. 'And who will pay your passage to that God forsaken part of the planet? I have read it's full of heathen natives who have no civilized customs, what's more the Arabs are completely untrustworthy and a murderous bunch of blighters.'

I ignore my father's baleful assessment of life in the East African Protectorate.

'I shall work my ticket on a cargo ship bound for South Africa. It will take some months, but the pay I receive from the shipping line will meet my needs until I reach East Africa and then I'll be in the pay of Mr Trimble's company.

'I shall save until I can use my capital to take a stake in a cargo going back to England. From then on, I expect it'll take five or six years to accumulate sufficient capital to return here and start up a trading company using the business contacts I've made overseas.'

'Well I salute your adventurous spirit – and good luck to you. But it sounds fraught with risks – health risks to start with…

I interrupt: "I want to see the world. James had his adventures in the Boer War and has settled down in Dublin. I'm not content with that."

'Hmph,' says Henry Clarke and picks up a newspaper to read. The interview is over.

I pocket the cheque and on the way through the house kiss mother on the cheek before taking a cab to Murphy's Bar in Kingstown. The team is there and the excitement growing among the supporters of Monkstown RFC in anticipation of the

Leinster Cup game against Lansdowne which has been written up in the newspapers. The club nearly won the trophy in 1902 and with several Irish internationals in the side we fancy our chances this season.

The 1st XV has won all of its matches except for two and we have already defeated Lansdowne earlier in the season. I am first choice on the right wing and have a turn of speed which many say might get me an Irish trial in the coming season if I stick around. I have already decided to hang up my boots and turn my attention to business.

BEST LAID PLANS – DIARY JULY 1905

I was supposed to link up with Frederick Trimble, the Belfast merchant to whom I had been introduced at the rugby club – and who offered me the opportunity of work with his import-export company.

I arrived in Mombasa and spent two days looking for Trimble, his office being empty and stripped of all furniture. I was eventually told that I'd missed him by three weeks. Frederick Trimble is bankrupt. He lost all his capital when the ship carrying his cargo of coffee to Liverpool sank in a storm.

So here I am stranded in the Dark Continent of Africa with about 100 guineas and little else except for a suitcase. Mombasa is hot, humid and dangerous. There are many rough whites around who made their way up from the Cape after the Boer War looking for easy pickings off gullible newcomers.

One morning I stroll around the Portuguese Fort Jesus in the harbour absorbed in my thoughts, not looking where I am going. I walk straight into a European police officer. The policeman, Charles Rimington, is angry until he realises he's collided with a white man – then he asks questions.

The upshot is that Rimington meets me later that evening in the Mombasa Cricket Club and I am introduced to several senior officers. It becomes clear gradually this is no affable conversation.

I am being interviewed for a job. I think to myself 'Why not! The alternative is the risk of becoming penniless.'

BASIC TRAINING – DIARY SEPTEMBER 1905

I have done four week's basic training at the Mombasa barracks of the 3rd Battalion, King's African Rifles, and am posted to Nairobi along with Charles Rimington. We travelled there by train through the African bush. The line has to cross the waterless Taru Plain, and then the Tsavo – a river where thousands of animals congregate to drink. It is my first glimpse of Africa's exotic wild life and I am mesmerized by what I see, smell and hear.

There in front of my eyes from the window of the carriage is just about every tropical species I've ever read about; lions, elephants, gazelle, buffalo, zebras and rhinos. The railway will be 576 miles long from Mombasa in the east to Port Florence on the shores of Lake Victoria when it is completed.

It is a testimony to the engineering skill of the British and the hard work of Indian coolies who do the physical work. It crosses the mountains, gorges, valleys, desert, great rivers and swamps of the Rift Valley. Disease kills many of the Indian labourers.

Yet the building of that railway has been a defining moment in the history of East Africa. I think to myself 'you are lucky bugger' and dream of an idyllic existence on patrol in the Aberdare Mountains, Mount Kenya, the Rift Valley and other far flung places.

INTO BATTLE - DIARY OCTOBER 1905

Unfortunately, I have been suckered - within hours of arriving in Nairobi I discover why they were so interested in recruiting me. A joint military and police expedition is being planned into the Rift Valley to punish the dissident Nandi tribe. The warriors wear ostrich plumes, grow their hair long in dreadlocks and carry spears with poisoned tips.

They have been in open rebellion since 1895 and have already killed several whites and many Askaris. These natives are so ferocious to intruders that white settlement in the west of the Rift Valley is being held up. Both the police and army units are critically short of white officers to take part in punitive raids against them.

Koitalel Arap Samoei is their leader and he exercises power over his warriors because he is an Orkoiyot, a diviner. The Orkoiyot are the most powerful of witch doctors with supernatural powers. Samoei detests our invasion into his lands and the railway. He apparently prophesied that a black snake would tear through Nandiland, spit fire and usurp tribal life.

He believes his tribe must kill or starve out the Indian coolies who are building it and ambush supplies brought up for them by rail. The Nandi also hate rival tribes, especially the Kikuyu.

In the absence of the rule of law – yet to be established by the colonial administration – they terrorize and murder other tribes robbing them of their cattle. Now an expedition is planned to round up all the various clans and exile them to a reservation.

The Orkoiyot and his Nandi people believe they can stop further British infiltration. They know the forests and the hills are difficult to supply and think that because Arab slave trading caravans were seen off earlier in the 19th century, they can drive off the whites too.

I find myself as an officer in the expedition to bring Koitalel Arap Samoei to heel. Wish me luck.

Officers of the 1st Battalion Norfolk Regiment shortly before the outbreak of the First World War in August 1914.

The men who held Commissions in county infantry regiments in Britain's peacetime army were largely drawn from the landed gentry and such families supplied officers to their county regiment for successive generations. The high casualty rate among officers during the early years of WWI meant that far more men drawn from the middle classes - with a grammar school education - were commissioned, breaking the cycle.

It was a long held notion right up to modern times that British rank and file infantrymen preferred to be led by gentlemen.

Courtesy of Royal Norfolk Regimental Museum, Norfolk Museums and Archaeology Service.

I
THE TRUSTED SERGEANT

The forest is alive with game and the sound of birdsong. The earthy scents blend with the fresh cool air filling his lungs. He leads the column on foot in well dispersed file, followed by four mules carrying ammunition, water and food. There has been a dramatic change in climate from thousands of feet below. Herds of elephant, buffalo, lions and rhinos also move unhindered from the sun scorched plains, sheltering within the mountain's shadow.

For two days the column of 30 Askaris, and 10 porters have followed forest tracks in the trail of wild animals that roam the passes of the mountain, leaving spoor, hoof and paw print along the way. The soldiers sense they are not alone.

Occasionally warriors call out in a strange tongue, having slowed their ascent to be abreast of the column, but still they do not attack. The column climbs gradually higher towards the escarpment. When they reach the beginnings of the forest, after crossing the plains of the Rift Valley, he follows Benjamin's advice and orders the men to walk in silence—which heightens the sense of foreboding. Some of the native policemen understand the language of the tribesmen and it is hoped the column might glean some indication of their plans from the calls in the forest.

The slopes are covered in giant Abysinnicus trees, with long distinctive beards that drift on the breeze. In the shadow of these trees, patches of wild berries are growing, attracting monkeys whose calls are relentless and monotonous. The thick undergrowth is dotted with blazing colours of gladioli and bright red flowers.

"My God, I would want to come here in my leisure—not under threat of an arrow through my throat or a spear through my heart," he thinks to himself. As the Commander of the raiding party he has to make sure he looks confident. He does not feel it. Breaking above the tree-line of the forest, the column passes through expanses of giant heather—the plants grow increasingly large as the altitude increases.

Surprisingly, the tribesmen do not use this as the cover from which to launch an ambush upon the column. Every now and then a salvo of arrows is fired at them but no one has been killed. The intensity of the volley of rifle fire which is returned in the direction from which the arrows are shot discourages enemy activity.

The heather eventually gives way in the higher altitude to bog land on steep slopes of tussock grass and rock, underpinned by rich black earth. Beyond the bog is a ridge of bare rock and grass, punctuated by caves and overhangs. Engulfed in mist, it is a place of total and eerie silence, where the only sign of life apart from the warriors who track them are occasional birds scuttling for cover among the rocks and large upright lobelia.

It is ambush country.

The ridge feels like the gateway to another world; the final approaches to the upper slopes are through a series of breath-taking valleys, surrounded by rock walls and patches of giant groundsel, with clear gushing mountain streams powered by waterfalls. There is so much cover for ambush that he senses some form of attack is imminent.

Despite all this he is curious to discover if the small rivers hold wild trout. He pauses by a waterfall while the rest of the column marches on. He gazes intently down to the depths of the pool 50 feet below but can see nothing moving. While his concentration is diverted he does not see the tribesman. The huge warrior wears feather plumes and long dreadlocks down each side of his face. He is covered in red mud and has appeared like a spirit out of the wall of water tumbling down the mountain. The African carries a long spear.

Frank feels himself fumbling for his revolver but realises it is clipped in the holster, impeding his ability to save himself. He feels constrained—like in a nightmare—by a great weight that slows down his movement. He is paralysed and screams out. He wants to move normally, but he cannot do so. Terror engulfs him. This man is going to kill him. He waits for the sickening impact of the tip of the spear and the pain that will come with it. He feels regret that his life is going to end so suddenly.

He thinks of his mother's anguish in losing a second son. The warrior seems in no hurry to kill him. The native takes a pace forward and the arm holding the spear is raised above his head. Frank gets a grip at last around his revolver and brings it upwards swiftly from the holster. Then he realises why the warrior has delayed throwing his spear. He carries a panga, a broad curved knife in his left hand.

"You're going to disembowel me you bastard," he hears himself shouting and at last fires a shot at the warrior but the latter stands his ground sneering—as if to warn his victim he is protected by supernatural forces. A moment later a second shot—this time from a rifle at close range—rings out and the sneer freezes on the African's face. Blood cascades from his chest and he staggers backwards and seems to disappear through the torrent of falling water down into the ravine. Now Frank is confronted by another black face and this time it belongs to Benjamin Amin, his trusted Sergeant.

"He want kill you Bwana. Kill white leader, make them policemen run away. Nearly happen. Now he dead instead by me—but they attack soon. Call men into defensive ring along forest path Bwana."

Later, the African Sergeant stares with deep concentration into the campfire, the flames are turning themselves into images from past military expeditions. Benjamin Amin sits on his haunches beside the blazing fire and eventually looks around in the flickering shadows upon the faces of those gathered around him. He senses they are willing him to give them leadership. On the face of the white man there is an anxious expression.

The resonant rolling sound of a lion's roar is audible and is complemented immediately by the demented laugh of hyenas. Not to be outdone, a bull elephant trumpets to his mate only a few yards from where the soldiers and porters are camped in the forest. Night insects, crickets and calling nocturnal birds, are close at hand in chorus.

The sheer intensity of sound, behind the voices of the men at fires, provides a symphony in the darkness, under the canopy of a million stars in the moonlit sky that only minutes before were glazed red by the falling sun. Dusk has given way to the fullness of night in less than half an hour.

Inspector Frank W Clarke of the East African Protectorate Police, a tall powerfully-built young man of 22 with dark-hair, a distinctive Roman nose and tanned skin, is unfamiliar with this world, but enchanted by the hypnotic magic of Africa. He is also fearful of the unfamiliar and unpredictable dangers that lurk in so many corners.

Benjamin speaks to him quietly: "Warriors attack after midnight Bwana. Nandi only try rushing us once, lose some men then go home."

Clarke's lack of combat experience is not something he could hide from his sergeant and in the past fortnight he has come to rely upon his Nubian non commissioned officer, who has been seconded from the King's African Rifles to the police unit which he commands.

"Yes Sarnt. I don't want anyone falling asleep at his post. If anyone sees any movement he should fire his rifle," he says with the customary authority of a white officer.

Benjamin Amin, son and grandson of soldiers who have fought for the British Empire in Africa and India, expects to receive orders in such a fashion from European officers. Anything less than sternness would make him feel uneasy. His massive frame stands rigidly to attention and he salutes his officer, which the latter returns.

Benjamin is correct that the attack will come after midnight. There is shouting in Swahili all around Frank Clarke as rifle fire breaks out. He is in his tent writing his diary when the tribesmen try to get into the camp. The young man sees the reassuringly bulky figure of his Nubian sergeant through the flickering light of a fire. The African is crouching by the Maxim gun and directing its fire.

The tribesmen are somewhere in the shadows firing arrows at the Askaris grouped around the gun. The advancing warriors now appear out of the darkness—lit only by the flickering remnants of the fire. The policemen are outnumbered and will be slaughtered in the next few seconds unless something happens to prevent it.

"No, you fire too high, you fire too high. Close range, close range," screams Sgt Amin in pidgin at the gun team, ordering them to lower the trajectory of the barrel of the machine gun. Three policemen are already hit and lie screaming on the ground.

Frank fires six shots from the revolver but his aim in panic is too high. A spear lands less than two feet from where he crouches with a thud, its shaft biting deep into the dusty ground.

Another native police officer is hit but he falls silently after the sickening sound of the impact of the spear upon his rib cage. He is killed instantly by the tip penetrating the heart. Frank reloads his revolver with shaking hands.

A few moments later the bullets from the machine gun take out the warriors at point blank range. At least 10 fall to the ground, many screaming in the shadows. The group disappears quickly, leaving no sign of the incursion. They have even removed their dead and wounded from the battle.

"Ceasefire," Clarke orders in a strangulated voice that he hopes will go unnoticed. It has been his first fire fight and he quietly considers that he has not come out of it with much distinction.

If the Askari had not obeyed Benjamin and de-elevated the firing position of the machine gun, it would have been a massacre—and he, being the only white man in the detachment, would have been disembowelled and hung up from a forest tree by his boots. It gives him nightmares and on two occasions he wakes up shouting—in fear of his certain death and appalled by images of himself being skewered by a long spear.

The reality of Africa, a continent where most natives do not know its name or understand why it should even have a name, is at last apparent to Frank. This is a dangerous place for white strangers—he reckons if the tribesmen don't kill him, then some awful fly-borne disease probably will within the year.

Furthermore, the winds, the sudden lashing rainstorms and the wide skies presiding over endless veldt—monitored by circling birds of prey and scavenging vultures—suggest a form of overwhelmingly destructive anarchy beyond the will of mere humans to control. It scares him a lot but he marvels at its awesome yet indifferent power over life and death. This is the force of nature in a form he has never witnessed in Europe.

2

THE VIRGINIAN GIRL

Thousands of miles away in America, Heinrich Horstmann trots his favourite mare through the vast orchard which he planted ten years before. The apple and pear trees descend in tidy rows on a hillside that run down to the banks of the Shenandoah River in the foothills of the Blue Ridge Mountains.

He hears the sound of his daughter's voice and she seems to be addressing someone. Moments later he comes across Emily seated on the grass beneath a large oak tree on the fringe of the orchard. She is surrounded by a ring of Negro children who are squatting on the ground around her. He dismounts quietly and listens.

Emily has spent her childhood with her older brother Pete on the apple farm. She is regarded as something of a "tom boy" and enjoys riding the steeply forested mountain slopes, the open pastures and crop land on the banks of the meandering river—where they also spend days and nights camping and canoeing in the wilderness. Although only 14 years old, the auburn-haired Emily is already approaching six feet in height and with a developing figure looks at least three years older than she is.

As she has grown up she has spent most her time at play with the children of the black domestic helpers in the house who also assist in the upbringing of the young Horstmanns. Martha the cook is strict about hygiene and being tidy around the kitchen. Hands have to be clean before they eat. The housekeeper Maisey is big and buxom with a hooting laugh.

Emily's earliest memories are of playing with the six or seven young Negro children of her own age. She has always preferred to do this than seek out other white children living in the valley. Now she is on holiday from school.

The younger children squat on their haunches out of the heat of the sun under a tree but sweating in the humidity—and brushing away the flies and insects. Emily sits in the middle of the group and tells stories about her school in Richmond and legends that she has read about in her large collection of children's books.

The black youngsters listen wide-eyed. It is a world away from the rundown single-storey building in nearby Boyce. The Negro elementary school is short of academic equipment compared to its spacious brick-built counterpart for the white children. Usually, after the gathering one of the black youngsters invites her back to his or her home and Emily eats a family meal with them. They live in wooden shacks where grandparents wile away the hours on the balcony and the entire family congregate in the evening, singing gospel songs.

Emily learns these songs along with the other children. The former slaves do not own much furniture and no one sleeps on a bed. Most families in the shanty settlement have meagre belongings that might consist of tin plates and cups, and a metal pot for meat and chicken stews tempered with corn maize, hunks of corn bread and hot sauces. Only a few have chairs, tables, mattresses and blankets

Heinrich listens as Emily reads aloud passages from *Alice in Wonderland* and *Swiss Family Robinson* to the children. His daughter has a strong voice and seems to possess a personality that attracts the affection of others. It is as if she is teaching them lessons they would not otherwise get.

They are neither restless nor bored by what she tells them but listen to every word. Emily is obviously a figure of respect to these children and her father is astonished at the way she seems to command their attention.

Heinrich is proud that she is a devout girl, can quote the Bible and seems to have a strong sense of right and wrong. She also has a deep affection for all animals—dogs and even cats follow her around—and she is always prepared to speak her mind, no matter whose sensibilities might be pricked.

Fox-hunting has long been a fashionable activity among the wealthy classes of Virginia society and Heinrich recalls how he was deeply embarrassed by his daughter's uninhibited reaction to the local hunt one day when she was still only 10-years-old.

Its Master had trotted past the entrance to the farm in all his scarlet finery—aping the hunts of England across the Atlantic. Emily had been walking hand in hand with two younger Negro children and she scolded the hunt master—the richest and most important man in the valley—for his cruelty.

"One day I'll hunt you down on a horse with my dogs and see how you find it," she says to the Master, causing great offence.

He rides off extremely angry and makes a note to complain to the insolent girl's head teacher about her outrageous attitude towards her social superiors. She is punished by having to write out 500 lines.

"I must never speak again with disrespect to my superiors or question their judgment."

It is something she will never learn to do. None of Emily's activities or beliefs at this time really serves as a warning signal to Heinrich and Ada. This is why they are so unprepared for the turn of events during the cold winter months when the snow comes to the foothills in Virginia.

It brings the family to a prominence that the Horstmanns have been trying hard to avoid for several decades—and will leave them with a reputation that endures long after the First World War has ended. Heinrich and Ada have become substantial fruit growers in Clarke County, Virginia, although their German background creates a glass ceiling against social integration. The Anglo-Saxon fox-hunting set and the thoroughbred breeders—with sights set upon the Kentucky Derby—are Heinrich's neighbours.

They treat immigrant families politely but in a detached manner that stops short of friendship. Mind you, the plight of the black man is not something that Heinrich and Ada think about much—but as a matter of policy the family never draws attention to itself. They do make sure that the five Negro families, all former slaves, who live and work for them are paid at least as well as those who work elsewhere in the valley.

Two older black children call for Emily one evening after the family supper and reluctantly Heinrich allows her to go with them despite concern on a winter's night for the well-being of his 14-year-old daughter.

He harnesses a pony for her and she rides a mile-and-a-half with the children through the snow along the banks of the river, until they come to the shanty settlement on the edge of woodland. The Negroes there do not work on the farm. The men are labourers employed casually by the local rail road company.

There is thick wood smoke in the air, rising in coils through the frosty night from the chimneys of the shacks. Emily follows the children into the candlelit shadows of a shack and finds a group of adults, some weeping, praying for the life of four-year-old Nellie.

She is one of Emily's favourites, has bright eyes and is blessed with considerable intelligence. Nellie's mother speaks softy, with tears in her eyes: "The Lord thank you for coming to pray with us tonight Miss Emily. We are asking Jesus to save Nellie. She has been in fever since last night and is getting weaker.

"She finds it hard to breathe, has a terrible cough, chest pains and fever—she goes from hot to cold in a few moments. We think Nellie has pneumonia Miss Emily and we sent for the doctor in Boyce but he would not come. He wants 10 dollars and says we must bring Nellie to him."

The wider family group pray with such intensity and sorrow that the girl wakes from her light and fevered sleep bewildered, eyes huge on her thin face. She listens to the prayers for a few moments and then returns to her delirious world of intermittent slumber.

She seems to have recognized Emily and smiles weakly before closing her eyes again. Emily says: "I am studying to become a nurse and I have read about pneumonia. Nellie has bacterial fluid collecting in her lung sacks."

She kisses the child on the forehead. "Nellie must have picked up a chill—I heard that she fell in the river last week, is that so?"

Nellie's mother nods and listens to Emily, who towers above her. "You must keep her warm and tucked up against draughts of cold air and make sure she drinks warm water constantly, perhaps with plenty of apple and clove in a juice to provide energy to fight the infection. Let her drink whenever she wants to do so."

"The doctor will also have pills and other medication and if she gains strength then I think we will have to take her on a cart wrapped up in fur to his surgery later this week. Apart from praying with you for Nellie, what else can I do?"

Tears are welling up in the eyes of Nellie's mother.

"We have no money for that white doctor Miss Emily. We would like you to accompany us to the Episcopal Church in Boyce where black folk are not welcome to worship—but where the churchgoers have money.

"We would like you to speak up for us because you are strong and brave and ask them to have a collection for Nellie so that she can have medical treatment. There is a service on Sunday morning and we think there may be as many as 100 people in the congregation."

Emily sees a vision of Heinrich and Ada Horstman in the church among the congregation and their horrified reaction and embarrassment if she does what Nellie's mother is asking her to do.

She does not give it any further thought. She must do the right thing to save Nellie's life in what is potentially a tragic situation. The sensibilities of her parents are not a consideration in the matter.

"Of course I will. I cannot guarantee they will listen to a 14-year-old child—especially one who has already been in trouble for speaking her mind about fox-hunting. Yes, I will go to that church with you on Sunday morning and I will address the congregation on your behalf."

When Emily returns to the farm later that evening she does not tell Heinrich or Ada anything about what has gone on at the shack but she suspects the black domestic staff have more than a good idea of what is going on. They seem to give her knowing looks.

She returns to the shack the following evening and is told there has been little change in Nellie's condition, although the constant supply of apple and clove juice has eased the coughing and also enables her to sleep in a less fevered way.

She tells Nellie's mother and grandmother: "When we go to the church on Sunday we need to time our arrival carefully. If we get there at the same moment as the rest of the congregation then the church wardens may try to stop us going inside, because of their policy of segregation at services.

"If however, we enter the church through its front door a minute or two after the service has started we can sit at the back and then gauge the reaction of the priest.

"I will choose the moment to go forward in front of the altar, mount the pulpit and address them. I think our boldness will confuse them at first and give me a chance to say what it is that I want to say. I have worked it all out and rehearsed it."

It does work out according to Emily's plan. When the time comes for Heinrich and Ada to take the trap into town to church on Sunday the couple look for their daughter—but they cannot find Emily on the farm. It is unusual for Emily to miss church but they assume she has gone riding on this wintry morning and has not been able to get back to the farm in time. The Horstmanns arrive at the church at 10am along with nearly 100 worshippers from the local community around Boyce.

The bells of the small church are ringing out as the congregation arrive. Five minutes after the service has started and during the opening hymn,

Emily leads Nellie's mother, grandmother and two aunts quietly into the church and ushers them to a pew at the back beside the baptism font.

The sudden entrance of the four Negro women into the church causes a sensation among the white worshippers and there is an exchange of astonished glances. Heinrich and Ada notice that Emily is among the interlopers and look at one another with horrified expressions just as their daughter has anticipated.

When the hymn ends, the entire congregation turns to face the back of the church to look with anger upon the Negro women who are kneeling in prayer behind them. The white worshippers make a strangely hostile hissing noise as they whisper among themselves—and they also gaze with disdain upon Heinrich and Ada.

They all know Emily as a regular churchgoer and have heard rumours she is a trouble-maker. The elderly priest interrupts the growing hostility and tension but is clearly embarrassed at this unexpected test of his Christian values.

"I must ask the four ladies who arrived here during the first hymn and are now seated at the back of the church to leave immediately. The regulations about segregated congregations are well known in this town. Negroes have their own time for worship and are well provided for. . . ."

Emily knows she must seize the moment and has already left her seat and is striding up through the church towards the priest as he starts speaking. He looks upon her in astonishment and with some trepidation in his eyes as he sees this tall young woman with long auburn hair walking quickly and purposefully towards him. Now, she is standing beside him and the buzz in the church intensifies.

"What can I do for you Miss Horstmann?"

"I should like your leave to say a few words," she replies and without waiting for his acquiescence walks to the pulpit and climbs the steps to face the congregation.

The priest shrugs and walks back to the altar to allow Emily to address the congregation which is now even more hostile. She ignores several loud demands from male and female worshippers.

"Sit down you bad child. How dare you bring these people here," shouts one woman.

Emily ignores the taunts. "I do apologise for interrupting your service this morning but as a fellow Christian I make no apology for being a child. As for my Negro friends, I can only say they too are Christians and they will leave this church as soon as I have had a chance to address you."

"Make it quick then—or I'll throw you and the niggers out personally," shouts a man angrily.

Emily does not appear to be intimidated by the threat and stares in silent contempt at the man for a few seconds before continuing.

"Among the black women here today is the mother of a four-year-old child called Nellie who is very sick. In fact Nellie is losing her fight for life because she has been struck down by pneumonia. The power of prayer has so far kept this little girl alive but I believe the Lord has guided us here today because he knows that the worshippers of Boyce can help to save Nellie's life.

"The good doctor in the town—not here this morning I note—has offered to treat Nellie at his surgery and provide her with life-saving medicines in exchange for 10 dollars. It is a sum of money the little girl's family do not have—and have no way of finding. I am here today to ask you to have a collection for Nellie during this service."

"If we do that for one nigger child we'll be doing it every damned Sunday!" exclaims a male worshipper and his words are endorsed with several hissed murmurs of "here, here!"

Emily's face is now clouded with anger and Heinrich, sitting with his head in his hands, knows that his daughter is about to say something— he has no idea what—that will be regarded as outrageous by the white congregation.

The worshippers are of a generation that expect children to be seen but not heard. Her detailed knowledge of the Bible astonishes him in the next few minutes. She is a born preacher, he decides.

"As you sit before me feeling reassured in your faith here in the House of God, perhaps you all believe you have done your duty today in just finding the time to come to church. Perhaps you feel satisfied about that. I ask you to think again—this is a church which excludes some of our brothers and sisters—a judgment based entirely on the colour of their skin. To evaluate whether that is morally defensible we have to look no further than the Gospel according to the disciple Matthew—specifically Matthew 25.

She picks up a Bible, finds the page she wants and is about to continue when the priest intervenes by taking the tension out of the situation in a spirit of conciliation.

"Thank you Miss Horstmann. You clearly demonstrate a precocious knowledge of the Bible and I, for one, endorse your scholarship, although I am not sure that your elders and betters here today will appreciate being preached to by a child. I also hear your plea on behalf of fellow Christians and the plight of little Nellie.

"If you would be so good as to ask the ladies at the back of the church to leave with you now, I shall see to it that there is a collection among the congregation during the next hymn.

"God bless you Mr Priest," cries a voice from the back of the church. It comes from Nellie's mother and she leads her three relations quickly out of the church. Emily smiles at the priest and follows them.

In the afternoon Heinrich summons his daughter to his study and without a word of admonishment hands her a 10 dollar note that the priest has given him after the service. Heinrich and Ada are horrified at the attention their daughter's actions have brought upon the family—they are scared of the Klu Klux Klan who will see in the actions of the daughter of this white immigrant family a dangerously subversive attitude. At the same time Heinrich is extremely proud of Emily for her courage and he never forgets it. Some miles away in Richmond the incident comes to the attention of a journalist two days later.

John Mitchell Junior has several letters to read but he scans the one referring to Emily Horstmann several times. It has been sent to the editor of *The Richmond Planet* by a correspondent based in the small town of Boyce and it tells the extraordinary story of a 14-year-old white girl who has chosen to take up the cause of discrimination against black people at considerable risk to herself.

Mitchell was born a slave and his paper—with its team of black journalists—has a crusading reputation supporting racial equality. He has been the editor of *The Richmond* Planet since the age of 21 and has won a reputation as a fearless and campaigning journalist determined to expose racial injustice wherever it lurks.

He calls his deputy editor into his office. "There's a great story from Boyce but I need to get there and do an interview. You'll have to take over laying out the paper while I'm gone. Here read this for yourself."

The other journalist reads the letter and whistles through his teeth.

"Wow man, I reckon a young white girl doing that for black people is about as rare as hen's teeth."

"Precisely, which is why I've got to talk to her and get a picture too. This could go national it's so strong," added Mitchell.

"I can get a train there can't I?"

"Yeah, Boyce is at the crossing of the Norfolk and Western Railway and the Winchester and the Millwood Turnpike about nine miles from Winchester and eight miles south of Berryville.

"It's got a real smart brick passenger and stock-shipping railway station, there's lots of smart white folk there too. It has a reputation for being one of the most hard-arsed Conservative little towns in the state—so you've got to be careful man."

Mitchell replies: "Mmm, smart or not, I reckon that little girl really gave it those white worshippers at the Episcopal Church in Boyce last Sunday. She actually got some money out of them too!"

They both roar with laughter.

The following morning John Mitchell Junior arrives by train at Boyce and attracts some attention by hiring a trap from the harness shop. The manager hasn't known of a black man doing this before. He might have stopped it had he thought of something to prevent it.

Instead, Mitchell is given the directions reluctantly to the Horstmann's apple farm two miles away. When he arrives the door is opened by a black domestic helper who looks astonished and fearful when he says he is John Mitchell Junior, the editor of *The Richmond Planet*. He apologises for arriving unannounced and without an appointment.

He asks to speak to Emily Horstmann's mother and father and is taken into the kitchen—rather than the study—to wait for them. The servants who work at the apple farm are aware of *The Richmond Planet*—and when they find out who John Mitchell Junior is, they are fearful that big trouble might be stirred up if the events of last Sunday are published in the press.

It is a view also held by Heinrich who eventually arrives back at the farm and asks Mitchell to accompany him into his study. He is impressed by the man's elegance and manners. The Negro seems to be well educated and speaks in a quiet clipped tone.

"Would it be possible for me to do an interview with Emily for *The Richmond Planet* and possibly other newspapers as well?" asks John Mitchell Junior.

"Why would that be so important?" asks Heinrich.

"Your daughter, Sir, has done something quite extraordinary in our society in taking a position, a stand against racial discrimination—and it's important for that reason to publish what she has done to highlight it as an example to others," says Mitchell.

"For God's sake man, she's just a child of 14 years-old. By publishing an article you would probably bring this child, and indeed her family, to the attention of undesirable fanatics who are literally prepared to commit murder to perpetuate segregation.

"Believe me Sir our family does not support the new laws on segregation. Emily is precocious and she has a distinctive sense of right and wrong—but she would have wanted to help young Nellie regardless of her colour. She's that kind of person."

John Mitchell decides to try another tack.

"How is young Nellie by the way?"

"She was taken to see the doctor in Boyce in our family wagon, was given medication, has started to recover and is not going to die. She's still very ill but gradually getting stronger and has come out of her feverish state," says Heinrich.

"Can I have your permission to go to see Nellie and her family?" asks the journalist, knowing full well he does not need the white man's approval and can do what he likes.

"That's up to you but I'm sure Nellie's family will take the same attitude as my wife and I. Any publicity will expose them to the crazy people who believe in segregation. In fact they would be in greater danger than us. People in Boyce are already buzzing with anger and those who were in the church feel humiliated by my daughter's preaching.

"If they read in the *Richmond Planet* that they have been cast as villains in this affair, then goodness knows what will happen in this valley. The black people I employ on the farm will also be at risk from the fanatics."

John Mitchell looks thoughtful for a few moments as he weighs up the pros and cons of the farmer's arguments. The farmer is right, he knows that. He sighs deeply then stands up and shakes Heinrich by the hand.

"OK Sir, I hear what you say and accept your argument for not taking this matter any further by publishing an article in the press. But may I meet Emily—just to congratulate her?"

At that moment the door to the study opens and Emily stands there in front of the two men. She has been summoned to the study but instead of knocking, just walks through the door.

If John Mitchell thinks he is the one who is going to do the talking he is mistaken. In any case he is so astonished by Emily's appearance he finds himself speechless.

He is expecting to meet a small child, but instead finds himself scrutinising a young woman who is nearly six feet tall, with long auburn hair, high cheek bones, a large mouth and full lips. She is one of the most naturally beautiful young white women he has ever encountered.

It is Emily who speaks. "I'd just like to say Mr Mitchell that I am honoured to meet you, having been an admirer of you and your newspaper for more than a year now, although I do not bring it into the house for fear of upsetting my parents. This state certainly needs a radical newspaper to fight against the oppression of segregation which is one of the most evil and unjust manifestations our so-called modern society.

"What I did on Sunday was nothing really—and I shall not hesitate to do what I see as my Christian duty in the future should the need arise. I am sure there are many young white folk in Virginia who feel the same way as me about the oppression of Negroes.

"Had Nellie not survived this ordeal then I would be strongly advising you to go ahead and print an article about the matter in *The Richmond Planet* and I'd be saying 'damn the consequences.' As it is, Nellie is going to live and she deserves to have the protection of a happy and undisturbed childhood. So thanks for agreeing not to publish an article and allowing what has happened to fade away in the memory of the people of this town."

When John Mitchell Junior gets back to his editorial office he is surrounded by his team wanting to know if he has done the interview—and the strength of the article.

"No, it was nothing," he says, adding: "It turned out to be a non-story, let's leave it at that."

3

AMERICAN BOXER IN DUBLIN 1908

The new yellow automobile is parked on the quay at Carlisle Pier in Kingstown Harbour where the mail boat *RMS Leinster* is due to arrive from Holyhead. The presence of the large car is already causing a minor sensation among the legions of horse-drawn wagons waiting for the vessel, which belong to the City of Dublin Steam Packet Company. None of the waiting porters have any idea who owns the car.

Half an hour before the boat is due to arrive a crowd of more than 100 people gather to meet the ferry and most are intrigued to discover the identity of the driver of the car. Automobiles are still rare in Dublin; the avenues around the centre of the city and the Liffey are the domain of double-decker electric trams and horse-drawn transport.

The automobile machines—which create noise and smoke and disturb the peace on the roads—remain a talking point on which the jury is still out. The distinguished sportsman, writer and wit Dr Oliver St John Gogarty was the first owner of a car in Dublin and he cuts a familiar figure when seen at the wheel of his second car, a recently acquired white six-cylinder Silver Ghost Rolls Royce.

The crowd assume that at any moment Dr Gogarty will arrive on the pier in his white automobile to greet the driver of the yellow machine and that both will then don goggles and sweep off in the direction of Sackville Street, or some other fashionable venue. The doctor does not come.

Every age produces its anoraks, and one steps forward now, for the benefit of the crowd. "She's French, a Dion-Bouton, type AW and she's a real beauty, capable of doing at least 60 miles an hour, built by a company belonging to the Count Albert De Dion. A car like this won the Paris-Madrid race a few years ago," says the know-all.

He lifts the yellow bonnet and tells the bemused spectators: "A four cylinder engine with an engine capacity of 1,328 cc. That's real power!"

A small boy steps forward and points to the horn. His father lifts him up and he squeezes the black oval rubber airbag to which the brass horn is attached, creating a loud honking sound. The crowd titter. The mail boat steams in at last and heightens the tension on the quay. Soon the 600 passengers have been greeted by the porters as they stream off the vessel carrying luggage.

No one claims the Dion-Bouton. The crowd is about to disperse when there is a buzz of astonishment at the approach of a shaven-headed man and a blonde woman, who turn and wave farewell to the captain as they walk down the gangplank. They are followed by several porters carrying boxes of luggage. The man is tall, about six feet one, of powerful build and wears a black leather coat over his shoulders that reaches down close to his ankles. He is smiling broadly and this reveals gold-capped teeth. He carries a walking stick in his right hand.

The woman on his arm is almost as tall as him and she wears a long silver mink coat. People in the crowd can see the diamonds mounted on the gold rings she wears. Her earrings and necklace are of pearl and her long blonde hair is combed back behind the ears, flowing down in ringlets. It is a hairstyle none has seen before in Dublin. The couple exude ostentation and wealth. The buzz in the crowd is not caused by the opulent appearance of the couple but by the fact that he is black and she is white.

The man ushers the woman into the passenger seat of the car, directs the baggage to be put onto its back seat and then addresses the crowd in a loud voice, as he stands on the running board. He speaks with a drawling American accent.

"I should just like to thank all you folk for taking the trouble to come and meet us on the first occasion of our visit to your beautiful country. Sophia and I will be staying at the Gresham Hotel in Sackville Street.

"While I am here I shall be giving a one-man public performance—in shadow—of the pugilist's art. I'm now going to a press conference with the journalists of your city, so you can read all about me in tomorrow's newspapers. Thank you."

He climbs into the driving seat of the Dion-Bouton and a sailor from the mail boat steps forward and crank-starts the engine. The great machine comes to life with a roar that sounds like an angry beast. The American drives off at speed with his girl and white exhaust smoke trails behind them.

"Who the hell was that?" the crowd is asking itself.

The Irish Times print a story the following day with the headline: 'Negro contender shadows champion Burns.'

James, Frank's older brother, is a friend of Paddy Delaney, a leading sports writer on *The Irish Times,* who smuggles him into the press conference in the banqueting suite of the Gresham Hotel. The Negro sits with a middle-aged white man at a desk on the stage at the end of the room.

There is no sign of the blonde woman with whom he has arrived on the *RMS Leinster* a few hours before. He looks relaxed and well groomed. He wears a well tailored grey suit, a blinding-white soft collared shirt, polka-dot tie, gleaming patent leather shoes and a large ruby ring on the middle finger of his left hand. Those in the front row detect that he smells of a fragrant perfume.

The white man, Sean O'Malley, whom James Clarke recognises as the owner of the *Red Harp* in Grafton Street stands up to speak.

"Gentlemen of the press, please give a big welcome to the next heavy-weight boxing champion of the world, the finest pugilist the planet has ever seen. I give you Jack Johnson, visiting this city from the United States of America!"

The journalists have been plied with free alcoholic refreshment, courtesy of their American host, and are in a good natured mood. They hoot support and give the boxer a round of applause. He stands up and smiles broadly, again exposing his golden teeth.

"They love to hate me in my own country because they say I'm a 'flash nigger'—they say I don't know my place. It's true I don't!"

He smiles before adding: "I'm black. They never let me forget it. I'm black. Alright, I'll never let them forget it!"

The Irish journalists roar with laughter.

"No law, custom, no black nor white, man or woman, is going to keep Jack Johnson from what he wants—and what I want is the world heavy-weight boxing crown. I am the son of slaves from Galveston, Texas and my daddy made sure I learned to read and write like the white man, so no bum's going to trick me out of it.

"When I was young, the only way for a young black boy to get on in the world was to learn how to box. They used to blindfold young niggers and make them fight bare-knuckled until the last one was left standing. He got the coins.

"They called it 'battle royal' in Galveston and by the time I was 16, I was the boy champion. By the time I was 18, I was travelling around America as a boxer earning $10 a night. By 1902 I'd won 27 professional fights and I was making $1,000 dollars a night. By 1906 I'd beaten every good nigger fighter in the USA.

"People who see me box today say I'm better than any white boxer in the world, but none of the contenders are prepared to fight me. The title belongs, as you know, to a Canadian bum called Tommy Burns, who arrives here in town later this week to fight your Irish champion, another bum called Jem Roche. You could put 'em both in the ring against me at the same time and I'd still whip their ass!"

The journalists rock with laughter. They have never come across such an amusing and cocksure sportsman in their life and he is going to make good copy for the next day's paper.

"So why am I here? Well, I'm following that bum Tommy Burns round the world till he agrees to fight me. I've watched him fight twice in London and I'm going on to Paris and then to Sydney, Australia.

"That's where he'll defend his title. When the purse gets big enough, even he won't be able to refuse me. His time will be up and he'll be whipped by the true champion. My time is coming gentlemen.

"If you want to see just how fast I am, come and see me shadow boxing next Tuesday night at the Smock Alley Theatre. Afterwards, for the press, the drinks will be on me. Thanks for coming."

Before he leaves the hotel James Clarke writes out a message for Johnson in the foyer inviting him and Sophia to come round to the house and to go on to enjoy the night life of Dublin. He doesn't expect to get a reply, but the next night a messenger boy arrives from the Gresham Hotel asking James to meet the American at 7pm the following evening.

Frank, who still hasn't found a job since his return from Africa, is delegated to go to the hotel to meet Jack Johnson. He stands at the hotel reception desk and is looking out onto Sackville Street when a softy spoken voice with an American accent says behind him: "I guess you'd be James Clarke, is that right?"

Frank turns abruptly and finds himself facing a black man slightly taller than himself. Johnson is wearing a long fur coat, a wide brimmed black hat and carries a black walking stick. He smiles broadly, exposing gold teeth, and offers his hand in a surprisingly soft handshake.

"It's very nice to meet you. Actually Mr Johnson I'm Frank Clarke, James' younger brother. He got held up but will be back at home by the time we get there. Is Mrs Johnson coming?"

"No, Sophia won't be coming out tonight. She'll stay in the hotel, have dinner in our room and go to bed. She's still tired after the rough sea crossing. So, young Frank, I'm all yours for the night—and mighty grateful for the company of the two Clarke brothers."

"We are happy to show you round Dublin and we'll make sure it's a trip you'll never forget. We've also got tickets for the Burns-Roche fight on St Patrick's Night in the Theatre Royal and we'd be delighted if you'd like to join our party."

"Well that sounds good to me Frank. I think you may find Sean O'Malley will join us and I'd like to open tonight with a trip down to the *Red Harp* for a few beers, if that's OK with you."

The session, with Sean O'Malley standing front of house and other hardened drinkers forming a circle round Jack Johnson, lasts three hours. O'Malley, it turns out, met the boxer in San Francisco before the 1906 earthquake. Johnson says he prefers the company of white Europeans to white Americans—because they are more tolerant racially.

"No, we just conceal our feelings better," says O'Malley, earning hoots of raucous mirth and a roar of laughter from Johnson who seemed to possess a self-deprecating sense of humour.

Frank is slurring his words before he extricates the boxer from his circle of acolytes and gets him into a cab. It is 11.30pm by the time they reach Amiens Street. Bert the butler opens the front door to let the two men in. He looked in lingering discomfort at the black man, who hands the servant his pair of white gloves, his fur coat and black hat, but keeps the walking stick. Frank calls up the stairs to his older brother.

"Are you there James? It's me Frank, and I've got Jack Johnson with me!"

"Oh is it! Well bugger off and you can tell that black bastard to get out of my house, or I'm coming down there to throw him out," is the reply from James who has a reputation for sailing close to the wind.

Johnson exposes his golden teeth in yet another broad smile. James appears at the top of the stairs roaring with laughter.

"I bet that got you two buggers going for a moment!" he shouts. Charles Rimington, a friend from Frank's years in the East African Protectorate Police, appears from a bedroom and asks in his drawling voice, "What the hell's going on?"

The ice has been broken and Jack Johnson is escorted into the drawing room at the front of the house where he is plied for more than an hour with cigars and Irish malt and meets several players from Monkstown Rugby Club, who have been summoned to meet the famous guest. At midnight somebody suggests it is time to visit the bars around Montgomery Street, which is close to Johnson's hotel.

Monto, as it is called, is infamous as the British Empire's biggest red light district. It is situated conveniently close to the Royal Barracks where soldiers are quartered in the city. At midnight in Dublin, on any night except Sunday, Monto is ablaze with bars and small vaudeville theatres featuring scantily dressed girls. The Jack Johnson story has appeared in the Irish newspapers, together with photographs of the boxer and his white wife. In every Monto bar the party visit, prostitutes target Jack. In one bar six women literally crawl all over him. He smiles broadly, kisses a few, buys drinks, but makes no effort to couple with any of them. If Jack Johnson is the philanderer that the American press makes him out to be, then he shows no sign of it and none of the girls get lucky.

People drinking in the bars greet the Negro with great interest and ply him with questions that he is delighted to answer above the din created by the band and the partying.

"What's your secret Mr Johnson? None of us have seen you box. Why are Tommy Burns and Jem Roche just bums?"

He tells them he's learned most of what he knows from a great white fighter of the 1890s called Jim Corbett, whose ring style appeared "scientific" in contrast to the stiffly upright, crudely aggressive heavyweights of his time, who were all forward-lunging offence but had no defensive strategies.

"Boxing is an art and I'm the supreme artist. It's all about speed, timing, the art of deception and finally surprise. Great strength is important, but it's never the key thing. I've whipped more big strong fellows who lumbered forward onto my right fist than my daddy picked cotton in his life."

"What do you mean by speed?"

"Speed in the feet and the hands because that gets you where you want to be to counter punch the guy coming on to you. Sure, your punch has to be as quick as a rattlesnake and you want to put in a combination of jabs if you can, but you have to sucker the guy to come forward while moving to avoid his punches.

"That's speed and I'm the fastest man that ever lived. Boxing really is like chess played at a 100 miles an hour—and I'm a good chess player!" He raises his shaved head again and roars with laughter.

"So you see I've also got brains and I use them in the ring. It's called 'mouth-fighting.' I taunt the bums to come forward. It always works because they've gotten mad and start swinging at me. I keep my shoulders rotating so my head is never in the place they think it's going be and my chin tucked in. So now you know the secrets of Jack Johnson.

"If you ever get to see me fight you'll understand that I win by gradually wearing down a fighter, letting him tire himself out, by hitting him with my left as he comes to close quarters, then by clinching and executing my right upper cut—and all the time jab, jab, jabbing. Then, when I want to finish him off, he gets my right to the body or the head and down he goes!"

At this point Jack Johnson is demonstrating the pugilist's art with air punches at the bar. He then picks up the black walking stick he's left leaning against a stool and hands it around to those who are listening to him. Some find it hard to lift with one hand.

"It's made of lead and it lives in my right hand 12 hours a day. It's the secret of my knockout punch!" Johnson puts back his head and roars with laughter again. The 'night out' continues until nearly 4am, having been extended by the arrival in Monto by Sean O'Malley and his cronies from the *Red Harp*.

Over the next few days Frank sees Johnson on several occasions. He genuinely admires the man and wants to get to know him better. He also suspects that beneath the man's cocky exterior lurks a more complex personality. He is correct and soon discovers some of his earlier assumptions about Jack Johnson are entirely wrong.

During that week, Jack and Sophia take Frank to lunch at *Lamb Doyle's,* a famous pub on the hill of Step-a-Side at the foot of the Three Rock Mountain. They sit drinking dark ale at a table on a warm spring day overlooking the blue expanse of Dublin Bay and the white tips of the swell in the sou-westerly breeze. The expanse of the great city lies to the left below a smoky haze. The Johnsons are wearing long mink coats and Frank wears the ankle length black leather coat in which Johnson arrived on the *RMS Leinster*. He has given it to Frank as a gift.

Both Johnson and his wife are more subdued than usual. Indeed Sophia looks glum. She has spent the morning in Clery's department store but she does not look pleased or grateful about her shopping expedition. Now tears appear in her eyes. Jack looks at Frank and says: "They don't forgive her, wherever she goes. It never ends. We had hoped Europe would be different. But it isn't. She can cope with the looks of contempt, even the unspoken hatred, but every now and then someone says something and it gets to her."

Frank replies: "Did someone say something to her in Clery's?"

"She overheard them talking about her. She spent 200 dollars in the store on clothes and jewellery—and then they just ignored her. They kept her waiting for more than half an hour before they wrapped what she had bought. Then she heard the floor manager saying 'Careful you don't under charge the nigger's tart. She's got more money than sense!"

For the first time Frank sees anger on Jack Johnson's face.

"I've had it to here with racial hatred. They call me a 'flash nigger'— because my fame and wealth has really gotten to them. When they pick on my woman I hate enough to want to kill someone." He put his large hands across those of Sophia and she smiles weakly in return.

The following day Frank goes to Gresham Hotel in Sackville Street to meet Jack and Sophia in their suite. He knocks on the door and is ushered in by the boxer. The music that is playing on a disc phonograph and speaker comes as a surprise. He had expected to hear Ragtime. Jack's cultural tastes are more sophisticated than he could possibly have imagined.

The Italian tenor Enrico Caruso is performing in a recording of his debut role as the Duke of Mantua in Verdi's *Rigoletto* at the Metropolitan Opera House in New York City in 1903. Johnson smiles at the surprised expression on Frank's face.

"Your finest opera singer, the tenor Joseph O'Mara, is Rodolfo in Puccini's *La Boheme* at the Theatre Royal next week. I missed his performance in London because it coincided with one of Tommy Burns' fights, but I can enjoy him here in Dublin."

Frank replies: "Leave it to us, it will be our treat. I'll get the tickets for *La Boheme* tomorrow."

"You know Frank if I hadn't been born black I would not have been a boxer. I had eight brothers and sisters and we were all clever. My daddy wanted me to be a scholar but I saw no point—those sons of bitches would have stopped me.

"Given the choice, I'd have been a classical pianist. One day there will be famous black opera singers because we are born to be baritones—but it probably won't happen in America this century. I've always loved music and inherited that from my slave parents. The Italian tenor Enrico Caruso is my favourite singer. I even listen to him during my training with weights in the gym."

The next day Johnson is due to be interviewed by Paddy Delaney of *The Irish Times* for a feature. He says he will be away for the morning and he suggests Frank should go round to the Gresham in the morning to spend some time with Sophia, who is still depressed. They sit on a Chesterfield at a coffee table by the window overlooking Sackville Street.

She is dressed in a red gown and wears a mink stole around her neck. Once again the diamonds are in evidence and they sparkle in the shafts of sunlight that pour into the room from the bright morning sky. The fragrance of her perfume envelopes him, creating a feeling of sexual awareness.

"I wasn't born for this Frank. I come from a simple Italian family. We had a tenement apartment in Queens. My papa and mama came to America from Genoa and worked in a fish canning factory. I have five sisters and papa just wanted us to marry Italian men and settle down and have big families. We had just enough money to get by, but by the time we were all working things were better.

"I had a good job as a waitress in a smart Italian restaurant. The future looked good. We worshipped our mama, went to church and lived sheltered lives in New York. I'd heard, like everyone else, that the famous

Negro fighter Jack Johnson was coming to town and then out of the blue there he was, in a mixed group of whites and blacks, sitting at the table I was serving."

She lit a cigarette and continued: "He noticed me at once and just stared with that big smile on his face, but said nothing.

"I found him attractive because he didn't come on to me. He was handsome and possessed an attitude to life I'd not encountered before. Jack was intelligent, witty and had a magnetism that attracted people. He was always dressed smartly and was forever the centre of attention."

He broke in: "It sounds as though you fell for him on that first meeting."

"Yes I went out with Jack the following day and quickly grew to love him, but as an Italian girl I soon found that loving Jack Johnson was a death sentence. In America I am thoroughly ostracized by white women who despise me for going with a black man and by Negro women who are jealous that he chose me."

She added sadly: "My mama and papa never forgave me for going with Jack Johnson and when I moved in with him no one from my Italian family wanted to know me any more. I tried writing to them, I even went round to my father's house but they shut the door in my face.

"All that means I don't have a friend in the world and when he walks out of my sight—which he does all the time—I am alone and trapped in a silent world, except for the opera music he leaves playing on the disc phonograph. I'm not supposed to tell anyone this but we are not married. I guess I'm just his whore.

"I have tried to compensate by indulging myself with all the trappings of wealth and material comfort. I'd exchange all the world cruises, the cars, the fur coats, gold, diamonds and expensive gowns for just one good friend."

She breaks down at this point, weeping uncontrollably into a handkerchief.

"There's more. You might not see it, but Jack is raging with fury beneath that cheerful exterior. There are so many powerful people in the USA who want to bring him down—even the Governor of South Carolina has called for Jack's public castration because he tells people he married me."

She beckons him closer to her on the Chesterfield and to his embarrassment pulls her dress up to her thighs to reveal gorgeously long legs. He is also confronted with a mass of black and yellow bruising. Frank gasps in horror.

"Sometimes the pressure from all the hatred and the racial taunts are too much and he explodes like a volcano when we are alone. I am the only person upon whom he can vent his rage. He hits me where he knows that the bruising will never be seen. Then he weeps in grief, asks for forgiveness and tries to repay me with overwhelming generosity. It makes me feel I'm being bought like a whore. One day I won't be able to take any more of this nightmare."

She removes the handkerchief from her face and looks at him: "I want my life back."

He is appalled. Her face is now close to his and their eyes meet in close scrutiny. He reads lust, hunger and desire in her expression and he feels drawn to kiss her—which he does lightly upon the cheek. Her fragrance arouses him to do more and in seconds they are locked in a passionate embrace, her tongue deep in his mouth. She feels his hands between her legs exploring and she gives encouragement seductively by touching him.

This is the first man who has been kind and considerate to her for three years and she decides at that moment to give herself to him—in her mind, by this adulterous act, she is unlocking the misery and constraint of subservience.

The act of making uninhibited love with a man she hardly knows seems to Sophia to shout brazen defiance against all that she has endured since meeting the boxer. She wishes the young Irishman would just carry her away into another world—and right then as they couple, in ecstatic passion, with her long legs around him, screaming out in her moment of climax, she feels she could love him forever.

4
THE RAPE OF LEUVEN AUGUST 1914

Nurse Emily Horstmann and her Red Cross field hospital unit arrived in the Belgian city of Leuven a few days after the fall of the Liege Forts in mid-August 1914. Leuven was a major rail junction and Dr Josef Lanz, the Swiss commander of the unit, believed that German trains carrying their wounded men and prisoners of war would soon arrive in the city.

There were few Belgian doctors left in Leuven as most had either joined the Army, or made their way towards Antwerp where the King was intending to make a stand in the fortified city. The absence of Belgian doctors and the scarcity of German doctors would be the opportunity for which Red Cross units like Emily's had been waiting.

"I think our real work starts soon," she told her room-mate, an Australian called Jackie Pretz from Woy Woy in New South Wales, who shared her passion for horses.

Jackie spoke German—like Emily—because her family also originated from Bavaria. It would be the start to Emily's war; her mission as a nurse to save lives in far away Europe. She had solemnly pledged to do this if a Continental war broke out.

Her medical colleagues at Culpepper Memorial Hospital, a small town hospital in Virginia where she had trained and qualified, were impressed by the resolve of their idealistic colleague from Boyce—but none shared her premonition of the coming war in Europe.

Emily was well known in the county where she lived. Having brought attention to herself for defending the rights of the Negro community when she was a child, she had moved on during her adolescent years to issues such as women's rights—she had joined the Suffragette Movement—and cruelty to animals, especially foxhunting.

It had not endeared her to the higher levels of society in Virginia and some had expressed satisfaction on hearing that she had left the USA for Europe. She also left a trail of broken hearts—having been engaged four times and broken it off on each occasion.

Emily had shown considerable foresight in deciding to take a long vacation across the Atlantic in the summer of 1914. She arrived—after passage on the *SS Lusitannia*—in Liverpool and made her way across the English Channel to Calais and then by train to the Munich home of her father's cousin, Helga Horstmann, in late May that year.

Within weeks of arriving in Munich, Emily's application to the Red Cross had been accepted as the European nations gradually teetered through failed diplomacy and hapless alliances to mobilization.

She wrote home to the family apple farm in Clarke County that she would not be returning in the autumn as originally planned. Emily now wore with great pride the white head dress, white apron with its red cross adorned at the front, and a full length white uniform. It symbolized her commitment to make her mark on the world.

Ada and Heinrich Horstmann were filled with anxiety, but resigned to the fact that their 24-year-old daughter would only return when she was ready to do so. The only mitigating factor for the Horstmanns was that people in the United States believed there would be only one decisive battle in Europe and then a peace treaty, long before Christmas, to bring an end to the fighting. No nation would want to fight a long war, it was argued, because conflict was damaging economically.

Emily cut a striking figure in her uniform. She was largely unaware that her beauty and innocent sexuality was already attracting attention on the streets of Leuven, both among the indigenous population and the Teutonic invaders.

She had high cheekbones, a large mouth, ice blue eyes, and stood six feet tall in her stockings. Her long curled auburn hair, kept tidily within the regulation plait, fell far below the shoulders to the lower regions of her back.

Emily had a full figure hardened from years of riding in the foothills of the mountains. She had been brought up to a life in the saddle. She knew about horses, but there had been nothing about men and their potentially lustful behaviour in this farmstead upbringing.

The Red Cross unit established itself on undeveloped land close to the entrance of the station. The German Surgeon-General had agreed with Dr Lanz that the field hospital should siphon off the less serious cases when the troop trains arrived and that it would treat only German casualties—so there would be no requirement for guards.

In the following four days while the Red Cross personnel waited, Emily explored the city and was struck by its elegance. It was tragic, she observed, that the people looked so dejected—but it was clear from the distant manner in which they treated the Germans that most of them retained, within their collective breast, a sense of pride for the bravery of their undefeated army. The King was the commander-in-chief and remained at the head of the Belgian forces in Antwerp.

The citizenry appeared confident that the Allies would soon rescue Belgium from her nightmare. Civilians meanwhile had been ordered not to resist. The German front-line troops had passed peacefully through Leuven on their way to the front but problems were created by the second grade Landsturm soldiers who were under orders to garrison the town.

These less disciplined troops plundered the cellars systematically and made such unreasonable requisitions that it became difficult for the citizens to get anything to eat. Emily was disturbed that most of the Germans were allowed to steal from the civilian population and pillage empty houses.

She complained to Dr Lanz but he shrugged his shoulders and dismissed it as nothing more than the historic custom of conquering armies. The vanquished, he told her, had to accept what defeat brought with it.

Emily was conscious of her neutrality. She was aware that she had—together with a smattering of Irish—German ancestry, but felt no sense of kinship with the men in their blue-grey uniforms, spiked helmets and leather boots. She had no experience of the American Army either—but was acutely aware that American soldiers were not terrified or awed by their officers.

The latter were expected to win respect not govern by terror. German army officers appeared to treat their troops with a disinterested contempt—like a lower life form—and their strutting manner, some with pince-nez spectacles on their great hooked noses, seemed to Emily to be laughably arrogant, haughty and humourless.

Things suddenly changed for the worse one afternoon when a siren was sounded and the German troops left their quarters hurriedly. The German Police Guard, which was stationed near the field hospital in a convent near the station, remained at their post, but quickly built a sandbag position around the entrance and mounted a machine-gun behind it.

Meanwhile, the nurses and doctors were summoned to meet Dr Lanz in the field hospital. Guns were booming loudly in the neighbourhood and the noise of rifle firing was distinctly audible.

Dr Lanz told the Red Cross unit: "I do not know what is going on but it is clear there is fighting in and around the city and it looks as though we could have a battle right on our own doorstep.

"Nobody seems to know whether this is an insurrection mounted by armed Belgian civilians, or a thrust from the south by French or British troops. I want everyone on stand-by to be prepared to receive casualties and we will remain on this state of alert until further notice."

Emily and Jackie waited for the influx of wounded men. Buildings were soon ablaze in the centre of the city and visibility obscured because of dense black smoke. The Rue de la Station became a battle ground when—for no apparent reason—the horses from the taxi-ranks and loading bays outside the station stampeded. The terrified animals bolted down the street overturning baggage wagons in the process.

There was a burst of rifle fire from the German police guard position. They had seen troops arriving in disorder from a distance and assumed it was the enemy. Now two separate detachments of German soldiers were firing on one another.

The members of the Red Cross Field Hospital Unit—caught in the middle—could see that a tragic mistake was being made and that Germans were killing other Germans. The heavy fire pinned them down so they were unable to intervene to stop the fighting.

"Crikey, this is ruddy madness," Jackie screamed in Emily's ear as they hid beneath the refuge provided by their ambulance. Flames were now soaring 50 feet above buildings in the street and around the station the air became thick with choking smoke.

Emily watched horrified as she noticed a group of German soldiers cautiously making their way up the street. They started shooting at fleeing civilians. She leapt to her feet and shouted as loudly as she could in German at the troops.

"For pity's sake you jerks—can't you see they are unarmed people—if you shoot them it will be murder . . ."

At once an orderly leapt upon Emily, pulling her painfully to the ground. "Don't sacrifice your own life for a useless protest. You are going to have important work to do," he told her.

She looked at him, adjusted her bonnet and shrugged, but there were tears in her eyes. Emily and Jackie noticed that wounded civilians— rather than soldiers—were now being brought in. There was a shoot to kill policy and gradually the field hospital began to admit men, women and even children with severe gunshot wounds. Emily was seething with fury and hatred towards the Germans as she dressed the wounds of the injured people with iodine.

A few yards away the surgical team led by Dr Lanz was trying to cope with the severely wounded. Dr Lanz and his assistant had already carried out more than 20 operations, mostly amputations. Their aprons were covered in blood which dripped off the operating table onto the floor. The scene resembled a butcher's shop.

One of the orderlies was pouring bowls of blood into larger buckets and a second struggled—ignoring the intermittent rifle fire—with the weight of two large buckets of crimson waste to a street drain, where he poured it away.

The surgeons directed the medical staff to dispose of amputated limbs and other human offal into dustbins at the back of the operating theatre. The field hospital presented a ghastly spectacle, well beyond anything that Emily and Jackie had ever experienced in civilian life.

Many patients were screaming in agony despite have been administered with ether or morphine. She took a cup of steaming coffee over to a frail old man who had brought in his injured wife. She had been shot below the knee in the right leg.

"What happened old man?" she asked him in French.

He replied in a high pitched voice between sobs. "We were forced from our house and tried to flee down the street. This senior German officer searched me and found shares, money, and my savings bank book to the value of more than 7,000 francs. He put them in his pocket and laughed. When my wife implored him not to take our life savings he took out his revolver and shot her in the leg.

"The officers and soldiers told us that we had been taken prisoner because civilians had fired upon the troops. Half-burnt corpses of our neighbours were lying in front of the houses in our street."

Emily was incandescent with rage at this callous injustice. Shortly before dawn, Dr Lanz found time to summon another meeting of the unit, following a conversation that he had had with a German colonel.

"I was told that Belgian civilians all over the city have risen up against the Germans and that is why they are shooting them and setting fire to the buildings. He told me 3,000 rifles had been found in a church and he warned us that shots had also been fired from Red Cross ambulances upon the Germans.

"Not our ambulances I should add—but nevertheless I do not have to tell you that maintaining strict neutrality, no matter what we see or hear, is absolutely essential if we are to be allowed to continue operating."

Emily heard herself shrieking in reply at the doctor: "Godammit, innocent folk are being shot down in cold blood here—what do you mean we can't take sides?

"You should tell that darned German officer that we are going to give a full account of what we have seen to the relevant authorities!"

The doctor replied sharply: "Miss Horstmann when I need advice from you I'll let you know—meantime just do the job you've been sent here to do and shut your eyes to everything else."

"The hell I will," she replied loudly and walked off. She heard a loud laugh behind her and turned to find it was Jackie.

"Good on you sport—you spoke for all of us," she said. When they got back a queue of civilians had arrived for either treatment or for sanctuary from the Germans.

The night had now passed and Emily calculated that she had treated at least 60 people herself and passed a further 20 on to the operating theatre for surgery. She sought out a coffee and a bread roll to relieve her nagging appetite—she had not eaten anything since early in the previous afternoon. At the field kitchen she found Jackie. Uncharacteristically the young Australian was weeping and shaking as she smoked a cigarette.

"Come on nurse, don't take it personally, or we'll have to send you back to Woy Woy," joked Emily. Her friend continued to sob.

"I've had a letter from Australia," she explained between sobs. "What's happened is awful and I can't believe it did in my country. The German community in Woy Woy is under siege from mobs of people coming out on the train from Sydney bent on destroying shops and homes.

"My people out there in Australia are completely innocent of what these bastards are up to—but how am I expected to feel when I see the terrible things that are happening here and the Germans, some of them could be relations of mine, are doing it. I feel ashamed."

"Goddamit Jackie, you're not a Kraut, you're Australian, just as I'm American. I'm not going to take responsibility for what these morons are doing—even though I do have a German name. Out there in the streets of Leuven you've got the sort of half-wits who my ma and pa took a lot of trouble to get away from and start a new life. I feel no guilt on their behalf and neither should you!"

Jackie explained tearfully that during the night a family had come in from a small farm on the outskirts of Leuven. The father had been beaten up brutally by the soldiers and his wife had been shot deliberately in the foot. Their 14-year-old daughter had clung to her mother in terror and was then forcibly torn from her. Two soldiers had stripped the girl naked and violated her.

Courageously she had resisted and was consequently bayoneted twice in the stomach. Dr Lanz had been unable to save her life and was himself in a state of shock. The entire unit was talking of nothing else.

"Christ someone get me a gun and I'll shoot some of these jerks myself," Emily shouted in an outburst to Jackie—forgetting her vows as a nurse to save life rather than to take it.

By midday Emily and Jackie had heard about so many atrocities that they decided to keep a book recording what they had been told. They would somehow get it to the US Legation in Brussels. Emily and Jackie spent at least 12 hours a day in the field hospital over the next week, but found time to walk the city collecting witness statements for the American Legation.

Dr Lanz called them into his office and ordered them to hand over the dossier and to stop collecting witness statements. He warned them it jeopardized the neutral position of the Red Cross. They refused to hand over what had now become a substantial dossier but said they would take no further statements.

In fact they ignored Dr Lanz. It was a highly risky undertaking but they agreed there was no need for him to know anything about it. They decided they should tell no one else in the unit.

"I think we'll be safe as long as we stick together, do this in daylight, and stay within walking distance of our base," said the Australian nurse. They continued to carry out their work at the dressing station, looking after wounded civilians rather than soldiers. Gradually their dossier was filled up with details of atrocities.

The accounts of the atrocities would have shocked any civilized reader. Emily called at a large house in the Rue de Namur. She wrote down a witness statement from a Belgian policeman. It had her literally shaking with rage.

He said: "My attention was drawn to a house by reason of a number of people who were close to the window of a room on the second floor apparently struggling with one another.

"A girl was trying to attract the attention of people in the street—so as not to let those in the room know that she was doing so. I looked and saw 14 or 15 German soldiers, some of whom were evidently trying to force some girls—who seemed to be from 17 to 25 years of age—down on to the floor.

"I then went with three other men into the house and we found the mother tied up in a chair in a room on the ground floor and afterwards found the dead father hanging by the neck from a beam.

"Four hysterical girls came downstairs. Their dresses were torn and their breasts were exposed, the youngest in particular having almost the entire front of her dress torn away. Only the eldest was able to speak, the rest being too much overcome to do so. She said she had been violated by two men, the youngest by four, the third by three and the second by two.

"The girl who had attracted my attention from the window showed me a wound in her left side under the breast where she had been pierced by the bayonet of one of the Germans when he saw what she was doing and the poor girl was in great pain for it was still bleeding."

Each night the nurses stapled all the pages into one manuscript and enclosed it in a large red folder before hiding it under Emily's mattress. They asked themselves repeatedly for an explanation for what had gone wrong with the German mind; a people who until recently had seemed to embrace the most virtuous and sophisticated of Christian values.

One night there was violent knocking on the door of the girls' quarters in the Hotel de Rail.

"OK I'm coming, have some patience please," called out Emily as she put on a dressing gown over her night-clothes.

When she opened the door she was confronted by a German officer, four soldiers and an anxious Dr Lanz. The German officer spoke first.

"I want the nurses Emily Horstmann and Jackie Pretz. Are they here?"

"Yeah, what do you want?" asked Jackie pushing her way to the front of the group crowding the door to the room. She whispered behind her hand to Emily who giggled.

"Bloody krauts, what do they want?"

"Red Cross nurses Emily Horstmann and Jackie Pretz are under arrest and will accompany me to the barracks. Dress quickly please," said the officer sharply

Letter to James Ernest Clarke August 23rd 1914

Dear old boy,

I've certainly had a few adventures and now we are waiting to do battle with Fritz tomorrow at Mons who is on his way from Brussels which is occupied by the enemy. We are eager to try our luck against him but unfortunately the news from the French is not good. They have been pushed back and our task is to confront the German Army here—for the moment we do not know where their forward elements are.

They have shown themselves to be aggressive and brave and prepared to sustain heavy losses. At the same time we are receiving reports of atrocities upon civilians from several towns in Belgium along the frontier in the Ardennes.

We arrived at Le Havre and were transported north by train disembarking at Le Cateau on the border where we spent three days in preparation for our march into Belgium. We were billeted in Pommereuil—a small village—and were ordered to spend the time improving the fitness of the reservists with route marches accompanied fortunately by the platoon corporals.

It left us sergeants off the hook. One evening the mess organised a lorry to take a party of senior NCOs into town. Le Cateau is the birthplace of Henri Matisse and also famous as a manufacturing centre of cotton.

In three weeks the population of Le Cateau has mushroomed to 50,000 because of the British and French troops quartered here. The character of the town has altered overnight with the influx of soldiers—the narrow streets are choked with horse drawn military transport and trucks. Brothels have been set up in some backstreet hotels and whores from Paris inhabit them.

We wandered up the slope to the town centre enjoying the aroma of nosh and flirting with the local girls. Our khaki uniforms are a stark contrast to the French soldiers who wear baggy red trousers and long blue coats, like the cast of some comic opera. We went into a brothel in a hotel down a narrow cobbled street. Its interior was lit by red bulbs and Chinese lanterns. After handing over the equivalent of a pound in francs, we were ushered by an elderly woman with a cigarette in her mouth to a salon on the ground floor.

A collection of whores from teen to middle-age sat in the salon. Some were knitting things, others read magazines and a group of four were playing a card game with their spare coins. I decided to catch the attention of a tall dark girl in her mid-20s with long wavy hair brushed back over her ears. She had generous red lips and wore hoop earrings, but too much make-up—probably to conceal her acne. She was reading a book intently but looked up when I coughed and winked at me.

'I am Marie,' she smiled as she placed her little hand in mine, before leading me out of the door and up a narrow staircase. The air on the landing—and more so in the tiny bedroom—was heavily scented.

A small basin stood on a pedestal by the single bed. She filled it with water and gestured to me to come to her. I took off my trousers and she washed my best friend in a perfumed soap.

'Tommy—Parlez-vous Francais?'

'Un petit peu, madamoiselle,' I replied politely.

'I will speak in English then,' she continued, obviously unimpressed with my schoolboy accent.

'No kiss, no touch le breast, or le minge,' she warned.

She then lay back on the bed and opened her legs to expose what reminded me of a small beaver run over by a cartwheel. Marie pointed at it and winked at me again.

You will be delighted to know old boy that I at this moment I realised I was not interested in sex with a woman who might give me a dose of the pox.

'Pardon, mademoiselle, mais je pense que peut-etre j'ai mal," I muttered, adding: "Vous etes tres belle," in a foolish attempt to redeem her dignity before making my hasty exit.

As I descended the stairs I met Colour Sergeant Sid Gunn who grinned and rubbed his genitals. I settled for a big meal instead of a tumble with the whore—having jugged hare like we used to get in Norfolk and a good bottle of Medoc. The whole point of the evening—as you will know as an officer—was to get rid of the stress that had been building up since we left Belfast.

It's the real bloody thing this time. I slept well that night thanks to the wine. We set off last week over some of the roughest cobbled roads in northern Europe, covering nearly 40 miles in two stages. It was tough in the heat wave,

It was gruelling stuff but only a few dropped out in my platoon. Some of the older reservists did not make it. They were left where they fell.

The rolling meadow vista of this part of Northern France is dotted with tidy farmhouses and cottages and the fields at this time of the summer are gold with corn and barley ripening for the harvest. Endless lines of poplar trees mark the roads.

Heavy vegetation grows along the sides the lanes, the hedges untrimmed and the edges of the fields and meadows covered in poppies, specks of bloodshot red on the golden canvas. There are orchards heavy with fruit and large white cows grazing upon the lush grass and wild plants. It all seemed a paradox that we were going to war.

Do you remember Cyril "The Voice" Bartram, who was lead tenor in the choir at the Church of St Michael and All Angels Aylsham? He's a Corporal now and he led the singing in our platoon with 'I didn't raise my boy to be a soldier' and other songs.

In some villages the local inhabitants stood outside their homes and shouted encouragement. The farms are now being cultivated by old men, women and children. Women in the villages offered cups of wine or cider but the soldiers were not allowed to drink because it could cause dehydration.

In the sky French scout planes flew overhead to mark out the progress being made by the columns below—there appeared to be no sign of German aircraft at this stage. From the air at 3,000 feet, in highly visible conditions marred only by heat haze, the advancing British Expeditionary Force made an extraordinary spectacle—not seen on this part of the Continent for nearly 100 years, when Napoleon made his last throw of the dice at Waterloo.

Each soldier carried the weight equivalent of a small man on his back and many were troubled by the thick material and prickly surface of the uniform. The roughness caused particularly unpleasant chaffing in sensitive areas of the body like the back of the neck and in a heat-wave the irritation was depressing.

When sweat from the body permeated the coarse uniform fabric, it lost even the faintest trace of softness and became stiff like cardboard.

The high neck collar is another daft feature of the British Army uniform. The men undid the three top buttons of the uniform and placed handkerchiefs around their neck to soak up sweat.

The white handkerchiefs became drenched within minutes but provided some relief to the discomfort. The general distress of the men was exacerbated by the brand new boots worn by each private soldier—it was the bright idea of Brigade's Commanding Officer to issue new boots on the eve of war. Feet were blistered and gradually the men limped. I had wisely kept my old boots, refusing to exchange them.

At dusk when we reached the turnip field chosen to bivouac two of the Companies, not one man volunteered a brew, not one tin of scoff was opened. The men placed their rifles and bandoliers carefully on dry ground and sank to the earth where they stood, head resting on kitbag. Most were asleep within seconds.

A few moments before, dozens of regimental horses and mules had been calling out in the fields around them. They had been unhitched at last from their wagons and were waiting impatiently for their fodder and water. As soon as they got their hay and drink they too fell silent, the evening breeze subsided and there was a discernible stillness as night descended.

The bright skies reminded me of East Africa. I was transfixed by the infinite number of stars blazing above, spread out in a colossal galaxy. As I fell asleep I pondered which of the stars above me would be the arbiter of my own particular destiny but felt neither fear nor apprehension about my fate.

As our father once said, we are but insignificant particles of dust in the universe. There is not too much point in worrying. I'll drop you another line old chap after the battle—please tell our mother not to worry about me.

Congratulations on your commission—see you soon in France!

Yours sincerely,

Frank W Clarke

5
THE BATTLE OF MONS 1914

The German bombardment along the Mons Conde Canal had started. They advanced in overwhelming force across the flat meadows nearly a mile away. The British infantry prepared their lines quickly under the lash of shrapnel so deadly that the men had to lie flat on their stomachs as they dug.

Artillery fire from British guns rained down upon the blue-grey lines of German infantry but they moved forward relentlessly. Those few who survived the Great War who were at Mons remembered the sabre and lances of the German cavalry glinting in the sun.

The massed but independent fire from the British positions at 800 yards had a devastating effect. Within minutes, the battlefield was littered with the German dead and wounded. The British were jubilant. They had taught the Germans a lesson in trying to move in massed formation against the best riflemen in Europe.

The Germans moved back to the screen of the woodland. In just a quarter of an hour, the contempt felt by them for the small British forces had been replaced by respect and fear.

The Germans were shouting: "The Tommies have got dozens of machine guns!"

In fact there were only two machine guns allocated to each Battalion. The enemy moved forward again and again. The German artillery high explosive and shrapnel shells, fired from the heart of the screening woods, continued to thunder down upon the BEF forward and outpost positions in front of the canal in a roar that perforated eardrums.

The sky above the waiting British became palled with the dirty clouds of exploding shrapnel and the earth was threshed with the metallic hail from down-slashing balls of hot steel.

Sergeant Clarke's men listened with impatience and frustration to the sounds of the battle taking place not much more three miles to the north-east. They were professional soldiers and these unfolding events were what many men had joined up for—to fight the Boche.

The Platoon Commander's attention was distracted from the thump, thump, thump, of heavy artillery by the sound of approaching aircraft over the Brigade's trenches. Two biplanes, with black crosses on their wings, circled directly over the positions of the four Battalions. They were flying at 2,000 feet, reporting the positions of the second line defences and gun emplacements to the rear of Brigade where the batteries were located.

Through his field glasses Lt Ernest Briard could see the observers were using hand-operated Deitz morse-disc machines to transmit information to the artillery on the ground several miles away.

The men turned over and aimed their rifles into the air hoping to kill the pilot and observer in each German biplane, or inflict sufficient damage upon the aircraft to bring it tumbling down to earth. Three or four initial volleys were directed at the aeroplanes as they circled.

Nobby Clarke crouched low in a dell next to the Platoon Commander and he exchanged glances with the young officer. Both realised the aircraft were out of range and he shouted at the men.

"Cease fire—listen to what Mr Briard has to tell you"

The officer addressed the men. "Thank you Sarnt Clarke. Wait until those aircraft descend lower to take a closer look at us. Right now they are out of range. Don't waste ammunition."

Frank knew that stalking aircraft from the ground would be similar to fishing. Calm and patience would be the telling factor. The German pilots were still relatively inexperienced at this stage of the war and they were probably over confident because no French aircraft were in the vicinity.

German pilots were recruited from the Junker (officer) Classes. The prospect of being brought down by a bullet fired from the rifle of a common soldier was unthinkable; beneath contempt. He reasoned there was a good chance one of the aristocratic young German pilots would soon succumb to temptation—and fly too low over the British lines. He was right. The leading biplane in the circling formation dipped its wings, rolled over and descended to under 400 feet. It was cocky arrogance.

"Right, he's coming," screamed the Platoon Commander. Wait for my order."

The aircraft was getting close and flew parallel to their position.

"Hold your fire, hold, hold, hold. . . . .fire!"

Nearly 100 rounds from the 30 rifles went skyward over the next few seconds as the aeroplane flew past at around 90 miles per hour. Frank was easily the best shot in the Platoon and managed to get off six rounds. The machine passed laboriously overhead and appeared to have been immune to the hail of bullets fired at it seconds earlier. The men were mute in their disappointment.

Then black smoke billowed out of the engine, the beating sound of the motor became erratic, the fuselage shivered, caught fire, crumpled and then fell in a trailing wreck across the sky. It was out of control and plunged into a slag heap about half a mile to the west. A huge cheer went up along the Battalion line as the German aircraft burned in fury on the slag.

"Oh I love this Sarge," said Ralph, his ruddy face beaming with happiness.

"I doubt we've seen anything yet," he told him. "But it's a good start nonetheless!" The Battalion waited for the rest of the afternoon in nervous anticipation for their turn to face the onslaught, or to plug a gap where one was required.

The flash and rumble of artillery was unceasing and shells continued to explode just behind them. Twice Nobby and several other soldiers were blown off their feet by the concussion of a bursting shell—the shrapnel missing them somehow. The whine of incoming shells and the resulting falling shards of red hot metal filled the air around the Battalion.

It made them crave for the opportunity to retaliate but they stood fast. He felt a strong ringing in his ears and realised his hearing had deteriorated. They felt a curious mixture of anticipation, fear and a sense of wanting to find out just how effective their meticulous training had been.

Was peacetime training like the real thing or was it a completely different thing? Parade ground NCOs—and many of the arms instructors—had always insisted that the rules had to be followed rigidly. The men were warned that to make up their own set of rules could be fatal.

Fatal—now that was a word. Death was something that none of them had considered too seriously. Maybe a serious wound—but not death. No one expected to die, yet the concept of fighting to the last man was somehow not alien to them because it was about their mates, not so much King and Country.

Whatever each man did that day he'd do for the lads around him and just that. If they were to die it would be together. It was the boys who mattered. Next in the list of priorities came the honour of the Regiment.

A man can be trained to the highest level but only finds out if he's a real soldier under the test of battle. They were well bonded. They were also virgin soldiers—like so many before and after them—and the truth was they didn't know a bloody thing yet. It wouldn't be long before they found out. By mid-afternoon the situation was becoming critical only four miles away on the right flank. The remaining troops lined along the canal on the left flank were in an exposed position.

The Germans were moving across to the west. At any moment the enemy might break through. The Platoon had waited in its position all day for the expected mass attack but to their disappointment it had not materialised. Now the Germans could appear any moment. British troops had been coming through their positions in orderly formation, but in a state of exhaustion. Some of the weary men who had borne the brunt of the fighting warned the soldiers that Fritz was not far away.

"Christ I hate this bloody waiting. I just wish we could have a shot at them," said Bill Bagley, the Platoon pessimist.

The men around him chuckled. Tension had heightened as expectation of a fight grew—the Germans had pushed back the canal line so could attack them on their flank. They were not frightened so much as frustrated. They'd soon deal with bloody Fritz. A cyclist orderly arrived at the Platoon's position looking for the Platoon Commander. Ernest Briard had already attended a meeting at Company Headquarters but was instructed to attend a further briefing at the Headquarters of the First Battalion Norfolk Regiment.

The Germans had called a halt to their advance in the darkness. The shelling had stopped but even the private soldiers knew it would resume again at dawn. The Platoon was despondent when Lt Briard returned with the news of the Battalion's move to the south-west as a re-alignment to cover the withdrawal of Division. The flankguard would comprise the Norfolks, the Cheshires and a battery of Field Artillery under the command of their own Colonel. Bill inevitably saw it as a bad omen which he expounded to the nearest men around him.

"We haven't even had a pop at the Fritz yet and we're bloody told we've got to withdraw. I hate bloody withdrawals—nobody knows what the fuck's going on and you end up having to fight here there and everywhere. The Generals gave us this bullshit about fighting to the last man. Why can't we just hold fast and take the bastards out when they come?"

Nobby overheard Bill.

"When Battalion needs your expert strategic judgement it'll ask for it."

The order to withdraw had come, nevertheless, as a disappointment to the men and there was murmuring in the shell scrapes as the dusk turned into night. The German artillery had ceased its bombardment. The men slept fitfully. Nobby was relaxed, filled in his diary and dreamed of cricket.

BOWLING REVERSE SWING—DIARY MAY 1914

A superb ground at Aldershot in Hampshire is the venue. The green wicket is in perfect condition having been pampered by the grounds man for three weeks in preparation for this game. No other match has been allowed to take place upon it since the end of the previous season. This is because today's fixture is an important cup match played annually between the 15th Infantry Brigade and the Cavalry—and I am playing in it.

There have been several days of rain in the previous week in Hampshire but this day is of the rare azure type—the kind of windless enchanting summer morning of which English poets write about in their romantic sonnets. The sun in a cloudless sky beats down in a heat haze remorselessly upon the players and gentlemen in the field and particularly upon the pace bowlers. The fast bowlers have to be exceptionally fit and we are.

I have been invited not only to play, but as a recognised seam bowler who can make the ball swing, to open for our side. It is an honour for me to travel from Belfast to southern England to play senior representative Army cricket. In fact it is the biggest sporting moment of my life—greater even than playing for Monkstown RFC in the Senior Leinster Cup nearly 10 years ago. Last season I took more wickets than any other seam bowler in the Brigade and at 31 years of age people say I am in my prime.

Some even suggest that if the Norfolks had been stationed at Aldershot instead of Belfast—and had I been an officer—I might have been asked to play county cricket. Actually I lack ambition. I play sport just for pleasure and am content to be involved in Army cricket enjoying the time I get off to practice. I am content that this season I am stronger, faster and more subtle than in any previous year. I have no real desire to progress any further. I enjoy being in a good team.

Play starts at 10.30am and the Cavalry wins the toss and puts us in to bat. The innings lasts for nearly four hours before we are all out for 225—my small contribution is 15 runs, going in at eight and that includes three boundaries before being caught deep in the field.

After lunch our captain gives us a briefing before the Cavalry opening batsmen walk out of the gentlemen's section of the pavilion. There is an excited buzz in the crowd of several hundred spectators.

'It's going to be touch and go chaps. They've only really got one batsman and we must find a way of keeping him off strike—while we get rid of the others.

'It's down to the quality of our bowling and concentration in the field. Nobby, I think you are going to open OK?'

I nod but am not given the opportunity to direct the fielders as I would want to—being a mere NCO. An officer is always right. I take my customary 12 steps up from the umpire's wicket before turning to see the opening batsman tapping the ground with his bat at the crease. It is Francis Grenfell. He is something of a legend in Army cricket and has achieved fame early in his life by scoring 80 runs at Lords for Eton—in the annual cricket match against Harrow in 1899.

Grenfell is known throughout the Army to be a fearless batsman possessed with an uncanny ability to anticipate—before the ball leaves the bowler's hand—what he is going to receive. Grenfell never seems to hurry into anything.

I do not intend to be overawed by his reputation. I will bowl right arm over the wicket initially and vary the speed and length of my deliveries with a good line just on or outside the off-stump.

I will also intersperse the regular deliveries with out-swingers bowling on the other side of the wicket while the ball is in good condition. This is the way I always try to play my game. Consistency is everything. I will stay patient and accept that Grenfell is going to get a few runs before he becomes over-confident.

I run purposefully up to the wicket and deliver a fast ball that whisks past the off stump and into the keeper's hand. Grenfell lifts his bat in a languid manner to avoid playing the ball and seems to be more interested in studying the flight of the ball and its acceleration off the surface of the wicket.

'Good ball Nobby,' cry the two fielders in the slips interpreting Grenfell's lack of response to mean hesitation and perhaps even indecision. Grenfell turns and smiles at them. I pitch the second ball further up the wicket, outside the off stump and slowing its delivery.

This will give Grenfell plenty of time to come forward and smash it to the outfield—perhaps with luck a lofted shot that might just bring a catch. Grenfell ignores this ball too.

'Excellent stuff Nobby—you've got him rattled old man,' cries one of the slips. Grenfell nonchalantly gives the ground ahead of him a couple of soft taps with the end of his bat and takes his stance again thoughtfully.

'Right, I'll see if there's any bounce in this wicket and deliver one short—right on the middle stump," I think to myself. I accelerate down to the umpire and use every ounce of my strength to deliver a short length on mid wicket. The ball hits the ground five yards ahead of Grenfell and pitches high into the air towards his head. He ducks and lets it pass without trying to play a stroke. The keeper just manages to collect it.

'Horrific stuff Nobby, that's horrific stuff,' the keeper chuckles. Grenfell smiles again.

'That bastard Grenfell is already getting to me and he knows it,' I say to myself as I walk up past the wicket to start my run for the fourth ball.

'For Christ's sake don't let him put you off your stroke. Just play your normal game Clarkey," I whisper.

I am irritated by the lack of response from Grenfell and bowl another short length which bounces past his head again. I am heading for a maiden, not a bad start, but possibly a pyrrhic victory. The fifth ball is a nasty 'Yorker' and misses the off stump narrowly with Grenfell again just watching it closely.

I bowl the final ball, a fast one just wide of the off-stump but swinging onto it. It is a dangerous ball on which to play an aggressive stroke. Grenfell will not let me have my maiden. He springs forward like a panther and cracks it with sublime confidence towards the boundary. It speeds with such force to the outfield that none of the fielders come anywhere near it.

Grenfell is off the mark and I feel instinctively that this batsman is in another class. I think the Infantry bowlers are going to suffer. I bowl a further six overs before I am rested with the score at 65 runs for no wicket. Grenfell scores 55 of them, including five boundaries off me and the Cavalry now appears to be getting the upper hand against our indifferent bowling.

I have tried my entire repertoire—but nothing in my box of tricks seems to disturb Grenfell's easy rhythm. Fortunately the Cavalry do not possess batting strength in great depth—as the captain has anticipated correctly.

The Infantry bowling gradually dismisses each of Grenfell's partners until the score is 185–5 with Grenfell on 120 and looking indestructible, having scored four sixes. I am recalled and instructed to get rid of the tail-enders as quickly as possible before Grenfell can take the Cavalry to 226.

"Don't worry too much about Francis Grenfell. He's a law unto himself. Just keep him under control Nobby and bowl the bastard bouncers," instructs the captain.

As I walk up past the wicket to make a mark I notice the poor condition of the ball—which has altered considerably since the opening of the innings. It has suffered in the impact with the pavilion roof from two of Grenfell's sixes.

In regimental cricket I am recognised as one of the few exponents around quick enough to get the ball to reverse swing. Most know the drill but few can do it—keep one side battered dry and rough, soak the 'clean' side with sweat and let the aerodynamics take over.

The ball should swing through the air either inwards or outwards—but late in the delivery it will suddenly change direction and confuse the batsman. In just a split second, as the trajectory alters, even an experienced batsman might "prod" in error at the ball.

Ball tampering has been around since before the turn of the 20th century but the question remains—is it cheating or gamesmanship?

I prefer to look at it as gamesmanship, indeed as an art form. Blatant scratching one side of the ball is cheating, but manipulating the ball, keeping one side dry and letting the other side rough up, is perfectly legitimate in my book.

There is a line you shouldn't step over but operating just either side of it is part of the game—something we ordinary players are content to call gamesmanship, whereas the gentleman players might not. Indeed, some players, not quite gentlemen, go as far as scratching the ball with a bottle-top kept in the trouser pocket or even a strip of sandpaper. A few are quite outrageous and lift the quarter seam before picking at it.

The wicket at Aldershot has been in perfect condition early in the innings and tricks like reverse swing are virtually impossible to perform on well covered wickets with a new ball. Now I feel it is worth a try especially since the afternoon is humid. I feel in the mood to give it a go with such an old ball.

I want to get Grenfell out—not draw blood. Bugger bowling bouncers.

'There is no bloody way Grenfell is still going to be around at the end of this innings,' I say to myself as I walk to my mark. I examine the ball again and realise that one of the other Infantry bowlers has obviously been scratching it with his finger nails.

"Now that is naughty!" I exclaim to myself—and chuckle. Someone else is after Grenfell too. I continue the process surreptitiously after and extend my run up to 15 paces from the wicket to give myself more time.

I have been successful with reasonable consistency at the nets in Belfast in getting battered old balls to swing early in the delivery and then to reverse—giving their trajectory an S-shape through the air. The way I place the ball in my hand is critical. The seam must be angled in the same way as in conventional swing—10-20 degrees to one side—and the net effect of the seam and rough side is that the ball should swing in the direction opposite to where the seam is pointing.

I now stand facing Grenfell for the start of my second spell and align the seam and the sides of the ball slightly to the left towards the slips. I run up and at the point of delivery rotate my wrist towards the slips while keeping my arm straight.

The ball moves away to the offside but on the bounce swings back into the batsman as it comes onto him. Grenfell misses it completely and nearly falls to an inside edge.

"What a beauty Nobby. You've really foxed him," encourage the slips. I manage to get reverse swing into two more balls during the same over and Grenfell scores two more runs. The Cavalry officer continues to survive my reverse swing—but four of the Cavalry's tail-end wickets fall in the next six overs.

The score creeps up to 222-9 with Grenfell due to face me for the first ball of the last over. A four will do it for the Cavalry. I feel instinctively that Grenfell might be vulnerable to an outside edge to the wicket keeper or slips—if I can maintain consistency with the reverse swing.

The ball is by now in extremely poor condition and I am surprised the Cavalry batsmen do not bring it to the attention of the umpires. I run up and deliver another bouncer which soars over Grenfell's head and I notice a smile on his face.

'No you sod—I'm not going to scare you out, I know that,' I say to myself.

I take a risk with the next ball and bowl a 'Yorker' on the middle stump which Grenfell comes onto with his immaculate footwork and drives the ball past me towards deep mid-off.

It is retrieved for two runs and the Cavalry now need just two to win—but they are defending their last wicket. Grenfell is on strike which means this could be it. I run in towards the wicket sprinting hard and deliver the dilapidated ball with every ounce of my strength.

It flies in towards the batsman, bounces and then performd its extraordinary shape as it comes on to Grenfell.

At first I think he is going to be cool and ignore it—but Grenfell cannot afford to take the risk. He has to play it and he knows it. The ball nicks the edge of the outside of his bat and it flies safely into the keeper's gloves.

"Ouzat?" and there is never any doubt in the umpire's mind. The Cavalry are all out for 224. The Infantry wins by just one run.

In the players' changing room where I am alone I find a bottle of stout and a note which says: 'Well played Sergeant, Captain Grenfell.'

'What a condescending bastard,' I think and chuckle to myself as I remove the top with my teeth—taking a long swig from the bottle in a not very gentlemanly fashion. I might as well enjoy it, even though the officers are drinking champagne in the pavilion. I doubt whether there will be any peacetime cricket next season; the Kaiser will see to that.

6

THE ACTION AT ELOUGES

"Now we'll have a go at Fritz eh!" Tinker whispers to Ralph They inch forward along a hedgerow looking out for German scouts.

"I'm just itching to get one of those fuckers in my sights," he adds.

In the distance they see the CO being approached by a staff officer—also on horseback—at a crossroads.

The latter then gallops off. Fifteen minutes later the Platoon Commander gives Frank an explanation.

"Sarnt, Battalion has been ordered to move back from here towards Elouges. Get the men on the road and moving now at the double."

They arrive at the position a mile from the village shortly after 1100 hours. The men are not so much cynical as bewildered. Why are they moving back again before any contact with the enemy has been made? The soldiery just want to have a crack at the Germans. Company Commanders are ordered to disperse their platoons along a north to south ridge less than three thousand yards long.

A narrow sunken road runs parallel with the ridge for most of its length. Two mineral railway lines intersect the road via two bridges over steep embankments. Slag heaps form the rear of the positions occupied by the two Battalions.

The ridge in front of Nobby's Platoon overlooks undulating meadows interspersed with hedges and rows of poplar trees which run down to thick woodland. Beyond it is the highway from Mons to Valenciennes along which the German Army is approaching. The position commands an excellent field of fire over the meadows—both to left and right—which are covered by corn stooks.

It is a good position, but overall the companies of both Battalions are too widely dispersed which in the absence of signals equipment will make communication between them difficult. Both Battalions will be visible to the enemy but the British will have a wide arc of fire. Their weakness is the undulating ground—and the distance between the Companies—because in some cases no visual contact will exist between them. Furthermore, there has been no time to dig in, apart from rudimentary shell scrapes large enough to accommodate two or three soldiers which are only deep enough to cover the body.

Bill points to the woodland in the valley below and says darkly to the men after taking a peek over the embankment:

"That's where the bastards will come from, you can be sure of that. It'll be just our luck if they decide to attack right opposite where we are."

Nobby hears him: "You're right Bill they will come from there and they know we are here so it's just a matter of time now. It doesn't matter though.

"We've got a textbook field of fire. They've got to cover 800 yards over open ground and they've got to get through our field of fire. It's the covering of our flank to the south and north that we've got to worry about when the other units of Division retire behind us."

As the men run up and down the embankment bringing up ammunition from the boxes carried by mules, they disturb swarms of butterflies including *Small Tortoiseshells, Peacocks,* and *Red Admirals.* These scatter in panic from the long grass which is covered with embankment brambles, ripening blackberries and red poppies.

The erratic flight of these butterflies and the sounds of the countryside—including the song of skylark and meadow pipit and the cooing calls of wood pigeon—add to the feeling of unreality. Is all this a dream on a hot summer's afternoon? It somehow doesn't seem the right backdrop for the coming hell in which people are going to die.

They have a fine view over the valley. Provided they are not decimated by German shellfire, Lt Colonel Charles Ballard estimates they should hold off any frontal attack for two hours. He hopes that is all the time Division will need to put some distance between themselves and the Germans as they fall back in retreat. He knows the men will soon have to deal with the enemy coming at them from the west and the north.

The men now wait in the sunshine. In the far distance gunfire gradually becomes louder. The men drink tea, play dice and cards—having made their final weapons inspection. Some sing to absorb the awful tension. The Battalion chaplain moves among the relaxing soldiers and many say prayers with him.

Ralph says quietly: "This waiting's really bloody getting to me Sarge. You don't think they've all fucked off back to Berlin do you."

Nobby grins at the men, concealing his own deep anxiety.

"No way Colby, not while they've got a chance of blowing your head off!"

The enemy shelling of their position starts shortly after Midday. The incoming fire is from a German battery somewhere along the main road from Mons on the far side of the valley which the two Battalions overlook. Both Commanding Officers know it is a prelude to a major attack. Twenty minutes later the Cavalry arrive. The men of the Platoon watch spellbound as a squadron of Lancers clatter over the railway line less than 200 yards ahead of their position. The Cavalry intends to charge at the German flank as they begin advancing up the meadow slopes.

Cocker says: "Christ Sarge look at this. It's a re-run of the Charge of the Light Brigade!"

"It looks bloody suicidal to me," says Frank as he watches the extraordinary spectacle and listens to the thundering of hoof upon hard turf. He has borrowed the Platoon Commander's field glasses for a few moments and follows the progress of the Cavalrymen as they charge down the valley. He recognizes the officer leading the squadron—it is his recent cricket adversary Francis Grenfell. The Lancers charge on regardless of casualties. Men are falling from their horses—others who are hit just managed to cling on. He detects the agonised screaming of horses in the cacophony of battlefield sound. The Platoon cheers as the front echelon of Lancers catch and spear several German scouts who have been hiding in the corn-stooks.

The Cavalry is taking heavy casualties. Impenetrable barbed wire, which has been laid along the valley by Belgian farmers to restrict the movement of grazing livestock, saves the German infantry. Horses and men cannot get through the wire and gallop haplessly along its length trying to find a gap. Men and beasts lay strewn across several fields, some dead, some wounded. Uninjured lancers and dragoons take refuge in a sugar beet factory before galloping in an orderly column across the front of the British lines to regroup in a wood behind the BEF - ready to cover the retirement of the two battalions of infantry and supporting artillery units. Later that day Francis Grenfell is one of two officers to win the Victoria Cross for saving the guns of 119 Field Battery.

The Cavalry has undertaken a suicidal mission but brings the advancing columns of the enemy to a brief standstill. The enemy is for the moment wavering but the surviving British cavalrymen gallop off having taken over 80 casualties. The Germans are moving towards the British lines slowly—for the moment out of range. Four hundred yards behind the Norfolk's position the artillery battery opens up and its shells tear into the German formations. The Hun still come on, however, and quicken their pace.

"Any moment now I'm going to kill my first fucking German and I just can't wait. Look at these goons—they think they can steam-roll us out of the way. Well we'll fucking see about that," says Jack to Randy, who nods.

The German shelling is now more accurate as their gunners find the range. Heavy casualties are being taken in the Battalion line and for the first time the young regular soldiers witness the agony of death caused by exploding shrapnel shells which burst open in the air 15 feet above the ground, spewing out shards of hot metal splinters.

These shards decimate humans instantaneously and dispassionately into bundles of flesh and bone that hardly resemble what a second before has been a living man. The victims are lucky if they die immediately. High explosive shells are just as deadly when they hit the ground with a heavy thud—releasing the splintered and fragmented hot steel into the air around the large hole it creates.

Baz sees the consequence of a direct hit upon one position one hundred yards away. A soldier's body disintegrates and disappears, blown to pieces, across the meadow. Slivers of flesh and bone tinge the soil crimson where the young soldier had been lying in his shell scrape a moment before.

"Bastards," whispers Baz to himself as the fury boils up within him. "I'll take some of these fuckers with me," he promises himself, with tears of anger in his eyes and revenge in his heart. He is fearful but not possessed by the horror and terror of the battlefield.

In the sunken road behind them, stretcher bearers, unable to get back to the Regimental Aid Post in the copse next to Battalion HQ, are doing what they can for men who have been hit in forward positions in the meadow—injecting morphine and applying tourniquets out in the open without thought for their own safety. The virgin soldiers of Nobby Clarke's platoon are standing fast.

The British barrage goes on as the enemy continue to spill out of the woodland in massed formations. Shells—usually in salvoes of six—continue to burst on the meadow slopes in front of the British positions. Others shriek over their heads into the fields, probing for the artillery. Presently word is passed along that every man will be issued with more ammunition. They are preparing for rapid fire.

Nobby makes sure each man in his Platoon is able to get his hands on the ammunition boxes and takes Ralph and Cocker with him to deliver them. He glances at the expressions on the soldiers' faces and senses immediately they will fight in desperation for one another. He runs at the crouch at the foot of the embankment before climbing it and sprinting across the meadow to join Corporal Horace Witherick in a section outpost. He has brought with him two boxes from the mule 100 yards away.

"Welcome to the fucking fairground shooting gallery Sarge," grins Horace.

"Yes, I'm quite looking forward to this," he says—with not the slightest intention of revealing his true feelings. The lieutenant is also in a forward position standing beyond the embankment—and now starting to direct the Platoon, oblivious to the murderous shellfire.

"Hold your fire until ordered to fire," he shouts.

The Germans are advancing at jogging pace. They are thinned out from their previous massed formations. The previous day's catastrophe for the Germans—who were victims of British skills with the rifle—has been learned at a great price. They come up the meadows through the corn stubble in a frontal attack that appears to be about a mile wide keeping low to the ground. Suddenly bugles sound and the enemy soldiers drop to the ground—they start firing into the Battalion positions from around 800 yards.

The Platoon, from their elevated position, can see the Germans lying among the corn-stooks firing at them. Thuds and spats of bullets fired from the enemy lines pinge around the embankment without causing any casualties. However, incoming mortar rounds and increasing artillery fire make their position desperately uncomfortable.

"Hold your fire, they are not in range yet," shouts Lt Briard. The men wait in silent anticipation.

"For fuck's sake come on you bastards. You're going to get it you'll see," mutters Cocker winking at Jack.

His finger is itching on the trigger of his Lee Enfield rifle. Half a minute later a bugle sounds again and the Germans move forward into range.

"Rapid fire, rapid fire," screams the Platoon Commander.

A fusillade of shots ring out and all down the line the salvoes continue ripping into the formations of field grey.

"It's a fucking turkey shoot. I knew it would be. I must have killed 30 of the bastards already—I can keep this up all day," shouts an elated Tinker. He ignores an incoming mortar shell that lands only 15 yards from where he and Ralph are lying. Dozens of Germans fall to the opening salvoes, but they go to ground at 600 yards again and continue firing at the British positions. Shells from the Battalion's mortar platoon start landing among the forward German positions where men fall writhing in agony—many screaming with terror. The advance has been halted.

"Cease fire!" orders the Platoon Commander.

"Jesus, we've shown those Hun bastards haven't we?" says Ralph triumphantly to Tinker as his sergeant waves away stretcher-bearers, and applies an entire ampoule of iodine to the red face in the shell-scrape.

Cocker's mate Alf chokes back sobs. Cocker has taken a shell burst almost full on—and coils of smoke rise in twisted arcs from his fragmented lifeless corpse. Alf is handed a fag by Horace, his Section Corporal. Alf had been less than 15 feet away from Cocker when he got it, but he was uninjured.

The men are entitled to feel they have won their first victory but in reality it is an attack to establish the strength of the British positions. Although the German infantry has retired, heavy artillery bombardment continues to rain down upon the two Battalions in their exposed positions.

He hears himself chuckling and wonders why. His head is ringing from the sound of shells exploding and he realises his hearing has been affected. All around him stretcher bearers are taking the wounded to positions to the copse in the rear of Battalion HQ for treatment. Some of the young soldiers like Jack have escaped injury only through a miracle. He is the sole survivor of an HE shell bursting on the railway embankment and is wide eyed in shock looking vacantly ahead. It is an eye-opener for the younger soldiers.

In the lull most of the men drink tea gratefully from mugs dispensed by a Corporal from a mule-drawn wagon in the sunken road. The NCO seems oblivious to the shells falling around him and goes on drawing cups of hot tea from his urn. They are smiling; they have tasted battle for the first time and have come through it. Frank knows there is much more to come and they will not be able to sustain this casualty rate for much more than another hour.

"If the CO tries to hold on for too long it will be disastrous," he mumbles quietly to himself. Ernest Briard has been called to Battalion headquarters and returns 10 minutes later. He speaks quietly to his Platoon Sergeant, away from the men.

"We've been ordered to occupy and defend that colliery 300 yards forward on the left of Battalion's position close to the right of the Cheshires in the fields beyond it. If the enemy gets inside there first with a machine gun, Battalion's entire position will be untenable.

"Get the men moving. We can cover a frontal attack but we've got to look out for them coming round on our right. The colliery is a landmark and will attract shellfire and mortars when the enemy discover we are in there—so get them to dig shell scrapes where they can. I'll organise ammunition mules and medic support and join you before 1300 hours."

The Platoon, three ammunition mules and a section of medics are soon in position in the colliery which is also occupied by a Platoon from the adjoining Battalion of Cheshires. They look relieved when the Norfolks arrive. A German assault upon the colliery looks imminent.

"Christ this is a bloody wonderful place to be—a real nightmare," he says to himself.

Lt Briard deploys an outpost section to the right of the colliery. There it can better warn against advancing columns of the enemy from the north using the cover of disused brick sheep compounds below them. The German attack continues on a massive scale with obvious signs of an enveloping movement.

Despite the German barrage, there seems little likelihood of the two Battalions being overwhelmed in the immediate future. The frontal assault continues relentlessly, however and there are now new columns of German infantry approaching from the north. Everywhere the Germans are checked except to the north where they inch forward in a gradual infiltration.

The sands of time are slowly slipping away and the CO of the Battalion knows he will have to pick the right moment to bring about his fighting withdrawal. The ferocity of the fighting is nowhere greater than around the forward position of the colliery where Ernest Briard and his men are positioned in the outbuildings.

The situation grows critical when the Germans manage to get a machine gun in place close to the colliery. It is firing from a small poplar coppice and threatens to cut off the two Battalions. The experienced soldiers in the platoon can see they are not in a tenable position, but their presence in the colliery might hold up the German advance a few minutes longer. Most of the British lads are country boys. They have never heard a din like it. Peacetime army exercises did not produce anything like this, the real thing.

Frank is now in an elevated position on the first floor of a building and gazes upon the three ammunition mules below. They have been mutilated in a direct hit on their makeshift stable. One has just survived the explosion but is screaming in agony. Its legs twitch for a few moments and blood cascades from an artery in spouting torrents before it lies still.

"Jesus, that's a horrible sight," he says to himself.

A moment later a shell explodes 10 yards away and the shrapnel hits the stone brickwork giving him shelter—the concussion knocks him flat.

He is unconscious for a few seconds and when he picks himself up he finds that he almost entirely deaf. Looking through his field glasses Lt Briard can see that German Dragoons have already made it along the valley and are threatening to overrun the Cheshires in the line to the left.

"Sarnt—we've got to take out that machine gun."

The Platoon Commander has noticed a ditch running into the copse to within yards of the probable German position. The concealed ditch is not in the machine gun's field of fire. If he can get men along it without being spotted they might find a way of disabling the German gun. Ernest Briard looks at his Platoon Sergeant and points.

"Nobby take those men from the outpost position to clear out the machine gun. We'll give you whatever covering fire we can from this upper floor."

Nobby runs at the crouch with bullets flying all around him to the outpost. The men are lying in a ditch firing on the forward German positions—as if they were at the butts. Bullets and shrapnel expose the frailty of the human body causing the indiscriminate flaying of stomach gut, mashed brain tissue and body parts.

It is like watching a nightmare, a preview of one's own appalling destruction. In training they did not take into account the effect of bullet and shrapnel upon the human body. This horrific spectacle is unfolding at close range. The screaming of wounded men 50 yards away is terrifying, even in the din of battle.

The German infantry is incredibly brave and still looking for opportunities to infiltrate between the widely dispersed companies. The disused colliery buildings are becoming a magnet for incoming shell and mortar fire.

"Christ these Huns will fight. This is bloody ridiculous," says Horace who lies beside the Sergeant behind a poplar tree.

"I must have shot dozens of them. Are they as ferocious as this with the bayonet?" he asks.

"I think you're about to find out, old chap," Nobby murmurs.

"But I don't think our boys will be found wanting."

He can't hear himself talk so he then adds in a louder voice to the 10 men who comprise the outpost section

"OK lads we're pulling out of here now. But we're not going back to the colliery just yet. We've got a nice little job first."

The Sergeant points to the ditch that ends 30 yards from the northern side entrance of one of the colliery buildings.

"Follow me to the end of that hedgerow ditch. With luck it should take us to within a few yards of a German machine gun emplacement. When we reach the end of the hedgerow we'll decide what to do."

Even at this critical moment he marvels at the capacity of the British soldier to laugh sardonically in moments of extreme tension. Incoming enemy mortar fire is falling with increasing accuracy upon the trees and hedgerow whose screen they are using as cover and shelter, but not one man cowers in fear.

"Fuck me, this is it," says Ralph, winking at Baz and Tinker who are checking their bandoliers are packed.

Ralph looks at his Sergeant. The old bastard was a perfectionist in training—if anyone is going to survive this he will. The Platoon Commander, ignoring that he presents a clear target to the enemy, sprints over to them from the colliery.

"Take care you don't get surprised by a German patrol—they may have come up under the cover of those trees and bushes. We'll give you cover from the first floor. Remember, speed, aggression and surprise."

Clutching a revolver he sprints back to the colliery with bullets flying all around him. Led by Nobby the section scrambles out of the hedge and starts sprinting at the crouch towards the ditch which leads to the German machine gun position.

As he runs he becomes acutely aware of the bullets all around them. He expects to cop one at any moment. Every man makes it and with their sergeant at point they crawl along the ditch in silence for more than 250 yards.

They reach the end of the dry ditch inside the copse and lie on the ground still invisible from the German position. Through a clump of nettles—which stings his face—Nobby can see the machine gun and helmeted men lying around it. The gunner is firing into the Cheshires on the ridge.

The men are all watching him closely—waiting for orders. Slowly he withdraws his bayonet from its sheath and looks at all of them in turn. Then he kisses the blade and smiles thinly. It is enough. They all unsheath their blade and fix it to the end of the barrel of their rifle. Not a word is spoken. Tinker the gypsy boy has a strange look on his face. It almost equates to blissful excitement.

"Don't use it until you run out of ammunition. When you've got off all six rounds there won't be time to reload," he tells them.

"Horace and I will lob grenades to stir them up. The timing's critical, but we've done it all in training so let's do it properly now."

"We've got to keep ourselves out of the arc of fire of that damned gun and not give them a chance."

They look grim. He takes a grenade off his belt, pulls out the pin with the ring and releases the handle which flies off. The men watch as Horace does the same. The grenades emit black coils of smoke which mean they will explode within seconds.

"One, two, three," they lob them with a practised finesse developed over the years. The bombs land and explode on impact hurling turf and mud skywards.

"OK? Go!"

The defenders are stunned, several are maimed. The British soldiers rush across the open ground yelling and are upon the machine gun. The Germans fire one or two shots at the charging soldiers, but only Baz falls to the ground. The enemy has been caught by surprise and believes he is being attacked in force. The German soldiers are not sure how many Tommies are coming at them in the smoke, haze and din of battle.

Several Germans drop their rifle and stand with their hands in the air pleading for mercy. Others try to escape. Nobby's men shoot several at point blank range from the hip, not sparing those who try to surrender. A heavily-built Feldwebel (sergeant) with blonde hair, a full moustache and barrel chest, implores his men to go on fighting.

The German NCO sees a British Sergeant coming at him but is caught off balance while manhandling his troops. He turns to face the Englishman with a look of terror on his face. The steel bayonet punctures his stomach and is turned sharply within him. He throws up his arms, drops his rifle and utters a scream of terror and self-pity.

The dying man has a deep voice and his final cry, as the bayonet ruptures and punctures his intestines, resembles that of a badly wounded bull. Blood cascades from his tunic. Nobby fires a round into the body and rips the bayonet out of the German's stomach using all his strength. His attention is now drawn elsewhere. As he turns he witnesses the death of Bill Bagley.

The Corporal is trying desperately to retrieve his bayonet from the punctured stomach of a young German soldier who screams in pain like a terrified pig and clings to Bill's rifle barrel—as if by preventing the bayonet's retrieval his life will be saved. One moment Bill is alive, in the next a bullet marks the front of his skull and blows off the back of his head—spewing brain and bone several yards behind his body. He falls backwards lifelessly as his legs collapse.

It is a clean and instant way to die and the Platoon's pessimist suffers no pain or awareness of his terrible wound. Nobby vomits but doesn't notice the puke on his tunic. Smoke from the grenades and the smell of explosive from the heavy two-way shelling hang in the air.

Any battlefield of this intensity is pervaded by the smell and sound of exploding ordnance—which shakes the ground. Bullets are cracking past the British soldiers but no more fall wounded. He doesn't care about the foul tasting liquid in his mouth; he wants kill again before he cops a bullet.

It is barbaric. All around him the men are screaming like savages led by Tinker who is hacking and killing with his bayonet and rifle butt like some crazy scene out of Custer's Last Stand. The surviving Germans plead for mercy with their arms in the air. Now, amused by Tinker, he is laughing hysterically. As he disables the machine gun by removing its working parts, he notices that he is shaking. He hears himself shouting to the surviving eight men.

"Let's get our dead out of here. The Germans know we've taken out the gun—we've got to get back to the cover of that ditch or we'll be blown away."

He picks up Bill's body in a fireman's lift and sprints back to the ditch. He is the first to reach it. Tinker carries Baz and is right behind him. As he runs towards cover a bullet ricoches off the back of the corpse and he becomes acutely aware of his own mortality in the madness of the butchery. Bullets are whizzing through the air and hitting the ground all around them, but they reach the ditch. He sits facing the German positions in cover feeling exhausted and shaking uncontrollably as more adrenalin surges into his bloodstream.

Horace drops down beside him next to Tinker and Jack. Nobby lights a cigarette and inhales it deeply, holding the smoke back before exhaling it through his nose, slowly and deliberately. He repeats this several times before throwing away the butt and stares ahead of him speechless, with a strange feeling of fulfilment and pride, but also of emotion and pity for his dead men. He does not want the others to be aware of that. He doesn't give a shit about killing the German Feldwebel.

It is then that he notices Ralph Colby sitting in a hunched position at the other side of the ditch. His shoulders are shaking and his head is between his legs looking silently to the ground. He has vomited and been slightly wounded again by a bullet. One tattered arm of his tunic is stained crimson.

"Get that wound seen to by an orderly Colby back at the colliery," he orders.

The apparently lifeless form of the young soldier does not respond to the Sergeant's instruction. "Didn't you bloody hear me?" he growls as he crawls over to Ralph and places his hand under his chin. He now speaks in a more gentle tone.

"You'll get over it son."

Ralph looks him in the eye and there is anger there.

"No Sarge, I'm just a fucking worthless coward. I let the Regiment down, I let my father down, and I let my mates down.

"When it really mattered I was found wanting for fucking courage. I wish I'd been shot. I couldn't do it Sarge, I couldn't do it.

"This Hun soldier stood facing me and pointed his rifle, but I couldn't shoot him. I let him go.

"Now that bastard could come back and shoot one of my mates. When it came to it, when it really mattered, I was useless, a fucking girl."

The Sergeant lights another cigarette and hands it to the young soldier who takes a deep drag. Frank remembers the incident with the tribesman by the waterfall nine years before

"Let's get back. We must take the bodies," he orders.

When the eight soldiers reach the colliery they discover that Ernest Briard has been seriously wounded and is no longer directing the defence of the position. While they were giving covering fire a shell exploded near Ernest and two other soldiers on the remaining ledge of the upper floor of the main colliery building.

The colliery is now rubble and wounded men scream in agony under the metallic storm. There are no trenches for shelter, just heaps of broken masonry. German infantrymen are getting close to the ruined building, moving round the right flank to cut them off from the rest of the Battalion.

The earth shivers continuously and the air is shrill with the flying shrapnel. Each explosion causes a new avalanche of dirt and metal splinters and the stench of shell fumes is heavy on the air.

Mortally wounded, Lt Briard is carried gently down to the ground floor where some of the other wounded lie. He smiles weakly at his Sergeant, now deathly pale, having taken shrapnel to the side of his head. The bandages wrapped around his temple by a medic are heavily bloodstained.

A syringe is used by the medic to inject him with morphine. To make matters worse, the platoon commander has also been wounded in the neck and chest. One if not both of his lungs are filling with blood and he breathes with difficulty, but is determined to say what he intends to say.

"I saw you do that Nobby. Copy book stuff Sarnt."

He faints but recovers.

"I'd like us all to get out of here but the badly wounded men can't walk. They can use a rifle though—so they'll remain here with me. Get the unwounded back to Battalion HQ. Tell the unwounded Cheshires to inform their CO they will be surrounded when we have withdrawn. Remind them Division expects us to avoid unnecessary losses."

He pauses and then finds the strength to remove his binoculars from the case on his belt.

"Before you go there's one more thing Nobby."

He hands him his field binoculars.

"I want you to have these. They'll be a damn sight better than that battered old pair you use for racing. Remember the day you took me to the Curragh?"

He smiles as he lies on the ground watching his Sergeant, who is kneeling beside him. They touch hands.

Nobby gets to his feet and salutes.

"Very good Mr Briard Sir—thank you."

The Platoon Commander falls unconscious again. It is all so sudden, like a nightmare and he hopes it is. Maybe he'll wake up in barracks in Belfast.

He tells Horace: "Let's move on the Platoon Commander's order before we are overrun. I don't like leaving him but orders are orders. I'd better tell that Corporal from the other Battalion what the Platoon Commander said."

Horace nods saying: "Thank God that machine gun you fucked is no longer a threat."

"Muster our unwounded men Corporal as quickly as you can."

Three minutes later 16 men stand in front of him.

"They're closing in—we've got to get out of here before we are surrounded. The wounded will cover us. We've got to get back to the ridge where the rearguard will still be holding. That means crossing 300 yards without any real cover in front of an enemy well within rifle range, not to mention shellfire and mortars. So it's going to be hairy."

He pauses before continuing, inspecting his remaining ammunition.

"Those of you who were in my sniper section will be familiar with the contact drills. We go in teams of four, breaking off two at a time while the other pair can give maximum firepower to keep their heads down. Retire 40 yards, turn and let the pair in front of you come through. We might just present less of a target to the enemy than if we all go for it in a line."

He looks at Horace. "You lead the first team Horace and I'll bring the last lot out."

Horace leads the first team of four out of the debris running at a crouch towards the ridge above the meadows. They take advantage of a short lull in artillery shelling to slip away while engaging according to the contact drill.

Mortar shells burst close but no one is wounded. He beckons the second team to follow Horace whose men have gone to cover in a shallow ditch just 50 yards from the ridge. They make it but two men in the third team cop a shell burst half way towards the ridge and are killed instantly. Fourteen from the original Platoon are left alive. Now he makes a run for it with the three remaining soldiers. Suddenly heavy rifle fire breaks out from the vicinity of the ruined colliery buildings behind them. It is followed by shouting, then there is silence. Ernest Briard has been killed by a bullet through the heart, after firing his revolver at German soldiers in a frontal attack. The final four reach the ridge employing copybook contact drill in the midst of falling artillery, mortar shells and wild rifle fire from the advancing German infantry.

The Battalion has held the sunken road for more than two hours, but has been thinned out considerably and now less than a sixth of it remains to form a rearguard. He manages to find the Company Commander for instructions. The officer is in conversation with another. Their measured and relaxed manner gives no hint of the gravity of the situation—a Battalion facing annihilation, surrounded on three sides

The Company Commander looks at the Sergeant and the remnants of his Platoon.

"Well done Sarnt. I take it Mr Briard has remained behind."

"Yes sir. He and the other wounded men covered our retreat."

"Good show. Well I've another job for you and your men now Sarnt. Get over to Battalion HQ and join the working party that is digging in around its perimeter to keep Fritz out. There's some defence work to be done—your men will be helpful."

"Yes Sir, thank you Sir."

The Colonel, a lean man with an Earl Haig moustache, is not a happy Battalion Commander as he paces up and down the ground floor of his HQ. The four Company positions are now almost surrounded by the enemy at close range and attacking from the north and west. They are certainly between him and the neighbouring Battalion. If he stays much longer his unit will be cut off.

He has sent off several runners to inform the Cheshires that he is about to retire. None have returned and are presumed dead. He has instructed an officer to find another soldier willing to volunteer to be a runner. The Colonel decides he will break off the engagement as soon as he is able to do so.

Suddenly a Sergeant he knows to be the Battalion's sprint champion from the peacetime years in Belfast stands before him.

"Sarnt Clarke of D Company reporting for duty Sir," he shouts and salutes. He has no idea when he walks into HQ and salutes the CO that he has been mistaken for the volunteer who will try to get a message to the Cheshires

"Well done Sarnt. I'm sure you're the man for this job. If anyone can reach the Battalion you can. Give their CO this message please. By the way Sarnt, don't shout at their CO like you are at me—it'll make him bloody irritated."

"Sorry Sir, I've gone a bit deaf."

"OK. OK, now listen. Several stretches of the lane are visible to the enemy and you may be under both sniper and machine gun fire. So take care. Their Battalion HQ is about 600 hundred yards from here. If you loop round running at full tilt towards the east and then come up behind the slag heaps you should avoid enemy forward patrols."

He salutes. "Thank you Sir."

The men watch in dismay as their exhausted Platoon Sergeant takes off at full tilt up the road carrying his Lee Enfield. Ralph takes a pat on the back from Horace to reassure him.

"Nobby sprints as fast as the wind son. He'll make it if anyone can," says the Corporal to the young soldier.

He sighs, but not loudly. Some of them are still kids.

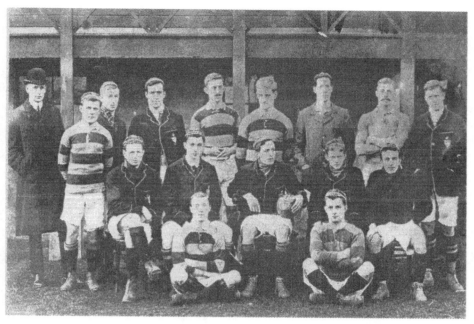

Monkstown RFC 1904-1905 season. Frank W Clarke
is standing fifth from the left.
Courtesy of Monkstown RFC Dublin

A regimental cap awarded to Frank W Clarke for cricket and athletics over three seasons in the years leading up to the outbreak of the First World War. It remained one of his most treasured possessions throughout his life as did his Monkstown RFC Cap for the 1904/5 season.

Frank W Clarke's representative cap presented by Monkstown RFC, Dublin in the spring of 1905.

77

1st Battalion Norfolk Regiment Skill At Arms Team (Shooting) 1910
Courtesy of Royal Norfolk Regiment Museum

1st Battalion Norfolk Regiment Skill at Arms Team (The Bayonet) 1911.
Frank W Clarke is standing in the middle of the back row
Courtesy of Royal Norfolk Regiment Museum

Battalion Hockey Team 1912
Lt. Ernest Briard(Captain) pictured centre of middle row

Sgt Frank W Clarke helped
to train recruits like these
throughout the summer of
1914

Troopships carried the 15th Infantry Brigade including the 1st Battalion Norfolk Regiment from Belfast to Le Havre in mid-August 1914

The 1st Battalion Norfolk Regiment stops at Rouen for refreshments en route through Northern France before the men disembark at Le Cateau

The Norfolks march to Mons from Le Cateau in the blazing August sun. Some reservists collapsed in the heat under the weight of the equipment. Most were spoiling for a fight.

The 1st Battalion Norfolk Regiment arrive at their destination near Mons on the afternoon of August 22nd 1914. The men were exhausted.

Many of the soldiers in Frank W Clarke's platoon were still teenagers. The Norfolks are pictured waiting in reserve positions on the afternoon of August 23rd as fierce fighting rages only two miles away.

August 23rd
The attacks on the line, along the Mons Conde Canal begins as thousands of German infantry swarm out of the woods opposite the BEF positions.
Artist Ed Dovey and courtesy of Osprey Publishing

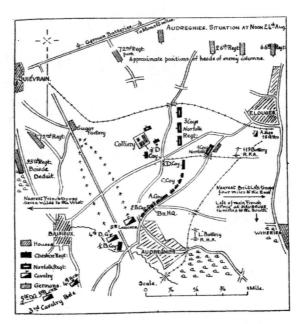

This military map shows the disposition of the British and German forces between Audregnies and Elouges at noon on 24th August.
Note the location of the colliery between the Norfolks and the Cheshires.

August 24th
The 9th Lancers, supported by Dragoons, attack the flank of the advancing Germans in front of the Norfolk and British positions but take heavy casualties before re-grouping in woods behind BEF lines to cover its retirement later in the afternoon.
Artist Ed Dovey and courtesy of Osprey Publishing

Battalion prepares for battle near Elouges (drawing)
August 24th 1914

The Action at Elouges on August 24th 1914 saw Battalions of the Cheshire and Norfolk Regiments fight a valiant rearguard action against German forces of overwhelming strength near the small town of Audregnies.

The action of the BEF forces on that day enabled larger elements of the British Army (5th Division) to retreat in good order and live to fight another day. Eventually the German advance was stemmed by British and French forces on the Marne and the Germans retreated to fixed positions. Trench warfare followed until 1918. Artist David Rowlands

Elouges cemetery
Many of the dead British soldiers were buried in a cemetery at Audregnies which is still cared for today. Among the graves is that of the 1st Battalion Adjutant of the Norfolks, Captain Francis Cresswell

7
LES FORTS TIENNENT TOUJOURS

The night before the Germans entered Brussels the people bolted their doors, closed the shutters and remained indoors to ponder their bleak future after decades of relative prosperity. The Belgian government had left the city the previous day and gone to Antwerp to join the King and the Royal Family in the fortified city.

Now the streets outside were thronged with hapless refugees. Some followed carts pulled by donkeys, a few by large dogs, while others pushed handcarts upon which pitiable possessions—tables, chairs and mattresses—were perched. On this crude transport children rode—curled up asleep in their exhaustion.

The peasants who did not have relatives in the great city had nowhere to go, so they clustered together in protective groups of extended family or village. Many had left their homes so suddenly they did not bring food. They had not eaten for many hours and tried to find refreshment in the narrow alleyway of streets.

The doors of the shops and cafes were bolted. Here and there soup kitchens, set up by the municipal authorities tried to provide for the thousands of distressed souls. Only the churches and the great cathedral of Saint Michel and Sainte Gudule thronged with local people.

The city's inhabitants, Christians and unbelievers, crowded like sheep into the comfort of the sanctuary. The priests prayed for deliverance from the German Army.

Almost exactly 100 years before, a British duke had saved Brussels from the clutches of Napoleon Bonaparte. In 1914 there was no Duke of Wellington to sweep away the enemy, but most clung to the belief that the British and French armies were on the way. Perhaps tomorrow they would come.

The sky towards the east was crimson and the setting sun in the west a vast ball of flame, from which people had to avert their eyes. Black smoke rolled ominously into the city centre—descending to street level.

The thunder of the guns and the vibration caused by the high explosive shells was so great that windows along the Rue de Marche and the Rue de Namur were shattered, sending lethal shards of glass onto terrified pedestrians below. There was fear in the air and tension on the streets.

By dusk many of the tree-lined routes into the city had become quieter. The refugees settled down to sleep in the parks. The narrow backstreets were empty. The buses were at a standstill. There were no fares for the horse-driven hansom cabs or motor taxis. Scheduled trains had been cancelled because it was said the city was surrounded.

Brussels, famous for its night life and gaiety, was in the dark. The gas lights had not been lit for the past three nights on the orders of King Albert—for fear of German Zeppelin airships dropping bombs on the city centre.

During a break from work tending patients on the wards of her clinic and nurses' training school, Edith Cavell matron of the Berkendael Institute had written to her family in Norwich. She explained that although she knew she would be regarded by the invading Germans as an enemy alien, she had decided to face any risks that this involved and remain in charge of her hospital—making it available to wounded soldiers from the armies of all nations.

As she wrote she glanced out of her window and watched a lone and dispirited Belgian soldier trudging in the hot sun down the road, sweltering in his heavy overcoat, his knapsack on his back, a tin cup and an extra pair of boots dangling from his neck and trailing his gun. He was powdered grey with dust. The soldier carried with him the symbol of defeat and despair. He had obviously given up the fight and was going home to his family.

"My darling mother and family, if you open this, it will be because that which we fear has now happened and Brussels has fallen into the hands of the enemy. They are very near now and it is doubtful if the allied armies can stop them.

"We are prepared for the worst. I shall think of you to the last, and you may be sure we shall do our duty here and die as women of our race should die. God bless to you all in Norfolk."

She made her way to the roof of the hospital with her beloved dog Jackie because someone had talked of the brilliance of the sky. She found she was not alone. A group of her French and Belgian nurses were sitting on a bench watching the explosions, hugging one another, weeping and trembling with fear. A wave of irritation washed over Matron Cavell.

"Goodness me!" she said in an authoritative tone.

"What is all this nonsense? This kind of self pity is just not acceptable among my nurses. Has all your training been forgotten and discarded so soon?"

"Ma'm there is talk on the streets of nuns being raped and children bayoneted."

She moved along the bench and peered closely into the face of each nurse with the powerful gaze for which she was both feared and well known. Younger women recognised a mildness and kindness in Matron Cavell's demeanour.

At the same time her reproaches could be firm and indignant when she was confronted by what she perceived to be unprofessional standards. She was not a tall woman and quite delicately built, but her rather masculine chin and grey-blue eyes conveyed a strength that imbued respect.

"I do not want to see these public displays of your feelings when you are in uniform. This is not the time to be expressing emotion or revealing your private thoughts.

"It is entirely inappropriate for a nurse to give way to her feelings and quite frankly it is not the way I have brought your all up to behave. Please consider your special calling and your vow that your life is no longer yours alone.

"You must all consider your duty as a nurse and the special example you are charged with setting in being a member of the staff of the Berkendael Institute—which provides the acknowledged benchmark for all nurses in this country."

The Belgian and French nurses bowed their head in shame and fell into silence. They listened intently to their matron.

"Tomorrow, or the next day, the Germans will come. We will deal with their officers just as we would with officers from the French, Belgian, or British armies. Our mission here is to save lives and to apply our rigidly professional standards in the cause of humanity without prejudice.

"Right now our wards are full of Belgian civilians—by next week there will probably be German soldiers dying downstairs as well. I do not expect the nationality of a patient to be of any consideration whatsoever. If there is anybody here who cannot cope with that, then please stand up, go to your quarters and pack your bags right away."

None of the nurses moved and most continued to stare at the ground.

"I want all those who do not have ward duty tonight to go out into the residential areas of the city, knock on doors and ask for clothing and food so that we can better feed our wounded soldiers. Take the names and addresses of those prepared to give and I will arrange collection.

"The Germans are about to arrive and they will bring with them not only their own wounded, but our own soldiers captured during the battle for the Liege forts on the Meuse.

"It is unlikely we will receive sufficient food from the German authorities to provide for all of those who are admitted here to the Berkendael Institute."

She paused and then added: "Do this good work ladies, get busy and you will forget your self pity—which is disastrous for the spirit and quite frankly not what Our Lord is expecting from you in the coming days when all of you will be sorely tested."

As Edith Cavell lay in bed that night she found it hard to get to sleep and her mind continually wandered back to the momentous events of the past 15 days

General Leman, who had built the forts and led the resistance of the Belgian army against the Hun, had been portrayed as a war hero and a brilliant strategist—who would outfox the Germans every time and gradually wear them down. Strangers walked up to each other in the streets of Brussels and said ecstatically:

"Les Forts tiennent toujours!" (The forts will hold out forever)

Edith Cavell was no cynic but she detected the somewhat brittle nature of this new found camaraderie, as if each Belgian nervously sought to reassure the other.

The matron noticed among her nurses that emotions were easily stirred—laughter and tears came just a little too easily. Gradually the propagandist reports in the press gave way to an air of greater realism, but surely, the people said, the British were on their way, now near Mons, it was reported. People sat in the pavement cafes in the burning sun and talked of a great battle coming that would settle the war—perhaps it might even take place on the fields of Waterloo.

Earlier that day she had been summoned to the office of the British Minister Sir Francis Villiers. She had been introduced to the white haired old gentlemen at a reception earlier in the year and had met him on several subsequent occasions. He stood up from his magnificent oak desk, shook her hand and offered her a chair. He then looked at her solemnly.

"Miss Cavell, all British nurses—apart from yourself and a number of others at the Berkendael Institute—were evacuated yesterday with the British military mission. Today this Legation is being passed into the care of the United States government and our entire diplomatic corps is being withdrawn to Antwerp."

He paused before continuing: "It is a frightful bore and the pattern of the war may be reversed within a few weeks, but we know that the German advance has brought its army to within a few miles of Brussels. Occupation is a certainty. It is not safe for you to remain in the city because you will not enjoy the protection of his Majesty's Government.

"I should like to offer you—and any remaining British nurses—passage out of Brussels late this afternoon. I am sure the Berkendael Institute will continue to function efficiently in your absence especially after all you have done to train its staff to such a level of efficiency in the past few years."

The British ambassador looked into the open face of Matron Cavell and noticed the resolve in her grey blue eyes as she gazed back at him. He had heard of the reputation of this woman who single-handedly had created a code of behaviour and ethics for the nursing profession in a country where none had existed before.

She spoke firmly: "I thank you for your kind and proper invitation Sir Francis. I have already sent the German nurses home. As far as the British nurses are concerned we have given this matter much thought in the past few days and we have decided to remain at our post whatever occurs, possibly working under the auspices of the Red Cross.

"Political and military events, whichever way they turn out, can have no bearing on our humanitarian work here."

As she turned over to go to sleep, Matron Cavell had no lingering doubts that she had made the correct decision. Tomorrow morning she and the off-duty nurses would go out to see for themselves the Germans marching through Grande Place.

They would get some idea of what lay in store for them through the occupation of the country. She was fearful for Belgium—but not in the slightest anxious for her own well-being which she was content to entrust in the hands of her God.

8

THE GERMAN OCCUPATION OF BRUSSELS

The boulevards were packed with thousands of people who could not resist the spectacle of watching more than 200,000 soldiers passing through the city in formations up to eight-men wide. They looked on in silence and with hatred in their eyes.

Among them were Edith Cavell and some of her nurses. She noticed with sadness that one by one the bright Belgian flags had been taken down from the white facades where they had fluttered in the sun for a fortnight. They had been a symbol of the hope and optimism of a nation that was still free.

Edith wrote later: "The parsiennes were drawn at all the windows of the public and private buildings, the old Quartier Leopold looked like a city of the dead."

The women stood and looked on as the soldiers came by in a column 20 miles long—undulating, glinting lines of bayonets and spiked helmets, heading to war at Mons. The soldiers in their field grey and black leather boots marched like robots, in step with fifes and drums and clanging cymbals.

The cavalrymen carried pennants fluttering in the breeze, lances swayed backwards and forwards to the trotting of the horses—hooves clattering on the stones of the uneven pavements of Brussels.

The nurses listened to the guttural voices as they sang battle songs to the beat of the music—a military band marched behind every regiment. Hundreds of artillery pieces drawn by powerful horses surged through the elegant streets in a slow trot.

The English nurses coughed frequently, caused by dryness of the throat as the dust of summer was beaten upwards by thousands of leather booted feet and heels fashioned in steel.

It would take 48 hours for the column to pass through, leaving a garrison of Landsturm behind it. The crunching of metallic heels simultaneously by tens of thousands of marching soldiers upon the road surface was so loud that Edith could not hear what the nurse standing next to her said.

Each young man carried a rifle on his shoulder with bayonet fixed and these glinted in the glaring brightness of the early afternoon. It was the only piece of equipment that did shine—for every piece of metal was covered and concealed by the same greenish-grey material as the rest of the uniform.

Spare leather boots were attached around the neck of each man—who also carried a kitbag and an entrenching tool.

Edith Cavell had never seen a convict but she imagined that these men resembled captives who had been squeezed of any drop of individuality. Their ice-blue eyes stared ahead in stolid indifference to their foreign surroundings.

The Englishwoman wondered what it was that occupied their thoughts—or was there just a void, a nothing? They appeared to have been tragically brutalized. They wore no expression.

In contrast to the private soldiers and non-commissioned officers, the officers who rode beside them on horseback conveyed insolent expressions of disdain. These were directed towards the awed crowds of subjugated Belgians as well as to their own soldiery. The only time the officers laughed was when they were in discussion with on another.

"Yes, these are cold fish indeed," Edith said quietly as she stood in the crowd watching the procession.

"I think perhaps we have seen enough," she said quietly to her nurses after an hour and they turned to look for a tram to take them to the southern suburbs and Rue de la Culture in Ixelles.

Two days later Matron Edith Cavell sat in her office facing a tall German colonel from the new office of the Surgeon-General in Brussels.

He had an open face and spoke respectfully with a cultured voice. She estimated him to be a man in his late thirties, although he looked older wearing pince-nez spectacles perched on his Roman nose.

"I should like to say Miss Cavell that as a doctor I have read much about your work and achievements over the past few years here in Brussels and I think it would be prudent to put some of this on record before a decision can be made on what role the Berkendael Institute should play under the present circumstances of continuing hostilities."

He opened a writing book, laid it before him on the table and produced a gold ink pen from the inside of his jacket.

"I shall take some notes before having my report typed out for the Surgeon-General and the Commanding Officer of the Brussels Garrison.

"It will of course carry my personal recommendation for the future use of the Berkendael Institute. We know you are an Englishwoman living in a city occupied by your country's enemy—but let's go back to the beginning of your life please."

Edith Cavell looked at the German disapprovingly for a few moments and then spoke quietly. "I was born in Norfolk where my father was the vicar of a parish called Swardeston, not far from the city of Norwich.

"I am the eldest of four children and received a boarding education at several schools before taking up various positions as a governess including one in the 1890s here in Belgium.

"I was attracted by a career in nursing following a holiday in France and did my training at the London Hospital in Whitechapel and later worked in senior nursing positions at infirmaries in St Pancras and Shoreditch before becoming matron of the Berkendael Institute in September 1907 at the invitation of Antoine Depage."

"Ah yes," interrupted the German officer. "Depage is one of Belgium's most eminent surgeons.

"He is now serving in the Belgian army in Antwerp. Does his absence signify that this clinic will henceforth be without doctors for surgery?"

Edith Cavell smiled and said: "Not at all. He made all the necessary arrangements and we are well served for doctors and surgeons. I am also matron and responsible for staffing the Hospital of St Gilles. Some of the staff nurses here are also expected to be working at the Royal Palace as and when required. We all expect to be at least as busy as we were before the War."

The officer spent the following three minutes in silence writing notes in his book—and then looked up. "I shall be recommending that the Institute be transferred immediately to the auspices of the Red Cross which will mean among other things that you yourself and the other English nurses currently working here—and wish to remain here—will have the provisional right to do so unless circumstances warrant their return to Great Britain for inappropriate conduct."

He paused before continuing: "There will be one further obligation that all English nurses will be obliged to adhere to."

Edith Cavell interrupted.

"My nurses will of course scrupulously abide by their code of conduct as defined in their contracts," she said firmly.

"I am pleased to hear that. I am referring of course to the obligation of all nurses at the Berkendael Institute, irrespective of nationality, to ensure that all allied prisoners brought here for treatment will be confined to the premises—and that their presence at all times on the wards will be strictly enforced by all nursing staff!"

Edith Cavell was both quick and emphatic in her retort.

"Our job, sir, is to save lives and care for all those who need medical care and professional nursing—irrespective of nationality. I can assure you that none of my nurses will be acting as jailers."

The German picked up his writing book, replaced his pen, stood up and walked swiftly towards the door before turning to speak in a firm voice to Edith Cavell.

"I can understand your sentiments. However your decision means no wounded prisoners of any nationality will be sent here in the near future by the medical staff at the garrison. Armed guards will be provided at the Hospital of St Gilles to ensure prisoner security.

"Your current attitude is misguided in the circumstances of you being in a country under German occupation at a time when your country is at war with mine. I shall return next week in the hope that you will have changed your mind and that you and your nursing staff will feel able to sign a declaration.

"In the meantime you will remain here now under the auspices of the Red Cross but receive no patients at the Institute except for Belgian civilians and each of these must be accounted for and recorded for weekly inspection.

"I have to add that your clinic, although out in a suburb, will be watched closely by the military authorities. I shall record that your state-ment to me can only be taken as hostile. Good day madam."

For the next 20 minutes Edith Cavell sat at her desk staring out of the window with her chin cupped in her hands. She knew there was no question of any waiver in her attitude or policy towards the Germans but now wondered how the Institute could justify its existence without being involved in some humanitarian way in the dreadful events unfolding around her. Her thoughts were interrupted by a loud knock at the door.

"Come in please," she said loudly.

The door opened and there before the Englishwoman stood a very tall auburn-haired girl with a large mouth and ice-blue eyes. She was pos-sessed of an elegant and dignified beauty heightened by the likelihood that she had no idea of the impression she caused. The girl was smiling broadly and almost looked childlike in her Red Cross nursing uniform.

"Are you Edith Cavell?" she enquired.

"Yes," replied the matron.

"I am Emily Horstmann. I'm American and although I'm a citizen of a neutral country I am fleeing from the Germans because they have ordered me out of the country. The American minister saw me this morn-ing when I handed him a dossier of atrocities committed by the Germans last week in the city of Louvain. It is because I compiled this dossier—with an Australian friend Jackie Pretz—that I have been ordered to get out of German occupied territory.

"Is there anything you can do to help me remain and work as a nurse? I am at you service matron and would like to be of use here in Brussels."

9
IN THE LINE OF FIRE

Frank follows the sunken lane before clambering onto the light railway embankment. As he runs his lungs feel as if they are going to burst, but fear keeps him from slowing down. It had been a normal country lane a few hours before, but is now so pock-marked with shell craters and mounds of red earth that it has become impassable for retreating transport. The flames licking round the roadside trees are fed by the dry August vegetation which has also been ignited by the shellfire. Blazing poplar and beech trees crackle as huge flames take hold on the timber.

After nearly four hours of battle the sky is black with smoke. The mutilated trees give the countryside an entirely new perspective—one of sudden catastrophe. Unhitched military trucks are parked up alongside the ditch—some blasted into pieces by the explosions and splintered by shrapnel. Dead horses and mules are strewn about—the carcasses often hideously mutilated.

He comes across the depressing sight of several bodies but he can see no sign of the enemy. An ammunition cart is upturned in the road with a horse still in harness lying on its side, its head lacerated and its huge teeth protruding from a gaping mouth in what looks like a crazy grin. The poor beast's carcass is astride an enormous pool of its own blood.

The remains of a British soldier lie hunched beside the mare. Somehow in the force of the explosion he has been hurled like a rag doll off the cart before coming to rest in the foetal position. The corpse has no head.

Horse and human body parts lie strewn around the road in grotesque bundles. He sprints past trying not to look too closely at the ghastly sights in case he knows the soldiers. Shells continue to fly overhead every few seconds in salvoes of six and incessant machine gun fire seems to be aimed at him personally. The air is thick with the smell of cordite, burning flesh, and the cinders from the corn stubble.

He can hear shouting in the distance from all directionsas he gets closer to the desperate action being fought by the Cheshires. He begins to feel sick, and his legs become heavy, but he runs on in both fear and determination. He takes evasive action by side-stepping because he is in the line of fire of snipers and scout patrols. He has at most a quarter of a mile of meadow to cross before getting anywhere near the zone of covering fire from the Cheshires—maybe he will be shot accidentally by them. He breathes in deeply and sprints towards a wooden gate. Despite the din of exploding ordnance he can still hear skylarks calling above him which he finds curious. His nostrils flare and his eyes scan every corner of the field as he runs in a zigzag pattern looking out for signs of rifle fire or movement from an enemy patrol or sniper ahead.

A German scout plane flies overhead at less than 500 feet but the pilot and observer show no interest in the running figure below them. He reaches the sanctuary of the hedge by the gate and goes to ground in a dry ditch. At the end of the field he notices a gap in the hedge. If he heads for that he might quickly get onto the road leading to the positions of the Cheshires. He remembers his infantry training. Soldiers are warned never to do the easy thing and make for gaps in walls or hedges—because such spots are likely to be covered by a sniper or even a machine gun.

"I'm going through there anyway," he says to himself.

His attention is diverted for a moment to watch a hawk hovering 150 feet above the mineral railway line—its gimlet eyes are probably fixed on a rat or small rabbit below. Perhaps the sight of the hawk is an omen. He has become prey too. Paradoxically, mankind might be at work creating hell on earth for himself here in the Belgian countryside, but nature and the animals remain unaffected amid this flaming human apocalypse—where death and agony lurk in the afternoon sunshine.

"Come on Clarkey get ruddy moving," he hears himself say. He clicks his rifle to safety and leaps out of the ditch, running four paces and timing his straddle perfectly over the farm gate. He pitches his rifle over a split second before leaping and lands cleanly. Instantly he picks himself up, gathers his rifle and starts bounding towards a gap in the hedge in the next field.

Just under 100 yards out he thinks he sees movement in the gap, side steps to the left, and feels the vibration of a series of bullets whishing past his shoulder. He collapses in a heap onto the ground and lies in a crumpled position quite still with his head pointing towards the hedge and his hand on his Lee Enfield. Four spiked helmets appear speculatively above the ground as the German soldiers scrutinize the spot where he has fallen. He can hear them talking. His gamble might pay off—they are inexperienced soldiers exposing themselves in such a reckless manner.

Now is the real test of years of marksmanship at the butts. Now he'll know the true value of the trophies won in the regimental tournaments at Aldershot. Now he'll find out if he really is the brilliant sniper they say he is. He springs to the firing position and brings the barrel of the rifle forward onto the targets—it is very close range at 90 yards but he has to be quick and he has to be cool. In the smallest of firing arcs he manages to get off four rounds in just a few seconds. One by one the Germans drop back off their feet, even though they have fired several rounds at him from close range and missed.

"Yes," he shouts, leaping to his feet and starts sprinting. If one of them is only wounded and able to fire off a round, he'll get it. There is no choice. He has to risk death—he cannot remain where he is. He goes through the gap in the hedge expecting to be zapped but isn't.

"Yes Nobby, yes!" he shouts as he races past the lifeless German scouts.

"Bugger me I'm going to do this."

A poplar tree 200 yards ahead catches his attention as he runs through the summer foliage along the side of the lane. He sees the boots of the man first and then his face below the spiked helmet as it comes cautiously round the trunk of the tree at a crouch. Then he sees the rifle. It is pointing at him—he is a sitting target at such close range.

"Oh shit, you bastard," he shouts—side-stepping violently to the left. It is not enough and it is the last word that he utters. He feels a huge force sweep him off his feet like an enormous ocean wave crashing onto him in an explosion of white foam. He feels pain and seems to see himself struggling on the ground unable to move with any co-ordination. Everything then goes black and he lapses into a deep unconsciousness—his mind exploring his past.

BREAM ON THE BROADS—DIARY JUNE 1904

Horsey Is the nearest Broadland village to the sea; the long beach and its dunes are just over a mile away from the Mere. It is one of the bleakest and most windswept freshwater fisheries in Norfolk—but always provides me with exciting sport.

I enjoy my bream fishing on the Broads because I crave solitude. I fish them regularly when in Norfolk during the summer. Sometimes I start fishing an hour before dusk, on others I am up with the lark for a session at daybreak.

Here at Horsey right on the coast, I am alone with nature; man is not at hand. The appearance of a car in this part of rural Norfolk would cause a sensation. The only sounds are the call of the wild and the pounding of the North Sea upon the sand. The only witnesses to my dawn adventure—as they pass by—are the foxes, the nocturnal badgers, and the wild deer who sometimes gaze upon lone fisherman when coming to the water to drink at daybreak.

The sun has just risen and the dawn is the herald of what will turn out to be a delightful June morning in the summer of 1904. So far it has been a long hot summer.

Insects are already rising from the surface of the Mere and the air shimmers in glorious warmth awaiting the beating stare of the rising sun. There is no wind. The surface of the water resembles a vast sheet of reflecting glass.

I pick up the rowing boat at Horsey Staithe from Harry Williams and row the 12 foot clinker quietly and steadily past the tumbledown windmill towards a favourite spot opposite a massive elm tree.

It has stood defiantly for nearly 100 years against the lash of the winter gales near where a colony of reeds reaches out upon a sunken bank 30 yards into the waterway.

There I hope to find the telltale muddied patches of water that will indicate to me that a shoal of big bream are rooting on the bottom of the Mere for food.

This is my own secret location, my own paradise, where I have sometimes spent entire nights—occasionally in the company of a close friend—out on the water and usually catching enormous shoals of bream. My record is 18 in one evening and each fish topped three and a half lbs.

Bream to me are the mother of coarse fish. They seem to possess an almost dignified feminine quality with their small delicate heads, elegant tails and deep bodies that flash silver in the water as they turn over and again in their struggle to evade capture.

The fight in a bream lacks the tenacity of a tench, the powerful dash of a carp, or the force of a wild river barbel, yet once a feeding shoal has been located, they usually oblige by presenting brisk and consistent sport to an angler.

Poor men take them home gladly as the main ingredient for fish and parsley sauce pie, having removed the vast number of fine bones and purified them overnight in a bucket of salted water. I try hard not to kill any of the fish that I catch. To me the flesh of the bream tastes like cotton wool.

I approach the great elm tree and stop rowing. The boat continues to cut its way silently through the water losing its momentum gradually. I turn my head to the bow and look closely at the surface of the water ahead. I carry an unusually long rod for boat fishing which means I can cast onto the shoal from a considerable distance away.

The bream is a shy fish, easily disturbed from feeding. It is a bright morning—not yet 5am—and telltale rings of muddy water appear just 10 yards ahead. I drop the anchor quietly and, before assembling my tackle, produce a bag of bread, bran and boiled potato which has been mixed with water to a moist paste by hand a few hours before.

I begin to throw the ground-bait in chestnut sized lumps into the muddy circles of water. I watch and wait for a further five minutes and note bubbles have come to the surface in some of the muddy rings of water. The shoal has found the ground bait.

On Horsey Mere I always use a nine foot greenheart rod, one of my star-back reels with an six lb breaking strain silk line, a red peacock quill float with four lead shot mounted—and a 3x silkworm gut to a number ten hook.

This is light fishing—risky if I encounter a five or six lb fish in the shoal—but that's what makes the sport of it. What I do next is extract from my backpack a biscuit tin containing a ball of greaseproof paper that has been tightly wrapped up. Inside this are the decayed and decomposed remains of half a dozen ears which have been cut off the heads of old cows in the local slaughter house—and for which I pay a few pennies.

I leave them hanging for some three weeks in a bucket in a barn at the farm, suspended on a wooden beam away from the reach of rats. The package is crawling with white grubs and its smell is foul.

The off-white maggots always appear mysteriously after a week or so of hanging—and I leave them undisturbed to get fat.

I am now ready to start fishing and bait the hook with two maggots before throwing a handful of the grubs into the area of the feeding shoal. I follow this with an accurate and unhurried cast out to the same place.

Now I wait tensely as the line sinks—having set the float so the last foot of gut line will lie on the muddy bottom of the Mere. After 10 minutes of sitting still and making no sound, I notice the float rise slightly. Its point appears to waver from side to side. I am tense as the float rises and then turns flat on the water before slipping under the surface and out of my sight. I count one-two- three and then none too firmly strike in an upright position.

"Got you, my beauty!"

The fish bores deep and I put sufficient pressure with my thumb on the wooden reel to move the bream away from the shoal—and thus to avoid their rapid dispersal in alarm from the disturbance.

The bream continues to fight deep for a further five minutes but gradually becomes passive—enabling me to reel it slowly to the surface towards the boat and into the landing net. I have brought my scales with me and the great silver fish weighs in a just under five lbs.

That morning I catch 12 fish of a similar size before the shoal stops feeding at 8am. It has been a brisk session of three hours and I am satisfied. The first six fish are caught on grubs, two with the tail of a large lob worm and four with bread paste.

I row the boat back to its mooring on the Staithe and walk down to the Nelson Head pub where I have stayed the night before. It is time for a hearty English breakfast, a strong cup of tea with plenty of sugar and then a short walk down through the sand dunes and onto the long beach to confront the blue panorama of the North Sea.

I know I will find several families of seal on the deserted sands— the white pups, born a few months before, romping playfully at the edge of the sea watched closely by their light grey mother and darker father.

10
TIME TO GO

Captain Francis Cresswell, the Battalion Adjutant and one of its most respected officers, is at his Commanding Officer's side in the cottage. Lt Colonel Charles Ballard hears him talking but hardly pays attention over the barrage of the guns. Then he realises Francis is volunteering to get notification personally to Dudley Boger, the Commanding Officer of the Cheshires. He cannot afford to lose an officer of Cresswell's seniority and importance on such a desperately dangerous mission, but at the same time he seems to have exhausted all his other options.

"I don't think Sarnt Clarke made it Sir. I believe that if I take a course riding south-east well behind the slag heaps, I will be able to get behind the Cheshires, avoid the enemy and reach their Battalion headquarters further down the lane. It will only take me seconds to deliver your order. Give me twenty-five minutes to get back here. If I don't make it by then, presume I will not be joining you."

"God go with you Francis," Charles Ballard murmurs to himself.

The Adjutant, a slightly built man admired for his horsemanship, sets off two minutes later on his charger carrying a revolver and galloping hard along the hedgerows behind the Norfolks. He heads towards the rear of the slag heaps where the Battalion HQ of the Cheshires is located less than half a mile away on the Andregnies—Elouges road. Shellfire from the German batteries spews shrapnel all around him but he pays no heed to the risk to his life.

Cresswell comes from one of Norfolk's well known county families and is a descendant of Samuel Gurney Creswell, the 19th century maritime explorer who was one of the first men to navigate the North-West passage. Cresswell covers nearly a quarter of a mile and having crossed two fields comes back onto the Audregnies lane galloping past the wounded and unconscious Frank. A troop of dismounted German Dragoons spot the British officer making haste for the Cheshires and fire a volley from close range that brings him down. He is killed instantly.

At Battalion HQ twenty minutes later, Charles Ballard looks at his watch. He now knows that neither Sergeant Clarke, nor the Battalion Adjutant, Captain Francis Cresswell, is coming back. There is a lull in the German advance. Now is the time to slip away, leaving a few men as rearguard.

He doesn't want to lose another officer in the rearguard action and chooses the remnants of Nobby's platoon for the job, led by Corporal Witherick. They dig in around the cottage.

"It's time to go," he tells his new Second-in-Command Captain Robert Brudenell Bruce.

"The Cheshires will see us retiring. We'll continue thinning out. I'll go with the first two companies—you cover our withdrawal and follow on. We'll take a route just south of Elouges and see whether we can link up with Division at Athis. The wounded men who can't be moved will remain here. Tell the Corporal in charge of the rearguard around the cottage to hold on for as long as he can and then attempt to make it to Athis. We'll see what we can do for our walking wounded there—maybe some vehicles will still be around to carry them to safety."

All the Corporal's men, members of Nobby's young platoon, are killed, wounded or captured in the heroic rearguard defence by the Norfolks. On the Battalion's left the Cheshires fight on heroically for a further four hours, eventually split into fragmented groups and completely surrounded by overwhelming forces.

11

THE ANGEL OF MONS

But I was looking at the permanent stars
Bugles sang, saddening the evening air
and bugles answered, sorrowful to hear.
Voices of boys were by the river-side.
Sleep mothered them; and left the twilight sad.
The shadow of the morrow weighed on men.
Voices of old despondency resigned,
Bowed by the shadow of the morrow,
Of receding voices that will not return.

Wilfred Owen

He regains consciousness three hours after being shot, having been disturbed and woken by the sound of two horses in panic and the continuing battle. Two horses bolt past him madly, shrieking in terror in the shadows of the evening. He guesses they have been released from their load by a bursting shell—which has killed the driver.

"My God, how am I going to get myself out of this one?" he asks himself.

There is a further crash less than 50 yards away. One of the horses has been hit by shrapnel and collapses, while the other continues in its bolting madness unscathed down the road. The dead horse has been disembowelled in the explosion. He looks away. The air is thick with cordite. Smog has descended to ground level. The cries of mortally wounded men calling for help disturb him deeply.

When he was hit by the bullet he was thrown like a rag doll ten feet to the left, into the dry ditch at the side of the road. The German who zapped him was aiming for his head at very short range and must have been a crap shot. He had sidestepped to the left which had saved his life. The bullet entered the front of his body below the right shoulder and passed through it without any major collision with bone or artery. The exit point is the size of a saucer.

He lies face down and relapses into unconsciousness again for more than an hour—although he is aware of the din of battle and guttural German voices all around him. At one point the muzzle of a gun pokes him around the body looking for signs of life, but no bullet is fired to finish him off. He would not have cared. Curiously, when he comes round again the wound is not giving him pain. He feels numbed however by the colossal assault upon his body. He can move, but only with agonizing difficulty.

He does not panic, in fact he feels carefree. He has no idea of the size of the exit wound in his back. Calmness overtakes him and a voice within his head reassures him that the wound is probably only superficial. He drifts back into unconsciousness but wakes again in great pain, crying out in agony. He opens his eyes to look up at the stars in the night sky and feels cold and lonely, perhaps nearing the point of death. The upper part of his body is so numb that when he pinches himself he feels nothing.

Now he experiences fear, real fear, which grips him so strongly that he loses control. He feels urine running down his leg. He prods his right arm, but he can't feel it. He begins to sob and wonders how long he will have to wait for death. He is desperately thirsty, craving liquid, any form of liquid. All around him are other wounded men and many are dying.

The cries of distress in the night are heart-rending, particularly those who cry and moan in English. He remembers suddenly the four dead men he has killed a few hours earlier. He staggers to his feet and walks drunkenly back towards the gap in the hedge where he knows he'll find the German soldiers. Then his foot strikes a solid object. It is a rifle. The dead German is lying alongside his weapon. He kneels beside the man, using his undamaged left hand to unbutton the soldier's pack.

None of the training exercises or pre-war manoeuvres have prepared him for the stench of burning flesh and shed blood that permeates a scene of deathly conflict. No soldier with real battlefield experience ever forgets it. At length, after groping around in the dark, he feels what appears to be a water bottle and sausage wrapped in grease proof paper. He takes both out of the pack and staggers away before falling to the ground at the gap in the hedge. He drinks all of the water in deep gulps and swallows the garlic sausage in a few mouthfuls. Gunfire and explosions diminish as the hours roll by. The British have retreated—the sounds of battle are being replaced by the more reassuring sounds of the countryside.A dog fox calls to a vixen, an owl hoots from a nearby tree. He is familiar with all this as a country boy and now falls into a deep sleep where the pain cannot pursue him.

THE ANGEL OF MONS—DIARY JUNE 1915

Something inexplicable begins to unfold before my eyes as I lie wounded near Mons. Suddenly I am watching the advance of huge numbers of men and transport. I am hidden in a thick hedge as they come streaming past in their tens of thousands wearing spiked helmets and field grey uniforms.

I cannot quite work out why so many of them do not have faces, even those who pass within a few feet of where I lie. I look up at the sky—which is crimson between the sparse clouds in the descending sun—and watch as a huge formation of men begin to materialise on the far horizon. They look like warriors, but earthly warriors do not have wings.

The warriors carry longbows and there are thousands of them stretching to infinity. On they come, obscured by a descending mist but marching forward to the sound of what I imagine to be heavenly music and the awesome beating of drums.

In their midst a leader appears on a gigantic white charger. He is a King adorned in a crown and above his head he brandishes a huge sword.

The mist slowly descends to ground level and acts as a carpet upon which the host of angels march. The heavenly archers draw back their bows and fire what become flaming arrows upon the advancing Germans.

Cries of fear and confusion greet the approach of these arrows upon the columns of Teutonic infantry and cavalry. The King ascends higher into the sky, his golden crown ablaze in the crimson of reflected sunlight as thousands of drums reach a crescendo. The arrows find their targets upon the advancing German columns and there is carnage.

Radiant light from the flaming arrows is so brilliant that men can only avert their eyes. I cover my face fearful that I will be blinded by the iridescent glare.

I look up again to find the King has been joined by a second figure on horseback; a woman in silver armour. She carries a shield bearing the Fleur-de-Lys of France. The woman cries out above the crescendo of drums and brandishes a sword as the ground is shaken by an erupting force of incalculable measure.

"Victoire, Victoire, Mon Dieu....."

The faceless columns of field-grey have halted and are prostrate. Immortal intervention by divine forces has stopped the Germans in their drive towards Paris and turned the tide of the War from certain defeat to ultimate victory. I am a silent witness to all this and feel warm tears upon my face.

I awake some hours later in the bright morning sunshine—still astonished and uplifted at what I have witnessed during the night. Now I have faith the Entente Cordiale will win the war, sooner or later and not concede defeat to the Central Powers, no matter how long it takes. Furthermore, I will live to see it. There is a God in heaven after all.

12
CLOSE TO DEATH

He felt in his tunic pocket and found his packet of Players and lighter were not damaged. He lay on his unwounded side inhaling the cigarette smoke deeply and pondered his fate. Frank was aware he probably faced captivity, but there was a sense of fatalism about this. He would do what he could to avoid capture. He felt stronger, but there was excruciating pain in any kind of movement.

He knew he must eat and he repeated what he had done during the night, by searching the kitbag of a second corpse. He found water, sausage and also black bread. He ate everything in a few gulps. Soon he moved, a step at a time, over to a corner of the field where he would be able to get out of the shade and into the midday sun.

He could hear horse-drawn transport, presumably driven by medics looking for German survivors from the battle. He knew he was gravely wounded and needed hospital treatment soon to arrest the infection in his wound, but he did nothing to attract attention to himself. He reasoned that if he could lie undetected for a day or two, eating the food and drinking the water from the remaining dead Germans, he might find local people prepared to help him get to a Belgian doctor.

He chose a spot where his body would be concealed by the thick vegetation in the ditch but where he could also feel the rays of the sun upon his face that would brighten his troubled mind. Within seconds, the agonizing throb from his wound ebbed away as he lapsed gently into sleep all alone in a world tottering into ruin.

He lay there for the whole of that day and the next falling in and out of consciousness but oblivious to the world around him. On the third morning he was woken by relentless drizzle falling upon his face in the black of the night. The moon was obscured by thick clouds, the peace shattered by a gale. The air temperature had plunged low for August. His uniform was drenched and he could find nowhere dry to conceal his face.

He could not light a cigarette because of the high wind and he felt extremely depressed. He felt weaker than he had the day before. His head was aching and he was partially deaf. The pain was increasing in his back and he realised he needed to get to a hospital quickly if he was to avoid septicaemia and certain death.

There were no longer any sounds from German rescue teams picking up their wounded. He presumed they would not be returning, so he could not give himself up to them. He realised he would probably not be discovered lying where he was and that he must attempt to make some progress down the nearby lane. He would try to reach a nearby village, but it would be wiser to do so under the cover of darkness.

It took several attempts and he used the last reserves of his willpower to get to his feet and he did so with the help of a rifle that had belonged to one of the dead German infantrymen. For several moments he stood still trying to fight back the waves of nausea that overcame him. He retched once or twice but only bile flowed from his mouth.

"Christ I feel bloody awful," he said to himself and began walking slowly along the sunken lane with its traces destruction at virtually every step. The heavy rains had produced pools of mud in the shell holes in which some of the corpses lay in grotesque positions.

He was aware of tripping over an object and going down. At first his face was submerged in stinking water but he managed to move it to the side so he could breathe. Then he blacked out. There was just darkness. He was waiting to die.

BINTRY MILL, NORFOLK—DIARY 1899

I often dream of picturesque Bintry Mill, one of the county's magnificent beauty spots. The miller there Robert Seaman is my grandfather George Printer's old friend. I stand before the two magnificent weir pools on the River Wensum—a chalk stream—and sense I will enjoy an evening's dry fly fishing on this humid June night. Wild trout of more than 1lb are rising continuously from the mill pool in a hatch of Mayfly shortly after 5pm.

I wade to the back of the pool in the shallows and cast upstream into the race. The Mayfly bobs back to me on the fast current and the response is greater than anything I ever remember.

It seems that the pool is crammed with fish and they rise to the fly with such ferocity that even a novice could hook them. I take 12 fish in three quarters of an hour, all over 14 ounces.

Having exhausted the pools by the road I take a wide berth off the path on the left bank running downstream and walk for a mile. There is still at least three hours of daylight although the shadows are beginning to lengthen and the sun glistens off the surface of the water. I decide there never was a better night for the evening rise and as I survey the river upstream the prospects certainly look plentiful.

Some fish are literally throwing themselves above the surface of the water in unbridled exuberance to feed. I open my fly-box and select four all-round flies that serve me well on Norfolk's rivers.

These are the Blue Dun, the Olive Dun, Greenwell's Glory, and the Alder for dusk. I finished the evening's fly fishing with the busy Alder on a pool darkened by shadow from the overhanging trees. On the second cast I take a wild fish of nearly two lbs, which fights for 15 minutes before I bring it to the net on my light tackle.

I decide to inspect the dam just above the Mill long after the sun has slipped below the horizon—and after starting a flagon of local cider with Robert Seaman. I have sharp eyesight and spot a large trout moving in the twilight near the surface parallel to the reed beds.

I swap my nine and a half foot split cane fly rod for a shorter six foot greenheart—and from the Seaman's skiff cast a silver spoon in front of the reed bed. Robert and his wife watch from the bank. On the second cast the cannibal attacks the spoon ferociously and with plenty of space to play the trout, I land him in 15 minutes. The wild fish weighs in at just below four lbs and I present it to Robert's wife to cook.

I have spent several summers on the Printer farm so have fished Bintry and other mills frequently, with particularly success at Sculthorpe and Fakenham. I love Ireland but yearn to return to Norfolk as a farmer and livestock breeder at some point in my life.

Georgie and James prefer shooting and riding to fishing and in winter we go after wild geese on the marshy coastal areas in the North of the county. The winter and summer shooting on the farm is good too—especially when the corn is being cut by the labourers.

The rabbits hide in the ever decreasing sanctuary of the crop—before running for safety to the hedgerows as their cover comes down. They are systematically picked off by the guns or chased by the Norfolk Lurchers—known as Longdogs—which grandfather George Printer bought as puppies from a local gypsy family and over the years has bred on.

Later in the year, after the fields are harvested, we venture onto the stubble to look for pickings with Ruffian and Snapper, a cross between a collie sheepdog and a greyhound. They have longer coats and more stamina than their greyhound ancestors and the infusion of the collie breed, every few generations, means that although they are slower than greyhounds they are hardy, more intelligent and aggressive.

Lurchers also run better lines than the greyhounds, especially in pursuit of the hare—which changes direction on a sixpence. Experienced pairs like Ruffian and Snapper work together driving the prey towards one another.

Norfolk's ancient hedge rows and its tens of thousands of small fields harbour millions of rabbits—their burrows lie deep below the roots of the elm trees that line the lanes of the county. The rabbit and the hare provide farmers and the country people with meat that would not otherwise be available throughout the year.

One of the most productive ways to catch rabbit and hare is

by using the long net which is laid along the hedgerows, also covering gateways and gaps. Both hare and rabbit, when being chased, make by instinct for the gaps and get enmeshed in the nets.

This Sunday I am invited to lunch at Grandmother Sarah Printer's house at Drabblegate near Aylsham. On Sundays after church the men in the family will arrive in their best suit and the women in their best frock. They are scrubbed clean but some of my cousins give off an inescapable agricultural whiff—as if they live in a dairy which of course in many cases they do.

They are not dirty people but endless scrubbing with soap is insufficient to get rid of the smell of cow dung and horse shit which permeates onto clothes and somehow into the skin.

The girls are sturdy, clean and pretty, do not wear any make-up but are fresh-skinned. Sarah has lost five of her nine children, all of whom are buried in Banningham churchyard. She never speaks of the loss. Sometimes the local priest, the Reverend Edmund Telfer Yates, vicar of St Michael and All Angels, Aylsham, comes to Sunday lunch and says grace in Latin. Conversation, when the devout and scholarly vicar is seated at the table, verges on the mock pious. Those seated around the table vie with one another to quote inaccurately from the Bible followed by hisses of laughter half-concealed under handkerchiefs.

The old clergyman never seems to fathom that he is being teased and corrects the inaccurate quotes with patience and in earnest. The girls fall into fits of giggles and run out of the room before they wet themselves—at which point Sarah refills the vicar's wine glass and encourages him to laugh with the irreverent humour.

It is better when the vicar isn't around. We can discuss freely the odds on the runners at the next race meeting at Fakenham and discuss locally trained horses and the jockeys who will ride them. Later on Sunday we will let off steam in the bar of the Black Boys Hotel where landlord Christmas Stapleton employs several attractive barmaids—with crude manners, rouged lips and fulsome breasts.

Drinking sessions sometimes continue until dawn—with the frequent participation of the local constables. Long live Queen Victoria who has reigned over the Empire for more than 60 years and soon no doubt she will be succeeded by grand old King Edward who appears to be the uncle of Europe.

Rule Britannia presides over a world order that looks set to last for generations and the Boer will get a good hiding for his making trouble. James says he's going to try for a commission in the Royal Dublin Fusiliers and get out there before the fighting ends.

Sister Madeleine drove the donkey and cart along the sunken lane shortly after dawn. Jacques, a short broad shouldered man who was the village blacksmith, sat beside her. They were appalled at the sight of the carnage all around them. Three days after the battle, fires still smouldered in trees and hedges from the sustained shellfire. Smoke trailed from the damaged military vehicles that took direct hits. The air was heavy with acrid fumes and a carpet of smoke lay close to the ground like autumn fog.

Sister Madeleine had already collected three British corpses and intended to search the lane for another hour before returning to the convent. It would be a sad business identifying the young soldiers—and even worse the planning of the burials in the cemetery with the Mother Superior, Sister Julienne.

A slender young woman in her mid-20s with striking brown eyes, the nun belonged to one of 10 convents in the district devoted to the teaching of St Francis of Assisi and she was part of the Order of the Grey Sisters. These women lived an active life in the community, begging for subsistence, but also caring for the sick in their convent hospitals. Many small Belgian towns relied on their convent and small hospital.

He was lying by the side of the road head down in a shallow pool of muddy water. Both Jacques and Sister Madeleine assumed from the amount of caked blood on his uniform that he was dead, until the nun administered the sign of the cross on his face and noticed from the touch of her fingers a flicker of movement in his eyes. She hugged him and was astonished when he blinked and then whispered in a hoarse voice.

"Thank God you've come. I don't know if there's much you can do but I'd appreciate a cigarette right now," he said wearily.

He accepted one from Jacques who pushed the bodies to one side of the cart, placed a blanket upon its floor, picked up the wounded Englishman and laid him gently down upon it.

Frank summoned the strength to smoke the strong French cigarette, felt better and then fainted again.

"Il faut sortir immediatement au l'hospital," Sister Madeleine said to Jacques "Peut-etre c'est possible sauver le Tommy."

The cart trundled along the uneven surface of the sunken road. The rough ride kept him conscious for the time it took to reach the convent. The pain was now constant but bearable. In the main street many pairs of eyes followed the progress of Sister Madeleine and Jacques. He was aware of very little except the deep odour of rot that emanated from the exit wound in his back.

"Christ, I reckon I'm a gonner," he whispered quietly to himself. He felt a deep sense of anxiety about what precisely that meant.

Another man joined Jacques and carried him gently into the hospital. Two cottages had been knocked through to form a ward in the front room. There were 10 beds packed in, with little space between them.

The kitchen of one of the cottages had been converted into a surgery and the other was a wash-room with a large tin bath on the floor next to a wood-burning range to heat water.

The atmosphere in the tiny hospital was pervaded by the distinct odour of chloroform and ether. It was immaculately clean. He was overcome by a sense of relief.

The men carrying him were ushered by an elderly nun into the wash-room and he was directed to sit down upon a wooden bench in the corner. The tin bath was full of hot water and on a tray on the floor next to it was a large bar of soap and a soft brush.

The nun used sign language to tell him that the men would help him to undress, which they did with surprising gentleness. His upper torso was covered in blood and his legs from his ripped trousers were caked in mud. As he was carried to the bath he fainted again.

He must have sniffed smelling salts given to him by the nun for he regained consciousness sitting bolt upright in the bath and he immediately felt embarrassed by his nudity. Now Sister Madeleine was gently sponging the mud off his lower body and cleaning carefully around his lower chest and back. The smell from his wound caused him to retch and she murmured something in French to console him. He noticed a tall woman, also a nun, standing by the bath. She spoke with an Irish accent.

"I am Sister Julienne and I want to tell you what we are going to do with you," she said.

"Unless we can eradicate the infection in your wound it will develop septicaemia, infection of the blood and you will die. We think you were shot at close range which means there are no traces of the bullet within your body. That is good because we do not have the means to operate here—this is really no more than a clinic and somewhere to convalesce. To halt the infection we should like to apply antiseptics to your wound, but we do not have any here.

"So we are going to pour ordinary table salt onto it, both at the front and the back. It is all we have. This will work but it will also be extremely painful. We will give you regular injections of morphine to fight the pain and sedatives to help you sleep.

"After we have put the salt on your wounds you will have to lie on your stomach and remain as still as you can except when we get you up for toilet. The process may take many days but we hope that eventually your wound will be free of infection and begin to heal."

She brought out a notebook. "Now, what is your name please and your regiment."

"I am Sergeant Frank Clarke, 1st Battalion Norfolk Regiment, number 7852. I was wounded on Monday afternoon, however long ago that is," he said.

"I shall also need other details in due course so that your family will know that you are saved and undergoing treatment in enemy occupied territory. We think that eventually the Germans will come here and take you away as a prisoner but for the moment the only important thing is to get you well."

He was given pyjama trousers and taken outside into the back garden of the hospital which had been planted with roses and shrubs. In the centre of it was a large well. The buzz of bees and other insects was just audible in his ringing ears. The August midday sun enveloped his face and for the moment he felt warm and contented.

The entry point of the bullet had been lightly bandaged and was stinging, but he did not know why. He was then laid face down on a long scrubbed table and Jacques appeared through the door and placed a wooden peg into his mouth. He made a sign and pulled a face. Frank realized he meant 'it's going to hurt mate, so bite on the peg.'

Jacques and the other man held him by the shoulders and pressed him into the table as Sister Madeleine tipped salt from a large white bowl onto his exit wound. For a few moments the effect of salt on the torn flesh and muscle fibre seemed minimal—sharp pains like dozens of pin pricks into the skin. Then there was an explosion of agonizing pain which felt as though the back of his head was being blown off. He was engulfed by it, drowning in it.

He heard himself crying out in distress and then he felt strong hands restraining him as he was injected with morphine. He was trying to get off the table and cursed those who held him.

Then there was darkness.

GUNTON HALL—DIARY FEBRUARY 1900

Gunton Hall in Norfolk is one of several grand houses close to Felmingham. I enjoy exploring the park where the 18th century palace is a derelict shell, destroyed by fire in 1882. I walk or cycle there from the farm just over four miles away and enjoy fishing it most during weekdays at the height of the winter early in the morning—when usually no other anglers are to be seen.

The lane from Suffield is pleasingly overshadowed by the trees of a forest and on this day—a late February morning in 1900—I walk through the icy woodland, now a frosty patchwork of white and green, past the lodge and on towards the saw mill. I am wearing Harris Tweed plus-fours, a heavy round-necked white woollen pullover, Norfolk sports jacket and a large canvas hat. On my back is a rucksack.

In my hand I carry a sturdy ten foot three-piece greenheart rod in a cloth rod holder and bait can for the live fish. I love this secret wilderness. The estate thrived in the 19th century until one night nearly 20 years ago in 1882 the Hall was gutted by fire.

Today I have time to explore Gunton Park before the weak sun rises in the sky, adding a few degrees to the temperature of the air. This will make the act of sitting still in a skiff marginally more bearable. I cross a cattle grid, which leads into a further jungle of rhododendrons.

Now I enter a glade. Here, dappled in the rising sunlight by oaks, elms and the ubiquitous cedars, is the chapel of St Andrew, a Doric temple. The architect was Robert Adam, his only church and the sole example of his work in Norfolk. It is a forgotten antiquity hidden in a Norfolk copse—which heightens its sense of unreality. I behold an almost pre-Raphaelite scene in the glade. The scene merely requires a host of harp-playing cherubims and seraphims to fly into the dreamy vista and complete the theatrical enchantment.

I light a Players cigarette and sit gazing at the scene upon a pile of cedar logs which have been sawn by one of the woodmen at the mill. In the next few minutes I enjoy the tranquillity, but the nip in the air soon moves me on towards the lake.

On this windless day the surface of Great Water resembles sheet glass tinted with a light blue dye. In the centre a dozen swans glide majestically and in their gentle wake swim duck and wild geese—the latter in winter quarters from the Arctic.

Gunton sawmill was built in the 1820s. It consists of a timber framework open on three sides with a thatched roof of Norfolk Reed. The mill takes its water power from a smaller lake which drives two enormous breast shot wheels via a guillotine gate. One wheel powers the main reciprocating saw and the other a circular saw and various pieces of ancillary machinery, including a small corn mill.

A single-storey brick outhouse stands beside the mill and is used as a smithy, a rest area and a workshop. Ten men work here under the head sawyer John Henry Ward and they all know I am the cousin of Reginald Printer, the dealer who supplies the estate with its work horses.

One of the privileges granted to the Printer family is the right to use the skiff to fish the lake.

'Is Mr Ward intending to use the skiff this morning?" I ask politely, directing my question to Charlie Lynn, the head blacksmith,

'Take it lad. He'll be at Aylsham market with Mrs Ward today. I saw him leave an hour ago in the trap. Good luck Mr Frank— you know what they say—December's good, January's better, February's best!'

I push the skiff into the water. First I have to catch sufficient live bait. Those in the 'know' at Gunton Park have learned exactly where to catch live bait quickly. I pick up the bucket and walk rod in hand to a willow tree.

This is the spot where the workmen from the saw mill congregate at lunchtime, when it isn't pouring with rain, to eat their bread and cheese. What they don't eat is tipped into the water under the tree.

It takes me less than half an hour to catch eight roach up to seven inches long. I put them in the bait can and row the skiff quietly across the lake towards a peninsula that cannot be fished from the bank because of thick reeds that form an impenetrable wall— and through which it is impossible to cast.

I know pike will lie here, lurking within the confinement of the reed bed camouflaged from their quarry. I drop anchor 45 feet from the reed beds and the bow of the skiff comes round to the suggestion of a westerly breeze which allows me a wider arc of casting—to cover 30 yards of water without moving the position of the boat.

I put the bait can into the water, attach it by string to the skiff and assemble the tackle. My heart beats strongly in anticipation. My pike line is made from silk and braided tightly in strands.

It gives me a breaking strain of around 15lbs and onto this I mount a red circular cork float with a hole drilled through the middle, into which I push a wooden peg.

Below the float I affix a swivel and an 18 inch wire trace with a hollow barrel lead attached at the end and running onto an attachment called a buckle swivel. Beneath this is the snap tackle with two large treble hooks at the end.

I take a roach from the can and attach one barb of the lower hook below the head of the fish and a barb from the second treble threaded onto the fish just below the dorsal fin. The fish can swim in a laboured manner which will attract a predator. I have an old wooden star-back reel bequeathed to me by George Printer.

I click down the ratchet pin with my right forefinger to switch it off so that the line escapes more freely and silently—and pull off sufficient line with my left hand to cover the length of my cast.

I swing the rod slowly behind me and the forward movement which follows is gentle but steady. The line rushes through the rings of the rod pulled by the weight of the float, wire tackle and the bait.

It lands just 10 inches in front of the reeds and the roach is pulled down to the four-and-a-half foot limit of its leash. For several moments the float stays secure in the spot where it has landed. Then, as the roach recovers from its shock, it begins to pull the float parallel to the reed-bed, bobbing the float in small spasmodic movements.

I enjoy the suspense of live-baiting as much as sea-trout fishing with a wet fly at night. The live bait patrols up and down for 10 minutes, towards and away from the reed bed. The impaled roach begins to quicken its movements in obvious agitation. The float skids for two feet across the water. Something is terrifying the live bait.

At this time of year the smaller jack-pike (males) are beginning to "team" with bigger female fish in preparation for the start of spawning in March. This is a disadvantage for the specimen angler because the jacks might seize the live bait before it is noticed by the heavier female.

Today I hope that the jacks are distracted and that my live bait will be confronted first by a hungry female predator. The cork float now bobs violently and begins to slide across the water parallel to the reed bed as though it is being guided by some unseen force.

I watch in fascination because I know what will come next. I grip the rod more tightly and draw several feet of line off the reel and wait for the jerk of the float as the bait is turned.

The unseen force is carrying the roach and the heavy tackle through the water taking with it the slack line and continues to do so for another three yards before the float slides quietly under the surface of the lake.

I remember my grandfather George telling me about the pike's bony mouth full of sharp teeth; there are only certain places within it for the hook to take hold. This is the moment where many pike are lost—because the angler becomes impatient. The mistake to avoid is to strike too soon, too vertically and too hard—before the pike has turned the bait in his mouth to swallow it by the head.

I count to five and then with a heavy, steady draw at 45 degrees pull the rod in the opposite direction to which the pike is travelling and bring the rod down so that its movement is parallel to the water, rather than upright.

The fish is hooked and shoots off at terrific speed towards the middle of Great Water. I have no problem holding this fish. I bring it to the boat, gaff it and pull it into the skiff. It weighs in at three ounces below seven lbs. I kill the pike and cover it in a cloth at the bottom of the boat. In the next hour I catch five more jack pike of a similar size along the reed bed, all of which I keep for the table.

I remain unfulfilled even with six fish in the bag. I want a 20lb pike and I know that there are many specimens as large as this in Great Water. There are fish left in the bait can and I thread one onto the snap tackle, pulling up the anchor and rowing upwind.

I will drift down with the wind travelling parallel to the bank of the lake—with the bait held within a foot of the reeds. The sun is now higher in the sky and it warms my body slightly. I smoke several cigarettes in succession.

The engine of the saw mill suddenly roars to life and creates a grinding, thudding agony of noise that submerges the softer sounds of nature. The birds on the lake fly off in fright. I won't listen to such a racket all day. It is approaching 11am and I am down to the last few roach—what's more, the breeze has stiffened. I am beginning to fight boredom as well as the cold and the noise. I shall enjoy the walk back to the Printer farm.

I will give this fishing expedition a further five minutes before packing up the kit and rowing the skiff back across the lake. I want to reach the workmen at the saw mill while they were taking lunch—so I can present them with some fish.

Then the drama begins.

The float stops dead in the water and bobs crazily, completes a wide circular movement and then shoots across the lake for 20 feet before disappearing. Intuition tells me this is something different. I strike with a steady draw of the rod and feel a dead weight which, within seconds, begins to thump violently and move relentlessly towards the reed-bed.

'Christ, this is a big fish I'm going to have to be bloody careful,' I hear myself saying aloud.

It is a big pike and I just manage to hold it before it reaches the reed-bed, where it would be sure to fracture the line. Once turned, the fish sets off at enormous speed towards the centre of the lake, pulling the unanchored skiff with it. I hold the reel in check with my thumb, conceding line every few seconds and allowing the greenheart rod to take the strain.

I will make the pike fight for every inch of territory as it moves around the lake thirty yards ahead of me. The pike has pulled the skiff for more than 50 yards and now brings the boat in the direction of the sawmill where I hear shouting from the bank and realise I have an audience.

Only now I notice the din from the saw mill has subsided. The workmen have stopped for lunch and are watching the spectacle unfold before them.

'Reckon you've got a monster there Mr Frank, don't rush him—

and watch he doesn't bite you when you get him on board,' he hears Charlie Lynn calling over the water as the men rock with laughter.

After 20 minutes the big pike begins to show signs of exhaustion. It has towed the weight of a man and a boat around Great Water. The skiff begins to drift towards the bank and I take in line upon my star-back reel until the fish is drawn to within 20 feet of the boat.

The pike is near the surface and in the clear water I see its deep shape thumping madly to resist capture. The boat is now alongside the bank and the workmen are gathered around it. The pike moves slowly from side to side a foot below the surface.

'I could do with some help,' I tell the workmen.

'Could someone grab the bow? I'll jump off the skiff and finish the job from the shore. Mr Lynn—could you take the net?' I do not want to use the gaffe on a big female fish full of eggs.

I spring ashore holding the rod high and gradually reel in the remaining line. The fish is now spent and she allows herself to come to the net submissively. The pike has fought for 35 minutes but is now safely on the bank. She is too heavy for my scales, but Charlie has brought across equipment from the forge.

She weighs in at just over 25lbs. Her body length is 44 inches and her depth nearly 11 inches.

'I reckon that'll take some eating,' laughs Charlie Lynn.

"Oh, she's going back," I say firmly.

'A female pike of this size might produce 200,000 eggs—increasing her body weight by five lbs. She'll be carrying those eggs now—so I wouldn't want to open her up!'

I pick up the fish and place her gently back into Great Water. She allows herself to be held before drawing renewed energy to return to the wild. The huge body glides out of my cupped hands and she disappears into the depths of the lake.

He awoke and for several moments could not work out where he was, or why he was there. He was lying on a thin mattress laid upon a table in the rose garden of the cottage hospital, his face bathed in sunlight. He realized later he was fortunate to have been wounded when the weather was warm. He would spend the long days of recovery ahead out of doors during the daylight hours—so that his wound would be exposed to clean air.

He lay upon the garden table for several days resting uncomfortably upon his stomach—the large saucer-shaped exit wound was not bandaged, but covered only with gauze to keep away the insects. Sister Madeleine attended to him constantly. She injected him with morphine when the pain became unbearable, administered ether when he could not sleep and spoon fed him so that he would not have to move his body.

Every few hours she gently guided him to do his toilet in the little shed at the end of the garden. At night shortly before dusk, as the air cooled, he would be brought inside to the ward at the front of the cottage hospital.

He spoke rudimentary French and Sister Madeleine knew only a little English, so for the most part they communicated through sign language—and in the process he noted she had a wonderful sense of humour. She was by no means dowdy and serious like some of the other sisters. He found her attractive with her large innocent brown eyes that gazed upon him so intently.

He wished he could get to know this petite young woman better—but language and respect for her status as a nun was a barrier for which he had no solution.

Sister Madeleine told him he was the only soldier occupying the ward—along with a small child suffering from tuberculosis and an old woman who appeared to have lost her wits and spent most nights weeping. The sounds from the unfortunate old woman did not disturb him.

He spent most of the time sleeping or dozing and lost all sense of time passing. Every day his wound would be cleaned by Sister Madeleine and treated again with salt—gradually the foul odour of infection dispersed.

The raw flesh was not visible to him without a mirror. By the end of the second week the wound began to heal slowly in its own natural way, but progress would be agonisingly slow. One morning, after what he assumed had been several days of treatment, he woke up to find a man standing in the garden beside him. He was not in uniform but wore a white overall.

"Good morning Sarnt. I'm delighted to see you are getting stronger.

He replied: "Good morning sir—may I know who you are?"

"I am a British officer, a doctor and like you a fugitive from the Germans. You are a lucky man. Lucky because the bullet that had your name on it didn't enter your chest cavity but tracked around the external circumference of the rib cage—that means under the skin and then through the muscles, before exiting through the shoulder blade which is quite thin at its central part.

"Your survival was largely down to luck and the shrewdness of the nursing sister who runs this hospital. Having your wound irrigated with an antiseptic salt solution helped you—as are the continual application of clean dressings. It could take several months before you are well enough to be active again. By the way, don't worry, because you will regain use of this arm."

He paused to write notes down on his white pad. "You now need to be admitted to a fully equipped hospital to ensure you do not regress and fall victim to septicaemia. Your continued presence here is exposing these good sisters to risk."

He smiled at Sister Madeleine who was standing beside him, also smiling and gazing intently upon her patient.

"There are many British and French soldiers in hiding in the district and the Germans have started to issue notices of warning to the local population. Some people have already been shot for hiding British and French soldiers.

"We think from our intelligence sources that a small garrison of the German Army's Landsturm is to be quartered in the town and in that case the discovery of British soldiers hiding in the convent would be inevitable.

"So we are going to have to move you out of here together with a group of unwounded men, who are currently quartered in the convent. I don't know where you will be going but it will be soon."

As he examined Frank he talked to him more about his wound.

"What happened to you Sarnt?"

"I was trying to get to an outpost position Sir with a message when I was shot from the front at less than 200 yards range." The doctor was now examining the exit wound with his gloved finger.

"Mmm, my own view is that it will be better to leave the wound wide open and drain it as required. In the meantime we'll pack the wound with dressings saturated in tablets of salt.

He continued work and then said: "We have been treating you in the garden because infection can be defeated by fresh air. Furthermore wounds like this smell foul so it is better to be outside in the open. Yours was no exception. We leave the wound exposed with only a thin piece of gauze to protect it.

"In two or three days your wound lost its odour and began to look cleaner, while there was no sign of your internal system and bloodstream having been poisoned. Salt was all they had here. In better equipped hospitals wounds are treated with other antiseptic solutions."

He had by now finished examining the entry wound, took Frank's pulse and listened to his breathing with a stethoscope. The doctor finally patted him on the top of the head in a friendly manner.

"Your body temperature is higher than normal and you are still suffering from fever as a result of the infection, but I am impressed with your condition. Do you have any appetite?"

"Sister Madeleine brings me fresh boiled eggs and French bread in the morning. I get a light lunch and a cooked dinner every evening. What with frequent cups of tea and cold water I am made very comfortable," he replied.

"There is still a risk of regression Sarnt and also of you catching pneumonia. The good news is there appears to be no bone damage in your chest cavity. The remedy for complete recovery lies in plenty of peaceful sleep and careful nursing. We must find you someone in the next hospital as caring as Sister Madeleine. She has in all likelihood saved your life and certainly you owe this woman a considerable debt.

"There is still no known medical treatment for most diseases—so recovery comes from knowing when to deliver hot packs and tepid sponging, on the careful lifting and turning of a patient.

"Good cooking of nutritious food is also a factor—and so is persuading the patient to eat it. It's the nurses who save lives, not the doctors."

The Sister had not understood much but she blushed at the obvious references to her loving and skilled nursing care. She spoke a few words in French that neither could understand.

It was clear to the doctor that she had a personal affection for the big Englishman—despite her vows. Frank spent the following week in anticipation of his move to another hospital and when awake was well enough to enjoy Sister Madeleine's constant company. She sat on a wicker chair next to the garden table reading short stories in French by Guy de Maupassant—which he began to understand increasingly because she read them over and over again.

He remembered the writer from his French lessons at school. Maupassant was a popular 19th century writer, regarded as one of the fathers of the modern short story. He assumed Sister Madeleine had chosen this author because his stories tended to signify the futility of war, and draw attention to the innocent civilians who were victims of it. Maupassant had written out of personal experience of the Franco-Prussian war of the 1870s.

Sister Madeleine had a deep voice—expressive but lilting—and he found it a sedative when she read to him. It eased the constant pain. Most of all, however, he was touched by the devout nature of Sister Madeleine.

He was moved by her habit of kneeling at his bed in the later hours of the evening before he slept—and praying for his soul.

It certainly helped him to sleep facing down upon his stomach. Sudden movement in the middle of the night could cause his massive wound to reopen. He lapsed into a deep sleep.

The war had moved on and he had no idea where—although sometimes he seemed to hear the boom of distant guns. On this night they did not disturb his dream which took him back to his youth.

TICKLING A TROUT—DIARY JUNE 1901

I am on vacation in Norfolk with cousins John and Thomas. They are typical English farmers. It is 4.30 am and the midsummer sun is rising—following a spectacular dawn chorus. The trap turns right at Helvingham and we trot through the flat lanes towards Felmingham. The country lanes are deserted except for the occasional wagon.

I am not used to 12-hour drinking sessions and am slumped unconscious on the bench of the trap. When I wake up I can remember nothing of the night before, especially why my underpants are the wrong way round and my socks and shoes full of straw.

We have been at Norwich market. We set out on Friday morning so we could be in Norwich for lunchtime. It's an important rendezvous time for the Printers because there are important deals to be set up and on the last Friday of the month there is an alcoholic lunch at the City Club in the Star Inn, Rampant Horse Street.

Pubs like the Market Street Tavern, the Grapes Hotel on Grapes Hill, and the Steam Packet are packed with agricultural types enjoying the social atmosphere and the opportunity to network. Business and lunch at the City Club completed, a night of drinking followed in the red light area around King Street and Ber Street where whores patrol in the shadows.

The appalling stink from the drains on the streets is familiar because I live in Dublin where the smell is the same, The odour of town gas and the ubiquitous pong of horseshit, the leather works—and in winter the choking coal smoke—is joined during market days by the agricultural whiff of cattle and pig dung.

People are oblivious to bad smells, not surprising since Norwich has a population of 25,000 horses and nearly as many pigs living in small gardens and in back yards. Twice a week livestock are driven into the city or transported there by rail.

Bidding starts shortly after 9am on Wednesdays and Saturdays for the auction sales at the Norwich Livestock Market beneath the sentinel of the Castle. The city market presents an exotic spectacle and is the reason the city exists as a centre of trade.

It attracts farmers from a 40-mile radius, horticulturalists from as far away as Lincolnshire selling seasonal vegetables, flowers and fruit and fishermen from Great Yarmouth on wagons loaded with trays of ice-packed fish.

Tens of thousands of poultry, from bantam chicks to full grown cockerels, dead rabbits and hares are also on sale. Other stalls sell domestic and farm ironmongery and bric-a-brac. Gypsy women stroll around selling springs of heather, wooden pegs and they offer to tell fortunes.

It is said a person can buy anything on Norwich market. The country folk say the din of human voices engaged in trade can be heard five miles from the city centre. The sound of commerce is interrupted only by the clanking of steam trains arriving and pulling away from the city's stations and the rattling hum of the electric tramway network.

The Edwardian era is a prosperous time for the landowning and tenant class in East Anglia, but poverty and squalor lurk on every street corner in the shape of drunks, beggars, homeless families and even child prostitutes. The sound of the police whistle is as familiar as the call of the street vendor engaged in his trade.

I am saddened at the sight of poor families, some in rags, congregating around the cattle market on Saturday mornings to beg unwanted milk for their children. The cows are in great distress having been moved from the farm the day before and long overdue for milking.

'Christ my head hurts,' I say to John as the horse trots through a village.

'I can't remember a bloody thing after that blighter with the mutton chop whiskers at the City Club kept passing me port and made me drink it as fast as all you older chaps," I add.

'All I'll say Frank," says Thomas in his slight Norfolk accent and with an air of mystery, "is that if you were a virgin yesterday afternoon, then you aren't one any longer!'

He explodes into another fit of high pitched laughter. I blush and dig deep into my consciousness to search for just one small shred of memory to corroborate what my cousin is saying. It perplexes me because there is nothing, just a blur, after that boring old man made me continue drinking the port as it was passed round the table.

I've longed to have a proper sexual experience with a woman—now I am told I've actually done it—but can't remember a bloody thing.

'You'd better watch out you ain't caught a dose," continues Thomas.

'It starts with an itch, but scratching doesn't do any good. If you don't get the doctor on it straight away . . . then your best friend will go black and blue—and it could even fall off!'

I am less than two years out of school in Dublin, and completely horrified.

'Christ, what am I going to do? Come on you guys you're older than me—what am I going to do?'

Already I detect my private parts are itching.

'You're having me on aren't you?" he says, attempting to laugh.

'Oh that's not the worst of it young Frank. Have a look in the wallet in your back trousers," adds John.

I am mortified to discover that none of the five guineas that were in my wallet the night before remain. I must have spent the lot, or maybe it has been stolen.

It is all the money given me by Henry for the month—and includes what I've been instructed to give my grandmother Sarah for my keep during the summer.

'Oh shit, it's gone,' I mumble. 'The bloody lot's gone! What am I going to do?"

'Thomas and me will lend you the money for the pox doctor, so don't worry about that," says John kindly.

'Trouble is Frank, you got into a card game at the Star and you thought you wuz going to win—and you lost the lot!'

Thomas breaks in: 'Then you started telling your woes to one of the barmaids. She must have felt sorry for you—on account you'd got no money and you still being a virgin.

'The next thing we found the two of you going at it hammer-and-tong on the straw in the stables. Two or three people watched you actually—and were having bets as to how long you'd last.'

The two brothers collapse with laughter and halt the pony. I sit there with an incredulous look on my face.

'My God! What was she like?'

'I don't want to malign the lady but I will only say that she's recently been charging a guinea a week for haunting houses,' says Thomas before collapsing in mirth for a second time.

"Yes, she used to be on the game too," adds John," but she couldn't make any money at it so she took up bar work!"

They both hiss with laughter again. The journey continues in silence for a further 20 minutes before I speak again.

'Look here chaps I'm just the young cousin. You're older and more experienced than me. I think you should have looked after me better than you did last night in Norwich. I'll take my chance with the pox doctor, but the money, that's important.'

The journey continues at the trot in silence for a few more minutes before Thomas speaks again.

'Well, we all like a bet—so let's find something to bet on. We could even make it double or quits,' he suggests.

'You name the bet young'un,' John adds.

We reach the village and cross the bridge over Kingsbeck, a stream, just below Felmingham Mill. A whitewashed cottage stands next to the bridge and I remember the old woman who lives there tipping her peelings and waste into the river one evening when I was passing by. I point to the stream.

'I'll tell you what. I'll bet you chaps the five guineas that I can catch a trout out of this stream and have it on the table ready to eat by dinner tonight!'

'I don't think anyone's caught a decent trout in any of these Bure tributaries for years. Our father was probably the last man to get one. It's not a chalk river like the Wensum or the Nar,' warns Thomas.

'Well I've seen fish rising and they weren't dace,' I insist.

'Go on then, you're on,' agree the brothers, confident that my mission to find a trout in the stream will fail.

I collect a ten-foot cane rod and a split can cane fly-rod with tackle from the farm at Colby and walk back to the bridge over the main street just below the mill. At the whitewashed Bridge

Cottage I knock on the door. An elderly woman dressed in widow black with unkempt grey hair opens it.

'I'm sorry for disturbing you madam, but I have wagered five guineas that I can catch a good trout for the table from the river by tea-time. I think you can help me.'

'Oh can I? How?' she asks.

'Well, when I was passing over the bridge one evening last week I noticed you throwing your peelings and stale food into the river," I say.

The woman looks back at me in a defensive manner. She is not used to visitors and I am a stranger, perhaps a busy body.

'And why shouldn't I? I've got no other way of being rid of it. As you can see I'm old and just a poor widow,' she replies.

'Madam, I do not seek to chide you. In fact I think because of it you may be able to do me a great service,' I say. "I should like your permission to come into your garden and fish the spot where the unwanted food is thrown into the river.'

'What's in it for me?" she asks grinning—exposing half a set of blackened teeth.

'If I can catch a trout from your garden I should be pleased to pay you a shilling," I promise.

'There is one more thing. Once I have dropped my line into the water I should be grateful if you would tip in some of your rubbish just upstream so that the fish might be attracted to find my bait.'

Five minutes later I am tackled up and I ledger a worm at the spot where the pool is deepest. The water runs fast and shallow under the bridge, but thirty feet below it—by the cottage—a partially collapsed brick wall juts out into the stream. It creates an eddy—where the water is over five feet deep and the river weedy. This is where the widow throws her stale food every day and probably has done for years.

I stand upstream of the eddy and sit down to keep out of sight. The widow soon arrives with a cup of tea and a bucket full of stale food.

'Thank you so much. Leave the bucket there and I'll throw in the bits and pieces to save you having to stay out here,' I say.

After 20 minutes I have thrown in all the contents of the bucket but there is no indication of a bite. Impatiently I reel in the line and change the drowned worm for one that is alive and active.

I wait a further five minutes. Suddenly the top of the rod twitches almost imperceptibly and then it dips strongly. Five seconds elapse. The line shoots through the rings of the rod. I strike vertically and feel a big fish. The fish dashes out of the eddy and heads downstream.

It is strong and I am careful not to put too much strain on the silkworm gut above the hook—It will snap if the weight of the fish creates too much resistance in the flow of the river. I know almost immediately this is no trout. It thumps hard and feels heavy but lacks the dashing madness of a game fish.

However, I take care to play the fish with caution. Ten minutes later, I bring the nose of the creature to the surface and see it is a chub.

It weighs two ounces short of four lbs with a healthy bronze and silver glow. I release the fish back into the water. There is probably a shoal of large chub feeding off the old woman's largesse.

HERE COMES THE TROUT THAT MUST BE CAUGHT WITH TICKLING . . .

William Shakespeare (Twelfth Night)

I walk downstream along a path by the bank of the river parallel to a railway line and look for fish rising. The sun is now high and it is going to be too hot to catch trout in the heat of the day. There has been no spate on the river for several weeks. There might be a good rise later—but I've undertaken to have an edible fish back at the farm by dinner at 6pm.

'They will be hard to catch in these conditions,' I hear myself say.

I walk for a mile down river, but nothing rises or swirls in the water to take a nymph from the river bed. I follow a straight section of river where the current flows fast and shallow through the colonies of weed which dance in the current. The river is about three feet deep in the centre and the water is as clear as gin. As I stroll I realise I am 'spooking' trout and other species because the sun is behind me—casting a silhouette upon the water.

They dash upriver out of sight into the weeds and some appear to take refuge under the banks. It is then I remember a conversation once had in a pub in Cork with a pock-faced Irishman called Micky O'Rourke, one of the notorious poachers on the Munster Blackwater and its tributaries.

In a lifetime of living by the river Micky has become an expert at tickling game fish. I choose not to believe him at first and am astonished when he takes me to a tributary of the Blackwater and demonstrates his art.

The swarthy Irishman explains that tickling is the art of rubbing the underbelly of a fish using the forefinger. If done properly, the fish will go into a trance after a few seconds and can then easily be thrown onto the nearest land.

The joy of tickling Micky says is that it requires no nets, rods or lines or any other incriminating equipment that could be used as evidence by police or gamekeepers.

'You buy me another couple of beers and I'll be glad to take you along with me young man,' he promises.

We work our way up the shallows and rapids of the tributary just above a weir.

'I'm watching for a trout under a rock or ledge that I can reach without drowning myself,' he laughs. I can see nothing—but Micky misses nothing.

'There's a fish gone under that rock in about three feet of water just upstream of where you are standing," he says, while shamelessly removing his boots, belt, pants and breeches, revealing a white body that looks almost ghostly in the warm sun.

I watch fascinated from the bank as the naked Micky wades into the cold water. The fish is out of sight under the rock in clear water. He says he can see its tail, stands up close to the rock, then kneels till his chin is level with the water and passes his hands, with fingers turned up, deftly under its body. The open palm of his left hand comes into contact with the tail.

He begins tickling the fish with his forefinger, gradually running his hand along the belly further and further toward the head until it is under the gills. His left hand is poised to grab the head.

He gradually tightens his grip around the trout's body. Still it does not move. Then in a lightning grasp Micky holds the fish hard in both hands.

There is a struggle for a second or two. Then Micky wrenches the trout out of the water and holds the fish high over his head before hurling it to the bank where I jump on it in excitement.

"I've got you. I've got you my beauty!" I shout.

Micky runs out of the river and kills the fish with two blows to the head using a small rock. He then dresses quickly and hides the fish—which weighs over two lbs—under his coat.

I bring my mind back to my current predicament on the Kingsbeck.

'The trouble is I'm not in Ireland, there is not a substantial trout population on this river in Norfolk and there are no fast pools with rocks," I say to myself.

I am reluctant to put my hand into muddy recesses beneath the bank where my fingers might get bitten by something. However, I keep remembering the five guineas and it spurs me on.

'It needs to be a place where the current has created a hole large enough under the bank for a fish to hide,' I say to myself.

Suddenly there is an explosion of sound behind me and a train rumbles over the bridge 20 yards away. I notice an entire shoal of dace shooting past—and several take refuge under the banks.

I choose a spot in front of a large elm tree and by a thick hedge, where there is a stile for people walking along the path to climb over.

Gingerly, I lay face down on the bank at the point where I think a large trout might choose to hide in the daylight hours. I dip my fingers into the fast-running water.

'You lost your wallet mister?'

The sound of a human voice is startling and I turn round to find a small red-haired boy with a freckled face standing above me.

'What is it Bert?' asks the teacher.

'I dunno Miss—but there's a bloke lying on the river bank with his hands in the water.'

131

At that moment a young schoolmistress, with her jet black hair tied sternly in a bun, comes over the stile. A group of children stand behind her.

'What on earth are you doing young man?' she asks primly in a reedy voice reserved for small boys behaving badly.

'As a matter of fact I'm trying to tickle a fish madam,' I reply.

'There is a peel of laughter from the children. The schoolmistress isn't sure whether I am being rude, whether I am from the local lunatic asylum, or just making a foolish and rather feeble joke to make the children laugh. She immediately turns her back, gathers her skirts and says to her pupils: 'Right class, we'll go straight home now please, let's hurry and no looking back.'

Teacher and class literally run up the river path back to the village. I call after her.

'Madam, have you never read Twelfth Night?'

She does not turn back. I light a cigarette and wonder how long it will take for the word to spread round the village that a lunatic has escaped. Perhaps they'll send the local constable down to find me. All the more reason, I reckon, for catching something soon to take back to the farm. I return to the spot and conjure up the courage to sweep my hands into the unknown.

Very gently I slide both hands—two feet apart—beneath the bank and move inwards in a pincer movement. I trail my fingers along the mud and make contact with something.

Is it a stone, a tree root, or even something horrid? I gingerly rub my left hand gently along it. It is not alive. There is nothing there. I walk another mile downstream, listening to the skylarks above the meadows and come upon a disused mill.

There is a strong smell of wild garlic in the air and at last I see something exciting in front of me. In the middle of the river is a small island surrounded by reeds. It has been created by deposits of silt in what has been the mill pool.

I notice there are fewer weeds in the mill pool than in most other places on the river and on one side of the islet the current runs fast along a ledge of bricks upon which I could lie. Here is a much more hopeful location. Micky's words come resonating back to me.

'You need a gentle and delicate touch young man, very much as though you are caressing a girl!'

I remove my boots, socks and trousers and wade to the island, carefully climbing on the ledge and disturbing a moorhen in the process. Very slowly I let myself down upon the ledge and peer into the clear water below. I decide to be patient and lie completely still for 10 minutes before dipping my hands in the water.

After a few minutes my heart races when a large trout noses its way upstream and halts just beneath me. It was a long creature of well over 12 inches in length and I can see its spots.

It appears to have no intention of going anywhere and wavers in the current, slightly upstream of me but within reach of my hands. I hardly dare to breathe as I lay watching the fish facing the flow of the current.

I remember what Micky told me—to keep my hands low and stroke the underbelly with just the forefinger from the tail end of its body, while keeping the other hand as the pincer with which to grab its head. After five further minutes I dip my hands into the water behind and below the fish. Inch by inch my fingers move towards the creature.

I will never forget that first gentle touch of contact with the smooth underbelly of the trout just above the tail. I expect the fish to shoot upstream in fright but instead it remains in its position facing the current after the first touch.

There is something sensuous about all this that reminds me of the art of seduction and the unpredictable response of a girl who is touched in an erogenous zone for the first time.

Suddenly I remember the slap across the face I'd received from the outraged Blanche, daughter of the miller at Sculthorpe, when I touched her breast after a long kiss in the darkness of a barn, while her father was away hay-making. I want to chuckle.

"Come on Clarkey—keep your mind on the job!" I whisper.

I move my right hand and its erect forefinger along the silky body of the pleasured trout and position my left hand underneath its head ready to grasp it when the moment comes. It is quite extraordinary, but the fish appears to have gone into a trance. I continue to caress the trout with my forefinger at a point under its dorsal fin and then move my fingers around its body and gradually tighten my grip. Still the fish remains motionless.

One, two, three . . . then I grip the creature firmly with both hands. It comes to with a start and its initial flapping catches me off balance.

"Shit,' I shout.

Down I go into the water with a monumental splash that terrifies and disturbs all the birdlife in the vicinity. In the instant of falling I know I can either use my hands to break my descent, or keep clutching the fish.

I retain my grip on the trout even though my head strikes the bed of the river. Fortunately I fall into only five feet of water and soon find my feet. I come to the surface still clutching the trout and jerk the protesting fish out of the water.

'Christ careful you don't lose it Clarkey,' I shout to myself as I stagger across the river to the side of the mill pool. Holding the fish at its gills I grope for a stone large enough to kill it.

'My God, I've done it! I don't believe it, I've done it!"'

I walk across to my rod and satchel and weigh the trout. It is twenty ounces.

Now I lie down in the grass at the side of the deserted mill and sleep for many hours in the sun to dissipate the excess alcohol still in my system. I am back at the farm by 4pm.

The Printers return from their work shortly afterwards and are astonished to find the trout on the marble slab in the parlour. They are speechless with laughter when I tell them about my adventure and the incident with the school mistress and her party of young children from the village.

'Perhaps you can let me have the five guineas as soon as you can?' I ask

John hands over the banknotes and silver coinage.

EDITOR'S NOTE: It wasn't until after he'd joined the army in 1909 that Frank discovered the banknotes the Printer brothers had given him were in fact his own. They had taken them out of his wallet for a jape the night before when he was drunk.

Although he spent the next few days scratching his genitals no infection developed—hardly a surprise since on the night in question he'd never been near a whore.

13
THE GERMANS COME

He woke from a deep sleep in the back garden to hear German voices shouting early one afternoon in late-September. Lorries had arrived carrying a platoon of soldiers who immediately sent the entire town into a state of panic. He could also hear horse-drawn transport arriving. There was shouting and then two rounds of rifle fire followed by female screams. He could hear doors of houses being slammed and then loud protests in French. A few moments later Sister Madeleine ran into the garden and lifted him onto his feet. She picked up everything, including the mattress off the garden table and whispered to him.

"Vite, vite, suivez-moi!"

He was bundled into the stables at the back of the garden and lay on the stone floor while she covered him with a mound of straw using a pitch-fork. A black horse was led by Sister Madeleine briskly into his stable and stood with its hind legs only a few inches from where he lay. Now, to his surprise, the sister spoke in haltering English.

"Be brave my Tommy. Lie still. Make no sound. No one can see you here. Don't worry about the horse—it will not tread on you or kick you."

As she spoke the animal defecated and the green brown droppings fell closely to his head below the straw. Working on the farm in Norfolk before the War meant he was impervious to the smell of horse dung. In fact he rather liked it. Once again he responded to the gravity of the situation, as he had done at the height of the battle, by roaring with laughter. He was admonished by Sister Madeleine—who also giggled—and they both fell silent. He could not see her but guessed that she was no longer with him.

What he heard in the next half an hour filled him with rage and he had to restrain himself from leaving his hiding place to find some kind of weapon with which he could attack the Germans. He then realised that this would only lead to the nuns being punished for concealing him.

Sister Madeleine had returned to the ward and within five minutes two soldiers burst in through the door. One strode across the room and hit her on the mouth with his closed fist and then pointed his rifle at her. He shouted in poor French.

"You are hiding Tommies. Where are they? If you don't tell us we will find them ourselves—and you will be shot. Do you understand?"

He then hit her a second time across the side of her face. She fell to the floor cracking her head on the side of an iron bedstead. She lay there helpless and dizzy—but felt a sudden pain in her stomach as he kicked her with his boot and screamed in her ear to stand up. Sister Madeleine was now bleeding from the mouth and nose but looked defiantly at the young German who towered over her.

"There is only a young boy and an old woman in this hospital at the moment. There are no soldiers here. This is a clinic for sick people from the village," she said.

He now held the rifle barrel to her bleeding face.

"We have just discovered six English soldiers in the convent which means you and your sisters have given sanctuary to the enemy. If there are unwounded soldiers in the convent then there will also be wounded Tommies in your hospital—so tell me where they are!"

He brought the butt of the rifle across her thigh and the impact sent her reeling onto one of the beds. A bloodied and badly bruised figure, she felt tears welling in her eyes but continued to gaze upon the soldier.

"You will find nothing here, look for yourself."

The other soldier now moved forward and pulled back her hood, exposing her cropped head. He spoke in German which she did not understand.

"Hey this one is young and attractive Klaus. I am taken with her. She's just my type. I don't mind screwing nuns, they're probably grateful for it anyway."

The German soldier who had hit Sister Madeleine roared with laughter and replied: "That's OK with me if it'll make her talk!"

Before Sister Madeleine realised what was happening, the second soldier bundled her into the washroom and began to rip off her robes. She screamed and tried to fend him off as he tore off her habit, undershirt and petticoat. He stripped her naked, revealing her small frame and threw her to the ground where she lay cowering in terror.

The German was unhitching his trousers and clearly about to violate her when an elderly Feldwebel strode into the room. He shouted at the soldier to take his hands off the terrified Sister Madeleine and then hit him on the head with his rifle butt. The young German uttered a cry of pain and protest. He fell to the ground beside the nun, now bleeding himself. The non-commissioned officer looked down in embarrassment at the naked figure of the young woman on the floor and spoke in faltering French.

"Excuse me Sister for this man's behaviour. Most of my soldiers know how to behave in front of chaste women. This pig doesn't—and he will be punished. However, unless you give up your Tommies I won't be able to protect you from the officers. They are very angry. So please tell us where your wounded soldiers are hidden."

She sobbed in reply as she put her torn clothes back on, gradually regaining her dignity and composure.

"I told your men that there are no Tommies in this hospital, only local people. Why cannot they believe me? I am a woman of God."

Four soldiers, including the one who had hit her with his rifle, walked into the wash room and dragged out the soldier who had attempted to vio-

late her. They beat him continually and he cried out for mercy. She continued to shiver with fear, but managed to compose herself and walked back
into the ward. Through the door Sister Madeleine saw six British soldiers
dressed in ragged uniforms being lined up in the street. They were kicked
and also prodded with rifle butts but none responded to the violence. A
British sergeant in the front rank ordered them to stand to attention and
look ahead.

"Eyes front!" he shouted, determined that the men should be seen to
be disciplined soldiers. Eventually they were herded onto the back of a
lorry and driven off. Sister Julienne and another elderly nun were bundled
into the vehicle beside the soldiers. Their arms were tied by rope and their
bruised and battered faces revealed that they too had been the victim of
German violence.

The tension in the town gradually cooled as the soldiers went about the
business of billeting themselves in the houses. It was clear these Germans
were intending to stay—and the town was about to become a dangerous
place for Allied soldiers.

Frank had heard the din caused by the Germans and had been appalled
by the screams of Sister Madeleine only a few yards from where he lay
hidden in the stables. Then he heard voices—speaking in German, which
he could not understand—coming closer through the garden.

They were now in the stable which fortunately for him did not have
lighting and was constantly in dim shadow. He sensed the scrutiny of
a German soldier, who was standing by the half-open stable door. The
young man, obviously a country boy, stroked the head of the horse lovingly, rather than making it his business to search below the straw inside
the stable box.

He was fearful the German soldier might use the bayonet on him and
prayed to himself that no sudden itch or sneeze would come upon him—
forcing him to shift in his total stillness.

"There's no one here Hermann, don't let's waste our time. I think we'll
have to widen our search. They'll have the bastards hidden somewhere—
perhaps in the woods over there. We'll be getting the dogs in later this
afternoon."

After a few minutes the soldiers left the stable and he was left in silence
feeling a sense of relief and he drifted into sleep. He regained consciousness some hours later and found he was in the back of a cart that reeked
of human shit. He looked around him and realised that his body was lying
under a pile of sacks and surrounded by barrels of human excrement.

"Christ, I'm on a night soil wagon," he exclaimed to himself loudly.

He then realised he was no longer wearing pyjamas but dressed in a
loose fitting Army tunic with sergeant's stripes and the insignia of the
Regiment on his arm. This was all the more of a mystery since his old
uniform had been nothing more than blood-stained rags.

"Mine not to reason why," he thought to himself.

The horse and cart made steady progress along a narrow cobbled road bordered by poplar trees but eventually they turned off the road and made their way along a track which ran between high hedges. Then they came to the side of a wood.

The wagon pulled up at the end of the track beside a stone farm cottage whose chimney belched fragrant wood smoke. It reminded him of Ireland. A large swarthy man with a thick moustache and long beard stood at the rear of the cart and eyed Frank with curiosity.

"Well Tommy, how did you find the stink of shit?" he asked in reasonably good English, helping him off the back of the cart and giving him assistance as they walked to the front door of the cottage. He offered him his handshake.

"My name is Albert and I live here with my mother. We've got to get you to a hospital soon but you'll stay with us until we can find somewhere that isn't crawling with the Boche," he explained.

"I've never been much bothered about the smell of shit—mine or other peoples' actually. I'm just extremely grateful to you Albert for getting me out of the shit in town, but I'm worried about the sisters, especially Sister Madeleine," he replied.

"Don't worry, it could be worse. Sister Julienne is still under arrest in jail but the other sisters are none the worse for their ordeal.

"They're as tough as old boots it may surprise you to know—you see in times of adversity they take refuge in their faith. So don't concern yourself about the sisters.

"The Boche won't close the hospital because it serves the town. We think they'll use it for their own wounded soldiers and if they do then Sister Julienne will just get a reprimand and be sent back to the convent to keep it running."

A large saucepan was suspended over the log fire in an inglenook fireplace and an elderly woman with short grey hair doled out portions of what appeared to be Coq au Vin. Albert sliced off two large pieces of bread from a loaf on the table and placed them on the plates before pouring wine into two tumblers.

"Just call her Mama," said Albert.

"She's quite deaf but knows exactly what's going on. She'll be pleased to look after you and will bring you hot food every few hours.

"There's no need to ask too many questions. The moment you step outside the door you can smell the shit in the pits. It takes time to get used to it. That's why the Germans won't come here—unless they have to because someone has informed. That's a risk we'll take, but I think you'll be OK for a day or two here."

"Can you tell me what the date is and what's going on in the War? I have lost all track of time but feel well enough now to take an interest in what is going on," he asked.

"You have been sick for more than a month and in that time the fighting moved south over the border. The Germans almost reached Paris but were stopped on the Marne and they were pushed back to Flanders. Now there appears to be a stalemate. They call it static warfare. Both sides have dug trenches and they fight from their own lines. We hear there are many casualties."

They both ate their food in silence for five minutes before he spoke again.

"The doctor has said you must remain in bed to minimise the risk of infection. Sister Madeleine will come to you tomorrow."

He spent the next week in the farm cottage being nursed by Sister Madeleine who cleaned his wound every day and gave him white pills to swallow. She placed his right arm in a sling and she held him gently while he used the china potty and she showed no embarrassment at seeing his naked body.

Mama fed him two pints of fresh milk every morning from Albert's herd of cows. He had never much cared for milk—but she stood over him while he had the mug in hand and bade him drink it without argument by making loud but toothless 'tutting' noises when he failed to gulp it all down his throat.

The food was faultless—various forms of garlic-based stew supplemented by crusty bread fresh from the oven at the back of the fire. One day mama brought him rabbit stew which compared with anything he had ever eaten.

He had been given Albert's bedroom which overlooked the front of the cottage and the track that led to it. It was by now early autumn, but Belgium was enjoying an Indian summer in 1914. Following the advice of the doctor to lie still on his stomach, get fresh air and sleep as much as possible, he left the windows open and tried to avoid moving around, except when cramp developed in his legs.

It was against his nature not to get exercise but he felt weak. He knew he was still vulnerable to infection that could lead to gangrene. Thankfully, the smell of human waste from the pits inside the wood—which bordered the cottage—diminished as he grew used to it. The wood itself was populated by a variety of bird and animal life and he enjoyed listening to the call of the wild, especially at night. Sometimes he could hear Albert shooting in the wood and was surprised he had been allowed to keep his shotgun. Apart from that there was silence.

The Germans could have been 100 miles away and he felt no anxieties about them. The only people who disturbed the peace and his dreams were Mama when she came to bring him food and Sister Madeleine who cycled several kilometres to tend to his wound, supply fresh sheets when required and read short stories by Maupassant.

They got to know one another and Sister Madeleine was becoming better at speaking English. She told him that she was originally engaged to be married to the son of family friends in Mons. He was a miner called Maurice. She had fallen deeply in love with him and was devastated when he died in a gas explosion below ground in 1912. She told him she had never wanted another man in her life after the shock of losing Maurice and had chosen to serve God. He wondered whether she had ever regretted that decision—but felt it would be improper to ask her. One afternoon two weeks later she was reading to him quietly when the peace was shattered by the sound of human voices.

"Christ, who on earth is that?" he asked her nervously. As two figures came nearer to the cottage they realised they were German. She stood back from the window and looked up the track to see the German soldiers on bicycles approaching the cottage. They both carried rifles slung across their back.

She said: "Get under the bed and lie still."

Fortunately for Frank, Albert's bed was a high double with wrought iron bedsteads, a thick mattress and generous bed covers which tumbled down to the floor. A small chest at the foot of the bed obscured the view of what lay beneath it. He took a pillow and blankets to lie on and managed to get under the bed despite the searing pain from his wound.

Having made sure that he was out of sight, and thrusting the surgical dressings under the bed too, Sister Madeleine rushed out of the door and went downstairs to confer with Mama, who had also seen the approaching soldiers. They were by now rapping on the front door.

Sister Madeleine whispered as loudly as she dared in her ear: "Mama, tell them I am your niece. Tell them I was visiting you and that I became ill with dysentery due to the disease from the sewage pits. I will lie in the bed and pretend to be ill. Maybe they will be too frightened to come near."

The old woman looked confused but Sister Madeleine had no further time to talk to her. She ran upstairs as quietly as she could and took off her habit and head-dress. She piled these under the bed next to him and then hopped into the bed wearing only her under-clothes. She pulled the covers over her face.

"Say nothing and hardly breathe," she whispered.

It was Mama who saved them.

The soldiers were so exasperated by the deaf old woman that they became impatient to leave. Frank and Sister Madeleine could hear the Germans shouting questions in poor French at Mama who kept telling them she was partially deaf and could not hear them properly. They told her that they were conducting an official census of every residential building in the district in order to find out who was living where and to make sure there were no fugitives lurking in the local houses.

"So who lives here?" one of the soldiers asked abruptly.

"My son Albert, the night soil man and I live n this cottage. We also have my niece here at the moment but she is ill upstairs," she told them.

The second soldier spoke: "What do you mean your niece is ill upstairs?"

"She came to visit me to check on my health because I am an old woman and my son Albert does not know how to care for a poor old widow. She came to cook and give me a rest but I think the germs in the air infected her. Now she is very ill and in bed upstairs. She is constantly sick and has diarrhoea all the time—perhaps it is dysentery, or even worse cholera. Do you want to see her?"

"I'll take a quick look to check the old bag is telling the truth," the first soldier said to the other.

They heard him coming up the stairs. Both became rigid with tension. Frank stopped breathing and Sister Madeleine drew the sheets even closer over her face and lay still—to appear as if she was sleeping. The soldier opened the door to the bedroom and peeped in for just long enough to establish there was someone in the bed. Then he was gone.

They heard the conversation continue downstairs: "So what is her name?"

Mama feigned deafness again: "You what?"

"Her name you old hag, what is she called?" the second soldier shouted in Mama's ear.

The first soldier interrupted: "Oh for pity's sake let's get out of this stinking place. I don't want to be ill. Just tell her the girl must report to the authorities when she gets back to wherever she's come from—otherwise she will be severely punished."

He then turned to Mama again and shouted at her: "If we catch you hiding Tommies you will be shot by firing squad—so don't even think of getting up to any tricks old woman. We'll catch you, even though this is a lonely place."

The two men left the cottage, climbed on their bicycles and rode off. The two in the bedroom remained motionless for at least five minutes. Once again he could not suppress his laughter at the absurdity of the whole situation. Once again he was chastised by Sister Madeleine. That evening they discussed over dinner what should be done with him as Mama served at table.

Sister Madeleine obviously did not want to lose her patient and was of the opinion that he needed further nursing to prevent re-infection of his wound. Capture was a risk they should take she argued.

"I don't disagree with that Sister but he has to go somewhere safe where he will not be discovered—and where he can also get the right treatment. What if he relapses here?" said Albert.

Reluctantly and silently Sister Madeleine accepted what Albert had to say. She departed after dinner bidding farewell with a friendly smile towards her patient. As she cycled back to Witheries, carrying just a miner's lamp on a cross country route, she told herself she had become too involved with the Tommy sergeant. This would be likely to cause trouble for her with Sister Julienne. Alone in the dark with the insidious chill and mist of an autumn night, no one saw her weeping in the sure knowledge that she would never see her Tommy again.

The following afternoon he awoke from a deep sleep to find Albert standing over his bed with another bearded man who looked like the Belgian. It was curious to see them together and he assumed they must be brothers.

In fact Anton was no relation but the men appeared to be close friends.

"Anton works in the Forest of Mormal for the Countess Jeanne de Belleville. He is one of her gamekeepers. Their house at Montignies-sur-Roc is just this side of the border, deep in the forest and even more isolated than my cottage. The Countess has agreed you should stay there for a short while. You must leave tonight," explained Albert.

"I'm not sure I feel strong enough for a long journey yet," he said wearily. He was enjoying the warmth and comfort of his large bed and the constant nursing of a woman for whom he felt a lingering affection and hoped would return. There had also been a gradual drop in air temperatures at morning and night as October heralded the autumn.

"It is not ideal you should be moved so soon, but the Germans are convinced the district is teeming with bands of English and French soldiers in hiding. They have been reinforced with new units of Landsturm whose main task will be to root out fugitives. There are even rumours they will sweep my woods with hounds in the coming week."

Now, as they shook hands Anton spoke: "You will be safer at the home of the Countess. There are many places to hide in her large house and the outbuildings. There is a great battle going at Ypres which is less than 30 kilometres away, so the Germans have more important things to do at the moment than organise hunts to recapture fugitives in the Forest of Mormal. That may change, but for the moment it is too dangerous here for you."

He nodded his agreement.

Albert continued: "Tonight, after food you will take my bicycle and ride with Anton south through the back roads and forest paths where the Germans are rarely seen. You will both be carrying game and Anton will have his shotgun. If you are challenged you must let Anton do all of the talking but be prepared to answer simple questions.

"Few of the old soldiers of the Landsturm speak much French—so they probably won't recognize your English accent, or that your French is poor. The journey is almost 10 kilometres and in the dark you will need to go slowly. Anton thinks that even with your wound you will be able to accomplish it within three hours—provided there are no delays. If at any point you feel too weak, or too ill to continue, do not be embarrassed to tell Anton because he understands you must rest."

He paused, then added: "The doctors would never sanction what you are about to do—so soon after being seriously wounded. There is a danger of re-infection or of you catching pneumonia. Sometimes doctors have to be disregarded and risks taken."

Mama wept when the time came for the Belgian and the Englishman to leave. She gripped him tightly to her breast and kissed him generously on both cheeks. Albert also hugged him.

"Come back when you are well big man, and help us to fight the Boche," he said.

Albert had presented him with a rabbit fur jacket and a thick wool pullover to wear over his vest and army tunic. He wore a pair of stout leather boots also donated by Albert. Anton had loaned him a black beret which kept his head warm. For the first hour as they walked in single file—with Anton carrying a miner's lamp—he perspired inside his warm clothing. The bicycles had front baskets which were loaded with hares, rabbits, partridge, pigeon, and a few snipe.

In his weakened state and with his right arm in a sling it was all he could do to push his machine along. The sheer effort made him want to vomit. He had been severely weakened by the lack of exercise in the weeks of convalescence. He hoped they would soon come across a track wide and flat enough to cycle along—he hoped he would be able to ride and steer the bike with one hand. It then began to rain heavily and he felt a chill running through his body. Drops of rain cascaded off his beret onto the fur coat. The journey through the forest involved one major crossing point over a main highway—which Anton did not think would be busy late at night. He was wrong.

Suddenly Anton halted. Gradually, the sounds of the nocturnal forest had been replaced by the growing roar of large scale motorized movement and the clatter of horses in harness.

"It is coming from the main highway. Remain here while I go to see," said Anton. He returned in a few minutes with an explanation.

"The Germans are sending reinforcements to Ypres near the coast where a big battle is going on. There are thousands of men moving down that road. We will have to wait here to let the column pass."

They had stumbled across an entire Brigade of front-line troops in motor transport—supported by dozens of horse drawn wagons and artillery pieces. They waited for nearly an hour for the column to pass. It was raining and the cold damp air seeped into his wet clothing as he lay on the ground beneath a large bush. He felt tired and weak and tried to ignore the sharp pain coming from his wound.

"Get a move on you German bastards," he kept saying to himself as he shivered.

At one point Anton handed him bread and cheese and hot coffee—but it provided only short term relief. He started shivering again uncontrollably and began to feel ill. The tail of the column finally passed through three hours before dawn.

"We still have nearly five kilometres before we reach Montignies-sur-Roc. We must move south as fast as we can. It would be dangerous for us to be seen in daylight," warned Anton.

The remaining hour and a half of the journey was a heavy undertaking for a man in such a weakened state, but he walked slowly, pushing the bike with his head down with his left hand—and keeping his thoughts to himself.

The dark forest path seemed to continue forever. He cursed his predicament silently. On several occasions he fought with feelings of nausea. He tried to contain the shivering which had taken hold of him from head to toe. At last they came upon an unexpected clearing in the forest which widened out into a field—in the centre of which they joined a drive-way leading up to an imposing gothic building with two columns at the front.

As they approached, the grand double doors opened and they were ushered inside by a male domestic servant who had obviously monitored their approach. A commanding female voice called out in the gloom in English—perhaps for his benefit and reassurance.

"Take the Tommy below to the servants' quarters, fill a bath with hot water and let him soak by the fire in its warmth for half an hour to see if we can revive him."

He could think of nothing in the entire world that he would rather do than that. Within five minutes he had been stripped of his wet clothing by two menservants and helped into a large copper bath in front of an enormous log fire. The hot steaming water enveloped his cold limbs and he had to fight off immediate sleep in this state of exhaustion. He did not remember being towel-dried, clad in pyjamas and carried upstairs where he was placed into a large bed that had been heated with a brass bed warmer.

He had a vague recollection of drinking a hot concoction that warmed the inside of his stomach and of a tall aristocratic woman gazing down at him.

"Drink this slowly Tommy," she instructed quietly as he raised the large cup to lips and tasted something distinctly alcoholic.

Brought up to have good manners, he tried to introduce himself—but the effort to do so was subverted by a greater desire to fall asleep and he fell into a deep dream.The tall aristocratic woman was sitting at his bedside when he woke, but he felt too weak to move. Her grey hair was clad in a single plait and she spoke perfect English with a refined accent.

"Welcome to Montignies-sur-Roc Sergeant Clarke. I am the Countess Jeanne de Belleville. Anton. One of my gamekeepers brought you here two nights ago. You have slept since then and we fear from listening to your laboured breathing, during your slumbers, that you have developed a fever, possibly pneumonia."

He replied wearily: "I feel terrible Madame, worse in fact than any time since I was wounded in August. Furthermore my back is hurting like hell again."

He found the effort of talking had taken all his strength. He lapsed back into sleep while the Countess dried his perspiring face with a dry cloth. She turned to a maidservant.

"Marie, sit by the Tommy's bed. If he wakes make sure he drinks at least two tumblers of cold water and ensure the bed warmer is sufficiently hot. to keep the bed heated. It is important to make sure his fever does not worsen.

"I think we will have to continue the salt treatment on his wound in case the infection returns. I will do that myself, so let me know when he wakes of his own free will. We should not disturb him. They say sleep is the best cure."

She had been joined by a young man in a Belgian cavalry officer's uniform who stood by the bed looking down at the tall Englishman.

"Strange thing aunt, he looks more like a British officer rather than an NCO. Perhaps there's a story of some scandal here. It's most curious!"

"Pierre, I don't care about that. What worries me is that if the Landsturm come when he is in this state, we will not be able to move him out of the house into hiding. His discovery would compromise the entire network. But I don't see what else we can do!"

"Trust in God, aunt—that's about all you can do!" said the young Belgian as he walked out of the room. Frank slept deeply and received intensive nursing from the Countess for the next week.

He had no idea of the risk they were running of discovery by the Germans through his presence at the house. He also did not know that the Countess was already under suspicion of assisting allied soldiers to escape.

One afternoon he awoke to find the British military doctor he'd met before by his bedside. The doctor produced a stethoscope and put it to his chest. He listened to his heartbeat and his breathing.

"You have been ill with pneumonia Sarnt. It is an inflammatory illness of the lung due to bacterial fluid collecting in the lung's sacks. You must have picked up the infection through getting a chill during your journey here.

"You have been well looked after and I think in the next two weeks you should be able to move on from this house.

"Typical symptoms associated with pneumonia include a cough, chest pain, fever and difficulty in breathing. Are these familiar?"

"Yes, I've had all of those," he murmured.

"The infection in your wound has returned and so we are continuing with the salt treatment which seems to have worked well. You are still weak but strong enough to be moved—not far though. The Countess has prepared another bedroom for you on the top floor of this house. It has a concealed entrance so that if the Germans come here they will not find you."

He was given a dressing gown and helped from the bed. As soon as he stood on his feet he collapsed back onto the bed and vomited.

"Christ, I'm sorry about that," he mumbled. His head was bursting with pain, his wound was throbbing and a chest pain made breathing difficult. After a few minutes, with help from the doctor and a manservant, he was moved from the bedroom and staggered painfully up a narrow staircase to the top of the house.

A large chest had been pulled forward from the wall. It normally obscured a trap door—through which he now was helped into what appeared to be the bedroom of a domestic servant. There was a single wrought iron bed, wash stand and bowl, pine drawers, wardrobe and a chair next to the bed. A print of Pierre Renoir's painting *In the Meadow* was hanging next to the door—and he gazed upon it with pleasure. The scene of the two women relaxing in the countryside reminded him of

Sister Madeleine reading to him in the garden in the sunshine.

It was a Spartan room, but he felt comfortable in it—while craving for warmth. Marie brought up a brass bed warmer and soon he found relief from the pain in his wound by falling once again into a deep sleep.

TROUT IN DERBYSHIRE—DIARY MAY 1914

The red sports car driven by Charles terrifies grazing horses that bolt to the far end of the field and upsets a small flock of sheep which scatter in every direction. Its roaring six-cylinder engine is heard a mile away across the flat Norfolk countryside and it rouses mother and I in the kitchen of the farm at Colby, near Felmingham.

Charles has purchased the car directly from the factory in Birmingham. She is an elegant and beautifully engineered high performance car with a six cylinder engine that roars like a lion and gallops like a thoroughbred.

The car comes to a halt outside the front door in a cloud of dust that silences our barking Labrador. He climbs out and shakes my hand before being introduced to mother.

'So what is she?' I ask.

'A Lanchester Sporting 40 and there's a six month waiting list to own one,' he says proudly.

I am impressed by her compact lines, substantial radiator, twin headlights and drop-hood and wonder if I will ever own such a car. Not if I remain a sergeant I won't. I joined the Army five years ago and am now a senior non-commissioned officer but unlikely ever to be an officer.

We walk into the oak-beamed kitchen and a maid comes in with pails of water from the well and sets about preparatory work on our large range, warming both food and the kettle. A coffee pot is on the long pine kitchen table with three Victorian Golden Jubilee mugs on a tray.

'How did you get leave?' Charles asks me, stooping to pat and caress a Labrador puppy with a drooling mouth.

'I've been invited to play in a cricket match for Brigade against the Cavalry down at Aldershot. The CO gave me a week off—so here I am in Norfolk.'

'I thought the infantry in Belfast were tied down by the Irish nationalists quelling riots and insurrection.'

'We don't get too worked up by that. I can't see why there's so much fuss about Home Rule—it seems to make a lot of sense to me. It's in the North that feelings are running high against it—some of the top Protestant families seem to have the ear of the senior brass in the Army.

'We turn a blind eye to their militias strutting about County Antrim armed with rifles. I think it'll all calm down so long as no one does anything stupid to muck it up.'

'What about the Nationalists?'

'They seem to be behaving themselves because they want Home Rule, probably as a first step to independence later—on the other hand they are smuggling arms from Germany—so the whole thing is a can of worms really.'

'How is your brother?'

'He's been promoted so he's up to his neck managing the Corporation's horses and its lorry fleet.'

'I thought he wanted to farm.'

'He talks of it. One day perhaps.'

'What do you make of the international situation?' Anna asks Charles.

'I think the same as Frank does about Ireland, Mrs Clarke. So long as nobody in Germany or Austria does anything stupid the international situation will remain stable. I think the Kaiser will avoid a war with England because of the Royal Navy. He knows the French Army is a match for his Prussians. Provided no one does anything stupid, I believe our Government will keep us out of trouble.'

I interrupt impatiently: 'What about the fishing? Where are we going?'

'Have you ever heard of the Upper Derwent?'

'Are you telling me we're going to the Duke of Devonshire's fishery at Chatsworth in Derbyshire?'

Charles laughs. 'It's teeming with trout. We'll be staying at the Peacock at Rowsley not far away from Chatsworth. The hotel has seven miles of fishing on the Derbyshire Wye and a short stretch of a few hundred yards on the Upper Derwent. That's where we are headed. Have you done your packing?'

We journey through the old Sherwood Forest, past Mansfield, skirting Chesterfield and on to Rowsley. The car rumbles through the lengthening shadows at around 35 miles per hour passing the remote hill and valley villages of middle England. We are conscious of the odours of the countryside; the scent of meadow flowers and mown grass—and the ubiquitous smell of cow and horse manure, together with the occasional whiff of pig dung.

Children are out of school and play in the road, jumping clear of the approaching machine with squeals of delight. Many run in bare feet . . . although they look well fed. There are a considerable number of younger men around gathered on street corners usually outside a pub with beer glasses in their hand. England has looked like this for generations and I am conscious these are snapshots of Edwardian village life.

Two days later I stand fishing upon a collection of small boulders on a stretch of the Upper Derwent just beneath the church in the Derbyshire village of Baslow. I have used them to walk across the river to within casting distance of a number of feeding channels.

I feel sure there will be trout in these channels—although none are rising. I hold a 10-foot split cane fly rod in my right hand and cast my line, which is tied to a silk 2lb breaking strain leader, with leisurely ease into one of several meandering channels of whisky clear water ahead.

The fly drops slowly and silently onto the surface of the water in a shallow run close to the churchyard bank. The Blue Dun makes its way downstream and there is a surface flurry before it travels more than a few inches. I miss the strike on what is a small trout because I allow the line to balloon too far downstream. I curse—but can hardly complain.

I have caught more than 40 fish up to three quarters of a lb, on a selection of duns. Most are Wye trout but I am also very successful on the Upper Derwent, on the Chatsworth stretch of the river. I am enchanted by the river's fast-running pools—many of which are several feet deep—and each of which seem to contain dozens of small wild brown trout in mint condition.

The Upper Derwent fish are fierce and strong fighters, flashing gold and silver with big red and black spots as they come to the net on the surface. They are wild and have to be played with great skill and patience even with a 2lb leader. Trout like this have to be stalked with care and are easily put down. This is not a river for novices.

I like this kind of fishing because I have to keep on the move, wading quietly upstream. Close range, I soon discover, is little use. I take most fish on flies with very tiny hooks at least 25 feet away and find they prefer dun hackle patterns the shade of light blue or green, although the ubiquitous black gnat always catches when all else fails.

The sky overhead is dull with low cloud cover. The humidity of the warm day suggests there will be heavy showers soon. Darker clouds are mounting up in banks to the West. Fortunately, the wind holds off and all this amounts to perfect conditions for early summer dry fly fishing.

On the Upper Derwent the angler can stay in the water once he goes into it and can wade great distances up the shallow margins at one or other side of the river. Upstream I can see Charles fishing a good run below an ancient bridge. He has attracted a crowd of onlookers watching the demonstration of the elegant art of fly casting. Charles is a show-off and loves an audience. I prefer solitude when I am fishing.

I laugh when I see that Charles has let his unlit pipe fall from his mouth into the water—but with surprising dexterity he continues casting while retrieving the soaking pipe from the water. There is applause from the bridge.

When we checked into the Peacock Hotel at nearby Rowsley, where the River Wye meets the Derwent, we expected to spend two days fishing only the former river. After dinner we get into friendly conversation with the landlord Harold as we sit on stools at the mahogany bar and later he introduces us to Frederick Kirby, one of the Duke's land agents.

Fred says he is happy for us to try our luck on the larger river for a donation to the estate fishery of a guinea each. He says he will warn the bailiff and his staff we are coming—so we will not be arrested for poaching. We decide to stay an extra day in Derbyshire and Charles agrees to take me straight down to Hampshire for the cricket.

On the first day we fish the Wye, a limestone river with its source way up in the Pennine foothills above Buxton. In its lower reaches the river becomes languid—with some fast runs—and meanders in a series of bends through a landscape of limestone dales. It eventually loops through lush meadows approaching Haddon Hall and continues down the valley towards Rowsley before reaching its confluence with the Derwent by the twin-arched Rowsley Bridge.

In early to mid-summer the river is blessed with abundant Mayfly and on our third and final morning—before we split up to explore the river separately—we witness the extraordinary phenomenon. It is as though the very river has come alive with living creatures—exciting both the birds and fish to feed in a frenzied manner.

They attack the swarms of magnificent and splendidly winged flies; the females nearly an inch long. It lasts only a short while and I put my tackle aside for several minutes to watch it in awe.

Eventually I rise from where I am squatting and join Charles to cast my fly into the orgy of feeding which seems to have attracted large fish from up and down the river. I catch my best brown trout of the day at just over a lb while these Mayflies are active.

However, it isn't the Mayfly fishing on the Wye that excites me the most during that final day. A local tips me off on the first night. The tip comes from Harold, the landlord of the Peacock. Harold has been the patron since 1890 and runs a popular establishment because of its faded and rather eccentric gentrification—the sort of hotel that appeals only to those who pursue old fashioned country sports. The aroma of pipe and cigar smoke, reinforced by the whiff of wet gun dog, pervades the smoky atmosphere at the bar.

'Ephemerella Ignita,' says Harold, sipping another scotch on my room account and taking it from his own personal bottle. He tips the malt down his throat in one gulp after extending his arm to the shelf without looking behind him.

'What's that?' I ask.

'I shall let you have some,' adds Harold, helping himself to another scotch.

'The Blue Winged Olive represents clean, clear and cool fast water. It's the life blood of summer fishing here. Constant trickles of hatching duns provide fishing throughout the day with the spinners returning later to lay their eggs and die . . . thus the evening rise.

'You can take a whole box full of flies and use every one—but the Blue Winged Olive will give the best yield in May and June. Come and see me before breakfast and I'll give you a few to be going along with.'

That night in my room I am ready for a deep sleep. It has been a long day with an exhausting road journey and I have supped 10 pints of ale. I keep my eyes open to read about the Olive in an old Victorian journal given me by George Printer. I read that the fly is one of only a small group of flies with three tails and is easily identifiable in its hatching and egg-laying stages.

These two short stages constitute the lifespan of the tiny creature during the course of just one day. The angling techniques required at both these stages differ considerably—which is the essence of the challenge.

The dun has slightly kick-back wings and a trout seeking them at the hatch has to be quick—from the moment of hatch, to flying from the water might only take a few seconds. This often brings about a rushed, splashy "take" from below. Late in the afternoon and early evening—having mated—the adult spinners fly upstream to deposit their egg parcels on fast water.

This upstream movement on the wing counteracts the downstream drift of egg, nymph and dun. As the eggs are dipped into the water, the flies begin to die. Tiny bodies are swept into the food channels which cause the evening rise, characterised by gentle rolling sips or calm 'ticks' from the trout, often rising 10 or more times per minute.

'I think this is going to be an epic day old man,' Charles says during our early breakfast at 6.30am on the first day. We decide to fish until noon, take a long lunch at the Peacock and then return to the water at 4pm to enjoy the evening rise.

'Yes but it is always tricky when you don't know the water, the local conditions, or what works and what doesn't,' I reply mischievously. I have decided not to share my knowledge of the Blue Winged Olive with Charles who tends to be a know-all when it comes to new rivers we have not fished before.

Charles gets an idea in his head and tries to make me follow his example, often against my better judgment. Charles has not heard what Harold said—he opts not to use winged flies such as Blue Winged Olive, the Gold-ribbed Hare's Ear, the Iron Club Dun, or the Ginger, Orange and Red Quills. Instead, says Charles, he will concentrate on hackle patterns and variants of the Mayfly. He will seek out the fish in the long wide meandering pools of the lower river.

'OK you do that and take your time,' I say.

'I want to cover as much of this seven-mile beat as I can in the morning session so I'm going to move fast upstream seeking out the fast snappy runs.'

I walk nearly two miles of river up the valley before I start to fish. I am not after big brownies—I want good sport and will fish the fast-flowing runs to see what I can do to move smaller trout. I stop just below a bridge where a shallow run sweeps graciously down to a sharp bend and turns the current into a rippling pool of more than three and a half feet in depth which runs for more than 20 feet on the left hand bank—the angler facing upstream.

The water is so clear I know I will have no more than three or four casts on each pool and so each one has to be directed exactly to the spot where I require the fly to land softly on the water. I tie on the Blue Winged Olive and crouch low in the water behind a bush swinging the line delicately up river making not a sound as I do so.

I take a fish on the first cast and although I know it is less than 10 inches long it bolts up the river like a young salmon and I have to surrender line as it makes its run up the shallows towards the bridge. I gradually increase the tension and turn its head—but showing great spirit it heads madly back down river so that I lose touch with it for several moments.

I spend a few minutes on each pool and cover more than four miles in the morning session before turning back to head downstream towards the Peacock. I have caught 15 fish in as many pools and enjoyed the forthright manner in which the Wye trout come to the fly. I remember what the book has told me about the very few seconds that elapses between the hatch of the Blue Winged Olive and its first skittish flight off the surface of the river.

The trout has to be quick—and so do I. I release all of the brownies—the largest of which is just over 12 inches with a deeper belly than the others. All the fish are of a yellow hue and in magnificent condition.

'What kept you old man?' asks Charles when I reach the dining-room at the Peacock shortly before two o' clock.

'Oh sorry it took me longer than I thought it would to get back. I've had 15 magnificent fish but had to cover well over four miles to catch them. It's been a wonderful morning session.'

We spend three hours at the bar in conversation with Harold before the evening rise. I know methods will have to change radically. The trout will be feeding on dead or dying spinners. There will be none of the enthusiastic grabbing at the fly, but a more gentle roll and suck at the surface. I would not need to venture far—the lower river produces feeding channels where the brownies can take advantage of the abundant fly coming to die on the water. No need to cast long—but avoid putting shadow on the surface or making footfall vibration in the bank.

Charles seems to have read the river wrongly again. Now he decides to follow in my morning footsteps walking hard and seeking out the fast runs up the river. He takes a torch and tells me not to expect him back much before 10pm—but to keep the bar open.

I set off shortly after half past six. I smoke on the grassy bank and observe the long meandering pools to watch for signs of life. Fish begin to rise an hour later but still I do not move. I have a hip flask of malt whisky and while taking small sips enjoy the sight, sounds and smells of the falling evening on an early summer's day.

During my time there day-dreaming, I spot nesting kingfishers, heron, linnet, and finches. At 8pm I finally stand up, assemble my tackle—with the trusty olive spinner on the end of the cast—and walk just 50 yards to a pool which has become a frenzied feeding ground of rolling trout taking the spent flies from the surface of the river.

It requires the most delicate and silent casting—always crouched low at the bank and never wading. In the space of an hour and a half I catch 20 fish and only cover half a mile of water. It is glorious fishing ending in the twilight with the sound of feeding fish continuing to gorge on dead insects into the darkness.

In his waking periods he missed Sister Madeleine and her deep resonant voice when she read to him. He thought about her innocent brown eyes and the way she would gaze at him and then, before departing after each nursing session, how she would kneel without embarrassment at the bedside and pray for his soul.

One day he even asked the Countess if Sister Madeleine could be asked to continue to attend to him during his illness. She looked at him blankly and said dismissively: "I do not know of this nun and frankly it would be better if it stayed that way."

He did not mention Sister Madeleine again. The Countess would visit him twice a day and check his pulse and body temperature. In the evening she would bring a large tumbler of milk reinforced with cognac. It warmed him inside and always left him wanting more.

A further two weeks passed and while he felt stronger physically, he felt in lower spirits emotionally than at any time since Mons. Early one evening in mid-December the Countess came to his room holding a dark three-piece suit and a shirt and tie, which she told him, had belonged to her husband.

"My manservant Pierre will help you to change into these clothes. Then I want you to come downstairs to my salon. It is time your spirits were uplifted," she said.

Twenty minutes later he was helped down the stairs by Pierre and ushered into a warm spacious room with cedar wood panelling and a high green and gold coffered ceiling. A superb silk Lyon tapestry covered much of one side of the room. There were luxurious soft furnishings and a marble fireplace in which burned a large coal fire.

The room was lit by oil lamp and what made it so spellbinding in the shadowy light was the large Christmas tree in one corner, from which were suspended at least 20 red and white candles. Under the tree were dozens of small parcels wrapped in pink or blue paper and adorned with silver and gold ribbon.

"I must say you look very handsome in my husband's suit with your black hair and moustache. This year you are my principal guest," said the Countess with a big smile on her face as she kissed him on both cheeks.

"Countess, this is so unexpected. I did not know there were so many children in the house, it has been so quiet," he said, pointing to the presents.

"The children are not mine but they will come for their presents soon— and in return they will sing carols to entertain us," said the Countess. She explained that every Christmas the pupils from the village school visited the big house to give an impromptu carol concert. Each would receive a gift—a doll for the girls and a lead soldier for the boys.

"It is important you sit quietly in the armchair by the fire before and during the concert. You will be introduced as a member of my family spending Christmas here, but just remain seated and smile at everyone. I shall make sure no one tries to engage you in conversation."

The children arrived and sang like angels in their innocence. The carols, although sung in French, were all familiar to him. It made him homesick, and he fought hard at times to suppress his tears. That night he slept soundly and dreamed of a Christmas in Norfolk many years before when he was a boy of the same age as the children who had sung carols. He remembered those Christmases in the early 1890s when he had been a choirboy and sang with the other village children at the Christmas Eve service.

THE GRAYLING—DIARY NOVEMBER 1909

Anna is still upset I have joined the Army and says she cannot tell any of her friends that I am just a common soldier. She scolds me for my lack of ambition. In fact I have adapted well to service life and have been promoted to junior non commissioned officer. Why shouldn't I be in the Army? Soldiering is natural to me.

I find that the peacetime Army allows me time to indulge my passion for fishing. On this day I am dressed warmly in thick tweed and waders on a cold November morning walking along the banks of the River Anton, a tributary of the Test in Hampshire.

The Battalion is based at Aldershot and the opportunity for winter chalk stream fishing cannot be ignored. I have a day's leave and take the train to Basingstoke where at 1.30pm I meet Charles Rimington at the station who is waiting there with a trap.

We begin our 25-minute drive to the River Anton near Wherwell and we talk about the prospects for the day as the sun shines in a watery pastel sky. We also use the time to soften and oil the new silkworm gut to attach to our silk fly lines. Dry silkworm gut is stiff and useless for casting, so each angler carries a small leader tin containing dampened felt pads between which we place our coiled gut leaders to soften for half an hour or so. It is a hassle to have to do it—like drying and dressing the silk fly line after each day's fishing.

Upon our arrival at the estate Charles goes off to meet the river keeper while I change into waders and prepare for my first experience of one of the finest small rivers in southern England.

I stand on a wooden bridge and look around me—my heart pounding at the exciting sound of the water which rushes gin clear beneath me. I can see a number of native brown trout and grayling on the riverbed edging about here and there at what the current brings down to them.

The nutrient-rich waters of chalk streams are so named because their waters rise through chalk formations, neutralizing acidity and adding mineral content. The source of the Test is in north Hampshire in the town of Ashe and at thirty-nine miles it is the longest of the Hampshire chalk streams. Through much of its flow, the Test and its tributaries are not one river, but a collection of streams, feeder creeks, mill channels and manmade sloughs created initially for irrigation.

Chalk streams have historically fostered vast legions of insect marine life at all times of year and fish grow well. Charles returns.

'From what he said I think we've got things right. We'll need a decently long cast—so he recommends a nine foot split cane rod with a small nymph tied on a light gut of seven feet. If that doesn't work, we should fish dry using a small fly.

'The depth of the water at this time of the year is around four to five feet and unusually clear. Before we start he recommends us to drag the tip of the fly line through mud—to sink it quickly—as the river is flowing fast. Luckily the wind is coming from the south and will usually be behind us.'

I say: "You walk half a mile upstream before fishing and I'll follow you in 10 minutes. I'm going to try a copper wire coiled nymph tied onto a size ten hook to resemble a fry. I don't suppose the local gentry would approve, but that's what I am going to do. The nymph will flash in the water if I retrieve it fast. I'll enjoy a cigarette while I'm waiting for you to clear the ground."

Working upstream with the hatches behind me I wade in the cold and clear water using a variety of wet and dry flies as the afternoon progresses. Picturesque white thatched cottages line the road with the Anton meandering gracefully beside them.

The river meadows behind the orderly rows of cottages, now devoid of livestock—which are in winter quarters apart from a few horses being exercised—fold into the distance, merging with woodland as the sun begins to sink to the west in concert with a rising evening mist.

Now and then a pheasant flies overhead joining the indigenous birds like crow, rooks, and pigeon—breaking the total silence with their calls in the damp air. I am always fascinated by the aroma of decay prevalent in the late autumn countryside. It is due to the fallen leaves—I can smell burning foliage and detect smoke rising from a copse that is being cleared ahead of me.

I expel air from my lungs and watch the condensation from my hot breath filter upwards into the atmosphere before disappearing. The damp air is by now permeating my woollen clothing and I quicken my pace to stave off the penetrating cold of the winter countryside.

I love the seasons of the British Isles. The hum of bees and the drowsiness of warm summer days are certainly in a different world to this.

My unprotected face and hands now begin to feel extremely cold but I am exhilarated by the experience of being on such a famous fishery.

As I wade along the left hand bank upstream, with the weakening sun in my face, I turn to look behind me and notice a small shoal of grayling fifteen feet to the rear, feeding off the insects stirred up in the clouds of silt caused by my submerged footsteps.

I let a pheasant tail nymph travel down in the current and watch the end of the sinking fly line for the sudden sign of erratic movement in the clear water. The line skids perceptibly across the current only 15 feet from where I stand in the water. It is a goofy way to fish but I enjoy it for a few minutes. I hook a good grayling of 20 ounces that dashes across the river and then whips upstream before being brought to the net.

By this time, about three hours into the fishing, I have already netted ten fish on various flies but have caught nothing anywhere near the two lb mark. I want to end the day with at least a specimen fish in my net. I have perhaps half an hour to do this if I am going to catch the 5.30pm train back to Aldershot.

I regard the grayling with its elongated dorsal fin to be among the most handsome of British river species, one of the wondrous manifestations of nature—of majestic appearance and certainly a true member of the salmon family.

I have always supposed the grayling must have been created with infinite patience by the sensitive female artist in the sky. It is a fish to be gazed upon. Its grey colour overall permeated with subtle suggestions of violet, viridian, amethyst and blue.

George Printer has taught me that big grayling will sometimes seize a substantially dressed dry fly at dusk, even in cold weather when few insects are around. So now I dry the fly line back to a distance of 10 feet with a cloth permeated in linseed oil and tie onto it a seven foot gut leader with a breaking strain of about two lbs. This is lighter than the one I have been using.

I open the fly-box and select a red Soldier Palmer—I have not used it since fishing a rocky river in County Galway in 1904 but believe its substantial body might interest a large grayling.

I look upstream and choose a pool which is deeper than the average—formed after the protrusion of reeds on the left-hand bank. This causes the current to swerve around it and sweep back into an eddy. It looks a good spot.

I wade to within 30 feet of the reeds and stand—without moving—watching the pool for a further five minutes searching for visible signs of movement. In the fast sinking light, which still bears the reflection of the crimson sun, I detect a swirl and the tail of a large fish. The shoal is still searching out nymph. The sight of a fly on the surface might just arouse the enthusiasm and the instinctive lightning quick grab of a grayling.

I draw off sufficient line in three arcs from the reel and in my much practised slow and relaxed style—with my right elbow tucked into my ribs—I flick the top of the cork handle of the rod as the line passes lazily overhead. It is all executed with the confident precision of a bowler going for a good length at the offside stump. I have good rhythm today.

My body faces exactly towards the aiming point, which was the head of the pool alongside the furthest reed. The fly lands silently and the current carries it at speed into the eddy two feet from the bank. I know it could work, but I only have one cast if I am going to succeed. Afterwards I recall the sucking sound made by the fish as it grabs the Soldier Palmer. I can just hear it.

The fish rolls over with the fly in its mouth and is aware immediately that it has been trapped. Grayling share several features with their cousin the trout—and fierce resistance to capture is most certainly one of them. It makes a headlong rush for the sanctuary of the reed bed. I keep the rod up and gather sufficient line in my left hand to draw the grayling back into the main stream.

The Grayling rushes up and down the river, at one point dashing below the point where I stand, but after five minutes the fish begins to tire and I bring it to the net. Charles Rimington is standing on the bank of the river and he already holds the scales in his hand.

"Trust you. You must have the eyes of an owl. That's one to talk about at the club. . . . a dry fly catching winter fish in the winter twilight—what next?

"Now are you going to catch that train or aren't you?"

The grayling weighs in at two lbs four ounces and is the largest of the species I have ever caught. It gives me great pleasure to hold the head of the fish upstream for a few moments and then release it into the evening gloom of the river.

The weak sun has now fallen below the horizon and the chill of the air requires the angler to keep moving and get busy. It is going to be a cold night.

Around me the nocturnal creatures are beginning to move about and I catch an early glimpse of an owl flying from an oak tree to a barn that borders a nearby farm.

This is England at her best and most peaceful.

14
CHRISTMAS DAY 1914

He was getting stronger. He threw off the virus and his wound gradually recovered from its infection. One afternoon, as the snow was falling, the Countess joined him in a walk round the gardens. He sensed that she had something important to tell him.

"Frank, we are going to move you to a Red Cross hospital over the French border on Christmas Day. We believe the Germans will be preoccupied by celebrations and less vigilant than usual," she told him.

"But won't that mean that I shall be a prisoner of war if I come under Red Cross jurisdiction?"

She laughed: "We don't intend to give you up that easily. You are going to be hiding in the hospital out of sight from the main wards. We are sending you to the Chateau de Bellignies. It is the home of Prince Reginald and Princess Marie de Croy, who are brother and sister and is run under the auspices of the Red Cross.

It is within easy walking distance of here through the forest and we plan to send you on Christmas Day afternoon. We are all part of an escape network for Allied soldiers who were left behind after the fighting at Mons and Le Cateau. One day in the spring it will be your turn to escape from this country and get back to England.

"We will see how your health develops in the coming weeks. The advantage of being in a hospital is that you will receive professional nursing care and there are both doctors and surgeons there. Your bed will not be on one of the wards and there is no reason the Germans should ever see you when they visit the hospital.

"However, you must obey instructions and never question what you are asked to do. There must be no contact with anyone outside the family and their closest circle. If you are discovered in hiding many of the French and Belgian people helping you could be shot."

On Christmas Eve, as the snow fell, they had dinner together. They sat at opposite ends of a long walnut table with candelabra and other silverware obscuring their view of one another. The Countess wore an elegant costume which swept around her feet and a tiara.

She was middle-aged but with her high cheekbones, full mouth and large brown eyes, looked beautiful in the flickering candlelight. He surmised she must have been stunning in her youth. He wore one of the Count's hand-tailored suits and it amused him to think that for this night he was master of the house, and an accepted member of the Belgian aristocracy.

"I shall look upon the completion of your successful escape back to England as something in which I have played a significant part.

"It will give me great satisfaction. Perhaps one day when this terrible war is over I can be your guest in England?"

That night, on Christmas Eve, he relaxed for the first time since his arrival on the Continent. He drank at least half a bottle of cognac, having previously devoured a strong French cheese and before that he managed a generous portion of duck soused in Armagnac and cream. He slept with the sound of carols from somewhere deep in the past ringing in his ears.

He woke late on Christmas morning. At first he thought he was dreaming. He could hear the unmistakable sound of a choir singing. *It came upon the midnight clear* by Edmund Sears. He dressed as quickly as he could, walked carefully down the long staircase and knocked on the door of the salon. The Countess was seated by a log fire on a four-seat settee, listening to a disc phonograph upon which was mounted an enormous speaker, emitting the sounds in a scratchy harmony.

He sat down beside the Belgian aristocrat and together they listened to the haunting sound of eight consecutive carols performed at the King's College Cambridge carol service in its 15th Century chapel on Christmas Eve in 1913. So much had happened in 12 months that it was painful to look back upon the elegant and ordered world that had once been, but was now probably gone forever. The future seemed so uncertain.

The double-sided 78rpm shellac disc was, the Countess told him, the first recorded concert ever made by the choir. As they listened they didn't care about the quality of the sound, but marvelled at the invention. The machine was manually operated. Every few moments the servant had to rewind it, which they both found highly amusing. The servant brought them coffee and croissants and as the fire warmed them, they were both absorbed in their thoughts of Christmas festivities in years gone by.

"Will you be sad to leave us?" she asked.

"You have taught me the meaning of compassion and generosity, not least because you stand to lose so much, if your work with Allied soldiers is discovered by the Germans. Have you thought of that?"

"Of course, but then we must remember the thousands of young men who are dying for their country at the front just a few miles from here, the innocent Belgian civilians who were murdered in August and the orphaned children who are now starving. We must do our duty—no matter what the consequences."

He added: "I suppose I was lucky to be a soldier in a uniform. I just had to obey orders. England has not been ravaged and so most of us have no personal animosity towards the Germans—they are just the enemy. Our job is to kill them. If we hated them we would be no better than murderers, we would be killing from personal motive.

"You know, in Belfast people went wild with enthusiasm when war was declared in August. I didn't share those feelings and from what I have seen already I know I was right. War is unspeakable. Yet, as a matter of paradox, I am happy to be a soldier and a few weeks ago I killed several men in cold blood, which is certainly a contradiction isn't it? For several minutes on that day I became a savage, a beast. I wanted to kill and kill and kill.

"I have always believed I possess an orderly and civilised state of mind. I like routine, everything in its place, properly and neatly arranged and I am a stickler for planned arrangements to happen on time. Indeed I am so punctual that if I have to catch a train I'll be on the platform half an hour before it arrives. I suppose it's all reflected in my hand-writing, it is the smallest and neatest you could imagine!"

He laughed loudly at himself.

"Actually Sergeant it sounds extremely boring—and I don't believe a word of it. I'd say you were a devil-may-care kind of character," replied the Countess.

"Not true. I would pack my case two days before I was due to leave the house in Dublin. I prefer everything to be planned and I hate surprises. I am a pedant when it comes to rules and details and I like to record everything in my diary. I've kept a diary since I was a boy to record my fishing adventures."

He paused and looked at her closely. "I'm being entirely truthful about myself Countess. Maybe it's some form of anxiety syndrome. Deep down I am full of tension and worry. Yet before the battle at Mons in August I felt no terror of dying or being wounded. Perhaps we never get to know or really understand ourself, let alone anyone else."

She replied, moving her face into his space and gazing closely at his brown eyes: "I think you are a survivor, whatever befalls you." She held his chin, then kissed him on the mouth gently and stroked his moustache with affection. He felt the kiss was intended in a sexual way and it stirred him, but he did not respond.

Later that afternoon he and Anton left Montignies-sur-Roc as the snow continued to fall. The Belgian wheeled a bicycle loaded with game and the Englishman walked beside him. They followed the forest paths, which took them across the border well away from checkpoints and heard only the sound of wildlife. It was as if the War had literally gone away.

"It is strange that we cannot hear the guns," said Anton.

"Normally you can hear the shells exploding and even the rattle of machine gun fire if you listen hard enough. Today there is only silence from the direction of the Front."

Neither man knew that on Christmas Day 1914 on ta long section of the Western Front a few miles away British, French and German soldiers came out of their trenches, walked across No Man's Land, played football and fraternised in a truce that shocked and infuriated the high commands of all the combatant armies.

The ordinary soldiers on both sides—who had been locked in combat for several months—made a spontaneous gesture which for a few hours placed goodness above evil, life above death. It did not happen again during the First World War.

Anton talked in his broken English continually to keep Frank from becoming too introspective in his exhaustion.

"One day you will get back to England monsieur, thanks to what we are doing for you—and then you will return to France to fight again!"

15
EMILY HORSTMANN

When they arrived at the chateau night had fallen. He was ushered into the gateman's cottage and given a bed in the attic which he had to reach by climbing precariously up a set of ladders guided by one good arm. It was a small hard bed but there were thick blankets on it and he felt warm and secure as he took his arm out of the sling and lay down on his stomach to sleep. His limbs ached from the exertion of the six kilometre walk, but he did not have any fever and soon drifted into a deep sleep.

The next morning he climbed down the ladder and came face to face with a tall auburn-haired woman. She spoke with an American accent and wore the headgear, uniform and cape of a Red Cross nurse. They made immediate eye contact—hers were an icy blue—and something stirred in both of thes young people. There was chemistry here.

"Hi, I'm Emily Horstmann and I'm going to be your personal nurse. I'm also gonna make sure you don't get yourself into any trouble. By the way don't expect me to call you Nobby—I've never heard such a weird name," she said with a toothy smile as she clasped his hand. For one of the few times in his life he was speechless. All he could do was gaze at her. They sat round the table in the gateman's cottage and drank coffee.

"It's a term of endearment—my nickname in the Army. A lot of English guys called Clarke get to be called Nobby for some reason. Excuse me but aren't you American—and if so, how and why are you here in occupied France?" he asked.

"Yeah, I'm an American nurse. I come from a small town in Virginia and joined the Red Cross while on holiday in Germany in the summer. But then I got to see how the Krauts behaved in Leuven back in August. My friend and I kept a dossier of atrocity statements for the American Minister in Brussels and we got arrested. We were kicked out of the unit and I was told by the Krauts I had a week to leave Belgium."

"So why didn't you," he asked.

"The hell I would," she laughed. "There's plenty of work for nurses to do here and some jackass Kraut ain't gonna stop me from doing it. Anyway, now I'm in France!"

She continued: "I went to see the Minister to hand over the dossier and he sent me to the Berkendael Institute, which is a nurses' school on the outskirts of the city run by an Englishwoman called Edith Cavell.

"She thought it was too dangerous for me to stay there and so I was sent over the border here to the Chateau Bellignies to work for the Countess—right under the noses of the Krauts. I'm still a Red Cross nurse—but now I'm unofficial.

"I'm illegal, like you, so I don't go on the wards. My height attracts attention. So when I heard you were coming here and still sick, I thought I'd look after you."

He thought for a moment and then said: "Well, I think you're the best bloody Christmas present I've ever had!"

They both roared with laughter.

It was as if they had known one another for years. They had a similar sense of humour and found many common factors, including horses, in their background. He was no great horseman like his brother but he knew how to ride and listened in fascination to her stories of apple ranching, the Negro community on the estate, the canoeing, mountain riding and training racehorses.

Her description of the little conservative town of Boyce in Clarke County fascinated him and after talking politics he realised she was a socialist and had also been a suffragette. After two days of confinement in the gatekeeper's cottage, he was dressed by Emily in an orderly's white coat and allowed into the chateau accompanied by his personal nurse. His arm was still in the sling which made him look decidedly odd.

"Keep your trap shut and let me do all the talking," she ordered. He hadn't seen or talked to another British soldier for more than 16 weeks, apart from the doctor. He was excited at the prospect of being among his own kind.

A huge doorway led into the panelled central hall of the building, the principal feature of which was an enormous marble fireplace. The hall was also paved with marble and on both sides it opened onto reception rooms where recovering patients sat reading. Facing the doorway a wide staircase led to the first floor which was occupied entirely by wards, each containing from 10 to 20 beds.

The wards were magnificent rooms, most overlooking the front court-yard of the chateau. There were 60 ward beds and a hospital staff of about 30. This all-French team included a surgeon, two doctors, 10 nurses, 10 orderlies and four ambulance drivers. In addition to the medical staff there were the domestic, kitchen and estate workers.

On the second floor were the office, common room and the operating theatre. The management of the hospital and estate was all based on the office, which was a small room and always crowded. Four people sat round a table in the centre and at a second table in the window sat the Prince and Princess, who was herself a trained nurse. She took him to the operating theatre.

Large windows meant it was well lit during the day and there were electric lights in the ceiling for surgery at night driven by a generator. The smell of ether and strong disinfectant made him feel slightly queasy. Emily said the wards were happy even though patients lived under the shadow of German occupation.

The soldiers lay in bed, smoking cigarettes, laughing and chatting. The ones who were too ill to talk, or were blind, lay still in their bed and listened to the banter. As he walked past one group, he overheard Norfolk men talking. He paused and was sorely tempted to join in, but a hand prodding his lower back guided him on through the ward. Then suddenly at the end of the ward—to his dismay—he recognised a face that he knew well from the Battalion. He walked past the bed looking away from the soldier and managed to get out of the door without being recognised.

"Christ! That was close. Corporal Harry Dickens is in the bed at the end. He's in my Company and he'd have jumped out of his skin if he'd seen me," he whispered to Emily.

She said: "Yeah, we're not going to allow you to take this risk again. You could easily be recognized by these guys. But we thought it best you saw the set up—just in case you ever had to escape from where you were hiding and mingle with the soldiers on the wards."

They walked on in silence.

She continued: "Some of these guys were close to death from loss of blood and exposure just a few days ago. The surgeons sometimes have to resort to an amputation because of the great destruction of the tissues in the wound. It's too late to do anything else. You were lucky you were wounded before this terrible trench warfare started. If the war isn't over soon it's going to mean the death of millions of men from both sides."

"Every Tuesday more than a dozen wounded captured soldiers arrive by lorry. Those who can walk go straight upstairs—the gravest cases go to the theatre or wait their turn in the great hall for surgery. On the day that the wounded prisoners are brought here, the German medical authorities clear out those allied soldiers thought to be well enough to travel to hospital in Germany. It is desperately sad for the ones that have to leave because they face prison camp—but there is nothing we can do to stop it. They get them out before they are strong enough to start thinking about escaping. There is a section of Landsturm who remain at the gatehouse to check in visitors but they do not come to the wards."

They climbed a smaller staircase leading to the upper reaches of the chateau, where the family had their personal quarters on the third floor and walked into a sitting room with cedar wood panelling. There were several imposing bookshelves around the walls. A log fire flickered in a wrought iron grate and three enormous settees were arranged around it. This was a room that smelled of good cigars, like a gentleman's club and it appeared to be lived in.

Emily walked up to one of the panels and leaned against it. It swung back to reveal a dark inner passageway leading to a secret hideout.

"Follow me," she said laughing. Taking him by the hand, she led him to a door in the passageway.

"Where on earth are we?" he asked.

"Welcome to our new home Sergeant," said Emily smiling her huge smile, as she opened the door. It revealed a room smelling of disinfectant with a large bed, a wardrobe, a bookshelf and long table, upon which was an array of medical equipment, bandages and ointments. It was well lit with double windows overlooking the front of the chateau. The room next to the ward was Emily's bedroom and there was an inter-connecting door.

"This is your own private sanatorium and it's where we'll get you well enough to make your own escape attempt back to England. When you are ready I'm going to come with you because I'm going to apply to the American Mary Borden to join one of her Red Cross ambulance units on the Western Front—my Australian friend Jackie, who was with me in Leuven has already joined the unit in Flanders. You know you are lucky. You lay in a field for three days. You'd lost so much blood. Perhaps you are as tough as old boots," she laughed.

"Right now I'm going to put you back to bed, give you a sedative, and get you to sleep for a few hours without stress or tension."

That evening he met the Princess Marie. She was a petite woman in her mid-30s with short hair cut above her ears, and pale blue eyes that were so large in a tiny face that they gave off an air of almost girlish innocence. She spoke with a high-pitched soft voice, which heightened her femininity. She was dressed as an ordinary nurse.

"I have heard a lot about you from my friend the Countess. Welcome to the Chateau. I hope your stay here will be comfortable.

"As long as we use common sense and discretion there is no reason why the Germans should discover you here—even though you are right under their noses. For now you can relax and gradually rebuild your strength for your escape, with our assistance, to Holland. I think the Countess told you there are six British soldiers in the tower of the chateau. Actually, it is where my ancestors used to lock up their enemies!"

The Princess laughed and continued: "It is an ideal hiding place because the walls are nine feet thick and so they obscure any sounds the men might make. The soldiers remain locked in and hidden during the day and only a few of the trusted staff are aware of their existence. At night they work with the gamekeepers trapping the rabbits, so they help to feed us, stay fit and are well fed. We provide them with identity papers that will get them to Brussels. A group of us act as guides taking them through to Brussels to our sister network. Most will be leaving in the next fortnight, but we are always finding other soldiers in hiding. So our escape network will continue to operate for the time being."

In that short conversation he realised that the petite Princess was not what she appeared.

The escape network had sprung up from nothing in just a few weeks and the people who were running it were of the most courageous sort. On New Year's Eve they met the escape network headed by the Prince and Princess in the lounge connected to the secret passage. He wore the loose fitting uniform he had been given by Sister Madeleine and was introduced to Prince Reginald, a tall dark-haired man with receding hair, a strong chin, bushy moustache and pale blue eyes like his sister.

The Countess was at the reception and greeted him with a warm kiss on the mouth. The grandmother of the Prince and Princess, a Mrs Parnall from London, was seated on the corner of a settee by the fire. She had been on holiday when war broke out and had been unable to return to England.

She told him: "So far we have had a spectacular war here. First of all Sir John French, the Commander of the BEF stayed for a night when the Army was moving into Belgium and then a few days later, after they had retreated, we had to put up with that awful General Von Kluck, who made the chateau his HQ for one night.

"Then a bunch of frightfully arrogant German staff officers arrived and said they would make it their field headquarters. Luckily, the chateau turned out to be too far from the Front so they moved off. After all that, we've had the turmoil of being a hospital and now being an important part of the escape network. It's all too much for an old woman like me!"

He met two British army officers who were hiding in the tower with other soldiers. They were due to make their escape the following day dressed as artisans. The party celebrated the New Year with vintage champagne and the guests dispersed quietly into the night.

Another week passed and the familiar relationship between them quickly developed into a deeper but platonic friendship. It seemed to each of them that they had known one another for years. They had hours to spend in each other's company and began to devote certain hours of the day to certain things—like reading, playing cards and dominoes and inventing word games. Their one regret was that they could not sing or listen to music on the phonograph—and Emily had demonstrated on several occasions that she was an excellent pianist. There was a Steinbeck grand piano in the lounge.

In the evenings they would exchange stories about their childhood. He was fascinated to learn about Clarke County and the history of the Civil War that had raged around Virginia, only a generation before. He admired Emily for her strong views and forthright manner. One evening she produced a photo album of her family, the town of Boyce and snaps of her canoeing expeditions on the Shenandoah River which her brother had taken. Emily loved to hear whatever Frank could tell her about his family, the English county of Norfolk and Dublin, Ireland.

He did not tell her that he found her sexually attractive; perhaps more than any other woman he had ever met, including Sister Madeleine. The informality of Emily's American manners continued to surprise him and when, one afternoon, she lay down on the bed beside him, fully dressed in her uniform, he felt embarrassed—but hid it from her. She obviously had a platonic relationship in mind in the confined conditions of their concealment from the outside world and felt she could treat him more like an old chum than a man who might be aroused by her sexuality.

Emily seemed to have no grasp of the effect she had on members of the male sex and as she lay next to him she took hold of his hand, sending something like an electric shock through his body.

"Maybe we can sleep a little this afternoon," she suggested and giggled.

He was silent and murmured assent, his pulse rising.

"I think it's time you told me a lot more about your days as a socialite in Dublin. I know very little about you and your way of life when you lived in Amiens Street. How many American girls have you met—or am I the first?" she asked.

"You are definitely the first," he lied.

She looked at him closely and moved her mouth almost to his ear before whispering: "You're a tall good-looking guy. The Prince says he knows a lot of British Army officers. You're so tall he thinks you look more like an officer than a sergeant—especially because of the way you talk and your cultured accent. So we were kind of wondering if you weren't hiding your real identity for some reason."

Emily came even closer and whispered: "Maybe you're some kind of spy—you can trust me, I won't tell anyone!"

He laughed loudly but wasn't sure if he was being teased. This American girl had him guessing in more ways than one.

"No I'm the real thing I promise you, even if I might look like a captain or lieutenant. I was supposed to go into the Army as an officer—that's what my mother wanted anyway—but I got rejected by the War Office Selection Board in the autumn of 1908. I hadn't expected to fail because my older brother had been a lieutenant in the Dublin Fusiliers in the Boer War and is now in the Army Service Corps.

"I should have known that coming from an ordinary Norfolk farming background I couldn't be an officer in a posh English county regiment, but my mother insisted I should try. She's a bit of a social climber.

"The old Colonel—the chairman of the Selection Board—asked me several questions about my private income and who we were friendly with in Norfolk. Did I know this family or that family? I had to admit we didn't know many of them. They were not impressed and soon came to the conclusion I wasn't quite a gentleman. I told them I had been left an inheritance by my grandfather, but that my father owned no land except for the Dublin house we had lived in. It was as though the shutters came down. They just lost interest in my application for a commission.

"The Colonel told me tactfully that without a private income I would not be able to live at a socially acceptable level in a county regiment. He said the fact I'd commanded native troops in the field on active service in Africa didn't really count in the British Army. The following month was Christmas and I was in Norfolk. I came across the regimental recruiting centre in Norwich and on impulse I joined up in January 1909."

Emily asked: "But you didn't come from a poor background—didn't you feel out of place? Common soldiers are a rough lot."

He shook his head and laughed.

"Some people thought I was a 'posh bastard' but no one picked on me.

Emily continued: "But you are educated. Didn't you get bored spending your life with rough and ready guys with a more simplistic attitude to life than you? And don't you resent not being an officer?"

"Being rough and ready doesn't have anything to do with a lack of intelligence. Some of the men in the ranks who left school at 12 were born with better minds than the officers. Those were the types who, if they didn't become rebels and trouble-makers, tended to make the best NCOs. From a soldier's perspective it isn't the officers who run things on an everyday basis in the army, it's the senior NCOs. It's them that make the British Army what it is. However, the men expect to be led by gentlemen—that's just the British way of doing things."

Emily said: "Wow, this is all new stuff to me. We don't have a class system in America—just rich and poor. You are as good as the dollar in your pocket and if you work hard the chances are you'll get rich enough to buy land. You get enough of that then you get respect. You certainly don't judge a guy by the way he speaks or the clothes he wears, or the school he attended."

He continued: "So in answer to your second question, I do think I'm good enough to be an officer but I don't resent not being one because I volunteered to join the Army. I'm happy in my own skin being a Sergeant and now of course it's all academic, because my wound will prevent me having any further career as a soldier."

He moved his head towards her on the pillow.

"So I'll have to look at the process of reinvention after the War. Maybe I'll try apple ranching in Virginia and move in next door to the Horstmann family!"

She laughed and squeezed his arm.

16

GETTING TO KNOW EMILY

He was awakened one morning by the sound of shouting in a foreign language which he recognised as German from the previous September. He pulled himself out of bed painfully and peered through the window, taking care not to stand right in the opening, so the outline of his figure would be seen from outside. A German lorry and a Red Cross ambulance had been parked outside the Chateau and elderly soldiers in field grey, carrying rifles with bayonets fixed, were unloading a cargo of wounded prisoners.

There were more than 20 wounded, wearing the uniforms of the British, French, and Belgian armies. They were carried out on stretchers wrapped in crimson-stained sheets, while the walking wounded, some covered in bandages, were pushed roughly through the front entrance and up the staircase towards the wards. He turned from the window to find Emily standing next to him.

"It's Tuesday. The wounded prisoners have arrived," she told him. "Don't stand too close to the window."

They watched together in silence as the intake of wounded men was admitted to the hospital and then the guards lined up outside the main entrance forming a line to the back of the waiting lorry.

"They will come soon, poor things," whispered Emily.

Frank's eyes filled with tears of frustration and anger. He watched the pathetic sight of Allied soldiers being herded out of the hospital by guards and into the back of the Red Cross and Landsturm vehicles. They were shouted at and bullied with the occasional shove from the butt of a rifle. The men were no longer laughing and joking and carried a resigned air.

"Jesus Christ, these men are not fit for long term captivity yet—just look at them. They need hospital care," he said.

"Yeah, most of them will end up in Army hospitals in Germany before they go behind barbed wire, but they won't get much tender loving care in an enemy hospital. At least they are leaving here well fed and much stronger than when they arrived," said Emily.

It was clear to him that the men being herded into the lorry felt defeated. They could look forward only to the prospect of many years on short rations. Corporal Harry Dickens was among the men being sent off to prisoner of war camp. There were other familiar faces in the group. They were all men who had recently enjoyed the freedom of years of peacetime soldiering in the 1st Battalion.

He turned to Emily. "My God, I hope I get out of this country and back home. I think I'd rather die than be taken prisoner by those bastards after all these months."

She sighed. "We will get you out of here and back to England—you can be sure of that. As for them—you'd be surprised at the resilience of the human spirit and what people can put up with. At least these guys aren't going to have their brains shot out in a trench or their limbs torn off by shrapnel—so perhaps in that way they are fortunate."

"Mmm, I'd rather take my chance in the line any day," he said quietly.

"So when will I be ready to go?" he asked.

"Do you want to go?" she enquired.

"You know, I just feel guilty being here enjoying a comfortable life with someone who is very good to me, while those poor devils are getting shipped off into captivity in Germany."

She moved closer to him and looked him in the eye. "Don't feel guilty. You were gravely wounded and you can't use your right arm properly. Your wound could still turn septic. You're frequently in pain without morphine. You're still an invalid—now come back to your bed this moment!"

He was now obsessed with her and had written about his feelings for her in his diary—kept well away from her eyes. His senses were heightened by her sound, touch and naturally fragrant odour.

Frank found her starched white uniform which covered her knees and swept down to the ankles very alluring. Soap was already scarce in both Germany and the occupied territories. He wondered where she got her supplies from. Perhaps the Princess had a secret store of luxurious French soap which they shared. When she stood before him at nearly six feet tall and displaying her full figure, auburn beauty and those radiant light blue eyes—he could hardly keep his eyes off her.

He did so almost to the point of risking embarrassment. Then she would smile that full smile with her large mouth and lips and the blue eyes would crease in amusement at his close attention to her. She left him with the impression that although she was by nature a tactile person she just wanted friendship and she would not welcome anything closer.

Emily, he decided, would not know the meaning of seduction, for she was a complete innocent, utterly unaware of the effect she was having on him sexually. Sometimes, he wanted to grab her and kiss her strongly on the mouth in the hope she would respond. He wondered if there had been many men who wanted to do exactly the same thing.

He would lie awake at night wrestling with his greatest problem—how could he tell her that he felt deep sexual desire for her, without ruining their friendship. He had waited weeks for just one romantic signal, but there had been no hint of encouragement.

She would put her arms around him, kiss him on the cheek, even pinch his arm affectionately, but that was nothing a mother or a sister wouldn't do. Sometimes in his erotic dreams they had sex. Then he would wake up to reality—she would be lying on the bed beside him and smiling broadly—right up close to his face, the hint of humour in her large blue eyes. There was no hint of physical desire from her. It was always a huge disappointment.

She would reappear later from her room spotless and begin her thoroughly efficient nursing routine which seemed utterly dedicated to restoring his health and fitness as a patient only. He craved for a glimpse inside Emily's mind but for the moment had to be content with just being close to her physically.

One afternoon, they were walking round the grounds with the Princess discussing the military situation at the Front and the difference between every day Army life in peace and war.

The Princess asked: "What was Belfast like? I think some of my Parnall ancestors come from near there, but I don't know the city—and I've never seen any pictures of it either."

He replied: "Belfast is a much more industrial port city than Dublin with its cotton mills and heavy industry—most of which supports the ship-building industry. When we got there shortly after the *Titanic* disaster in 1912 the city was still stunned by what had happened. The Harland and Wolff shipyard completely dominates the place and the great gantry upon which the huge passenger ships are built can be seen from the top of virtually every inner city street.

"As for the noise—when we arrived the *Titanic's* sister ship, the *Britannic,* was on the great gantry and you could hear the riveters banging away on the giant hull for 18 hours a day. It took time to get used to it—especially if you wanted an early night which, in my case, wasn't very often. Those years in Ireland were some of the happiest times of my life. Ireland has a unique atmosphere and its people are the best in the world."

The Princess was beginning to spend more time with them and they would often talk in the drawing room next to the secret compartment. One day she came with a warning.

"The Boches are apparently stepping up their efforts to round up fugitive soldiers who they believe are still in hiding in significant numbers in this district, from last summer's fighting at Mons and Le Cateau. We have been told by the local gendarmerie that the Germans suspect an escape network has been formed and a number of us are on their list of suspects. Despite that, we'll send you both to Mons to have your new identity photos taken and papers signed. You must both have a talk and decide what you want your identities to be."

The following day they went for a long walk in the forest around the chateau. They were excited at the rich variety of leaf in the trees, evergreen pines, the shrubs and the woodland flowers. There was now heat in the sun and a haze in the air. They were both aware of the fecund nature of the early summer. Birds tended to their chicks, baby rabbits scuttled out of their path and the foliage had become dense.

The rhododendrons had already been in full flower and were now fading away to signal the end of the spring. In their place there was a blaze of colour from other plants including wild roses. The only reminder of the grim state of the world was the distant but constant sound of the guns 20 miles away. Hell and paradise lived cheek by jowl.

17
CARP FISHING

By mid-June the power in his right hand was returning. He had been able to move his fingers around with ease for several days. Now was the point when he might become more ambitious. He decided to stop using his sling. The recuperation period prior to an escape attempt was now beginning. He had to get physically fit again. The clock was ticking down to the time when he would be ready to make an escape attempt and he felt excited by the prospect of going down the network with Emily. The wounded soldiers had stopped arriving at Chateau Bellignies after the Germans launched a chlorine gas attack at Ypres in the summer of 1915—setting the stage for continuous gas warfare.

Prisoners streamed into field hospitals that were better equipped to deal with the appalling eye, skin and lung damage that gas shelling caused. The numbers of allied soldiers and the medical staff at the chateau gradually diminished.

They watched in sadness as the final group of soldier patients were driven away in a lorry. Now, apart from a handful of fugitives in the tower, they were the only occupants of the hospital. In the following days the remnants of the medical team and many of the domestic staff, were paid off and departed to fresh assignments. The small detachment of Landsturm at the gates was posted elsewhere and so the War, which was in fact so close, seemed even further away.

Before Doctor Henri Delamare left, he examined Frank and pronounced the wound in his back free of any trace of infection. The scab around the exit point of the bullet had been replaced by light pink flesh and he had regained feeling and some strength, in his right arm. His hands and fingers did not appear to have suffered any damage.

One morning the Princess came to the private ward and told them: "The departure of the patients does mean we can relax security slightly and if I were you I'd take advantage of the fine spring weather and use the estate to get some exercise. I'll have some suitable clothes delivered to you so that you look like staff in case anyone from the German military authorities should spring a surprise visit on us.

The following day they walked around the forest for about five miles and were ambling along a path back to the chateau when they came across the lake. Its shimmering water looked blue, like the sky above it and rays from the sun glinted on the surface in explosions of brightness from which they had to shield their eyes. Duck and moorhen glided about its surface.

Of all the sensations experienced in the joyful moment of stumbling across this enchanted lake—the greatest was the sense of smell. The freshness and purity of the lapping water, combined with the scent of pine trees, filled them with a sense of wellbeing. They stood hand in hand gazing out upon the forest lake. Emily had the perception that somehow this idyllic place had been waiting for them to discover it. "Oh my God, this is the most beautiful place I've seen for years," she said quietly.

"Can we come back here and bring a picnic?"

He replied: "I don't know about a picnic but I can tell you I'm coming back here with a fishing rod. This place looks like it hasn't been fished for years.

"I can't wait to come back and find out what's in here. Of course we'll bring some food and a couple of bottles of wine. But not for a few days because if there are big carp in here—and I'll bet there are—I'll need to bait several swims for about a week beforehand."

"What are you talking about"" she asked.

He replied: "The carp is not just an ordinary fish. Some people credit him with uncanny wisdom. You have to coax him to come to a place where he knows he will find food. So by baiting the swim I mean preparing that place with his food beforehand."

"What kind of food?" she asked. I'm used to trout fishing in the Blue Ridge Mountain streams with lures and fixed spool reels."

"Whatever I can get from the kitchen of the chateau—finely chopped potato peelings, stale bread, cake and raisins, grated cheese, and chopped up worms, mixed into a doughy mush with water and thickened by some sand. I might add a few spoonfuls of Pastis to the balls of dough—if the Princess has some in her cellar."

"Ooh, that sounds disgusting," she laughed. "I'm sure it'll smell awful."

The Princess produced a sturdy cane rod and a steel reel that had an oiled silk line coiled around it. There was also a lighter split cane rod of about eight feet in length with a similar reel mounted on its cork butt. Her search turned up a large landing net, several tins of hooks and gut leaders, lead weights and a selection of painted cork and quill floats. Two large wicker baskets, which could double as small seats, were also hanging on the wall of the saddle room. Someone had looked after the Prince's fishing tackle with loving care.

The Princess said: "Everybody talks about how beautiful it is by the lake and for several summers before the War we had a large skiff down there for people who wanted to get out on the water. The Prince hasn't fished it for years but some of our gamekeepers say there are huge carp in the lake whose ancestors were once an important food supply for the house. The lake is fed by fresh springs and so the water is quite pure."

"I think we might have carp in the Shenandoah River. Pete my brother used to catch them, said Emily."

They stood back from the shoreline of the lake while he tackled up the rods keeping shadows off the surface of the bright water.

"Most really large carp, the 201b fish and above, are lost in the struggle to bring them ashore to the net. The carp breaks many hearts I can tell you."

"Is your heart ready to be broken?" she murmured.

He laughed. "We'll see. You have to be patient. It's no good expecting things to happen quickly.

He cast the bait and the ledger weight hit the water without any great explosion at the right distance. It sank rapidly to the bottom of the pool. He laid the rod to rest on a small branch with a V-shape at the end of it which he had pushed into the ground.

"We have to wait and be very quiet," he said.

"Does that mean we can't even talk?" she asked ruefully.

"No, we can chat away quietly but we must avoid making a vibration, even shuffling our feet, or getting up and walking about," he replied.

"So I can open up the wine and the sandwiches?" she asked hopefully, also handing him one of his cigarettes, which he refused, but accepted a sandwich.

"I haven't had a cigarette all day and I shan't while I'm fishing. Tainted hands that carry the stink of tobacco are absolutely taboo. These fish are fussy and will sniff and snuffle around a bait under the water before committing themselves to eating it."

She looked astonished: "Are they that intelligent?" she asked with doubt in her voice.

"Oh yes—if you don't do things properly then you won't catch the big fish. They have an uncanny sense of what is going on in the world around them. Once they are disturbed they won't feed on any account. The monsters group in ones and twos and they look out for one another."

He handed her a shorter fishing rod: "Your job is to catch the smaller fish for the table—we want about a dozen carp. They swim in shoals and we'll try by casting alongside those lily beds. They often nose their way towards the surface working along the stems of the lilies looking for insects and snails. But we won't start float fishing until I've caught a specimen because we have to wait quietly for the big fish."

They waited for 20 minutes and then he looked down at the coiled line on the newspaper beside his seat and saw the line being pulled quickly out into the water. He picked up the rod gently.

"We have a bite. The line is coming off the coil on the ground. It's still going and I'm going to strike into him in the next few seconds. Watch how he takes off!"

Emily watched in suspense as she waited for him to strike.

"Yes, he's on and he's a big fish. There are monsters in this lake!"

He allowed the rod to take the strain and it buckled into a deep loop as the line hissed at speed off the reel and through his fingers.

"My God, he's raced off at about 100 miles an hour and he's still going!" she shouted. It was true. The fish was running out to the middle of the lake in the direction of a large bed of lilies 50 yards away.

"There's no point in trying to stop a carp of this size when he's at his strongest during his first run. You need soft hands and a gradual process. However, I'm going to have to stop him reaching those lilies because if he gets in there or I'll never get him out."

Frank gradually began to win back line but the fish fought him every inch of the way returning again and again to the centre of the lake before being gradually retrieved.

"Now when I've brought the carp to the shore get the net underneath him and lift it until he is right at the bottom of it—then bring the net towards the bank and I'll lift him out of the water."

They accomplished this without mishap. He brought the carp up onto the bank and proudly laid him on top of the net on the grass by the path. He must make an entry in his diary about this carp.

"Hey, he's a beauty! How big do you think he is?" she asked.

They weighed the fish and he was two ounces short of 18lbs—not the biggest carp in the world but enough to convince him that the lake probably held specimens of more than 20lbs.

One day in the future, after the war, he promised himself he would come back to catch one of the really big ones, but for now this specimen would satisfy him. They spent the following two hours drinking the wine and using the smaller rod to catch the fish for the table. Emily caught most of them.

18

THE PAINTING BY THE LAKE

"Now it's your turn to come and be with me when I do what I do," she chuckled one morning as they ate breakfast in his sanatorium after she had inspected his wound.

"Oh yes—and what's that?" he asked. He was reading *Moll Flanders*, a book by Daniel Defoe from her bookshelf, and was hardly listening to her. She had been reading a magazine.

"Well I may be a Virginian farm girl but I nearly dropped my plans to become a nurse and go to art school instead in Richmond. I love sketching and painting and am particularly fond of the work of the French Impressionists.

"So we're going painting in the forest?" he asked putting down his book.

"You betcha we are. The Princess has found me an easel, brushes and a set of oil paints."

"When are we going?"

"Well what's in your diary for today Sergeant?"

An hour later they were at the lakeside. He had taken the fishing rod and sat on the bank gazing upon a red quill float that he had cast about 20 yards across the water. He was fishing with a large worm on the bottom and wanted to find out if the lake held a shoal of tench.

The sun was up and it was too late in the day to expect good results, but much pleasure was to be taken in just being there with the love of his life, even though she didn't know how he felt about her.

He told her: "I wasn't taught much about Impressionism except that it was a 19th-century art movement among a group of Paris-based artists in the 1860s, who included Claude Monet, Pierre Auguste Renoir, Alfred Sisley, Frederic Bazille, and Paul Cezanne. I like the style, particularly the countryside landscapes."

"Well that's more than most people know I'm sure. Yes, it's all about visible brushstrokes, open composition, emphasis on light in its changing qualities. The Impressionists concentrated on ordinary subject matter, the inclusion of movement as a crucial element of human perception and experience and unusual visual angles. It was all a bit like the radical way in which photographers were approaching their compositions in the middle of the last century."

She continued: "I like them because they were radicals who broke the rules of academic painting. They gave brushed colours primacy over line and painted realistic scenes of modern life, giving emphasis to overall effect rather than detail. They also took painting out of the studio and into the world. They found they could capture the transient effects of sunlight by painting outside like we are doing now. They were much more interested in painting landscape and contemporary life than in recreating biblical scenes from history."

He watched his red float dip gently beneath the surface into the depths of the lake and waited for two seconds before striking upon the fish. It dashed across the lake boring deep, at the same time shaking its head in frantic attempts to disgorge the hook.

It turned out to be a perch weighing nearly two lbs which he decided to keep for the cook. Through his landing of the fish, Emily had continued to work at her easel refusing to be distracted by what was happening on the river bank. He killed the perch, re-baited his hook with another worm and continued to fish. There was silence for 10 minutes. The red float did not move during all that time.

"So what are you painting, a general view of our secret lake?" he asked.

"Yes of course. You are in it too. I shall call it *The Fisherman* and when it is finished I shall hand it over to you to frame . . . and always remember me by," she said mischievously.

He didn't speak the words but thought to himself: "Silly girl, how could I ever forget you?"

He replied: "That oil painting will be my most prized possession. I am lucky because it will mean I shall own two special treasures—the other is a pair of British Army field glasses. I was given them by Ernest Briard, an officer in my regiment, a few moments before he died in 1914."

19
LOVE AT LAST

The Prince and Princess held a dinner party the following week to which they were invited. There were eight British fugitive soldiers and a tall Frenchman called Gaston Quien seated round the table. Most of the fugitives were about to move down the escape network and they discussed their plans—assessing the strength of each one.

In Frank's case it was agreed to make the paperwork simple and straightforward. He would take on the identity of a French speaking Belgian mining engineer called Walter le Clerc. Emily would travel at the same time on a German ID card and remain dressed as a Red Cross nurse until she reached Brussels.

The Prince would escort them as far as Brussels and they would make their own way to the Berkendael Institute in the rue de la Culture. They would meet up with Edith Cavell and she would arrange for Frank's onward journey to the Dutch border with an appropriate guide. Emily would always keep her American nationality papers and true identity—and seek diplomatic help in Brussels at the US Mission.

She reasoned she would have the legal right of entry to Holland—provided her name was not still on file. That was considered extremely unlikely.

Emily told the Prince: "If they issue me with new US papers and give me some form of diplomatic protection, then I don't think I'll have any problem in travelling by train from Brussels and crossing the Dutch border that way."

The Prince warned Frank that his ID papers would be of limited value when he moved on from Brussels and it would probably be necessary to re-create another identity for him while he stayed in the city. He told them that Louis Dervaire the photographer from Mons, would forge their identity cards from photos taken by the Princess on her old box camera.

Only one thing a marred perfect evening for him and that was the presence of Monsieur Quien to whom he took an instant dislike. The Frenchman was a garrulous individual who wanted to swing the topic of conversation around to his own activities—and his personal heroism. He claimed he was an officer in the French army who had been wounded at Landrecies in August 1914.

He told the guests he had been hit by shrapnel in the leg and that it was still troubling him. Quien was tall and good-looking with a presence—although to Frank his narrow eyes suggested a man capable of deceit. His lingering looks in the direction of Emily began to infuriate the Englishman as the evening wore on. Quien smiled at her continuously. It wasn't helped by Emily appearing to return his flirtatious banter.

She flashed her eyes at him and offered to give him an examination so that she could advise on the right treatment for his wound.

"Oh, there's no need for that Emily. I still have my surgery in the hospital for the local people and I shall examine Gaston there tomorrow. If we need to call back a doctor it can be done," said the Princess.

Emily had obviously been taken by Gaston and so had the Prince who seemed to be treating the Frenchman with undue respect. Something about this man wasn't right—Frank was sure of that. To make matters worse, Gaston talked of Paris, the theatre, the opera, museums and the galleries, which were outside the realm of his own experience. By the time the brandy was served he was in a foul mood and felt his fists tightening. He drank the brandy heavily. If Gaston didn't stop showing off and forcing eye contact with Emily, he'd have no choice but to drag him outside and give him a good thumping.

At midnight the evening was over and together they walked back to their rooms behind the panelled walls of the sitting room upstairs. He was so fired up he rather haplessly began to reveal his true feelings for her.

"I didn't like that French blighter Emily. He did nothing but show off all night and he had the cheek to come on to you in front of me as if I wasn't there. I don't think I could have stood much more. I'm glad that dinner's over."

She smiled but said nothing. They reached the sanatorium in silence. Frank—who never ceased to be amazed by Emily—was speechless when instead of picking up a book and lying on the bed fully clothed, as she did sometimes before going to her own room, she took off all her clothes in front of him and then sat naked on the side of his bed. He was transfixed by the first glimpse of her body and stood there with his mouth open, unable to communicate.

"No don't say anything," she whispered, her large blue eyes revealing a sense of excitement and anticipation. "Just come to me now. We have waited too long for this moment. You don't have to say a word."

He stood by the side of the bed, bent towards her and she kissed him on the mouth. He felt the softness of her tongue and smelled the familiar fragrance of her skin. He adored her and was almost overcome by his passion and desire to possess her. She understood his desire and gradually undressed him, garment by garment, while she talked.

"My darling I admire you for your restraint and decency towards me over these past few months. I was hoping you had fallen in love with me and made every effort to conceal my own feelings for you. I have loved you all this time—and I am glad I have kept myself for you. I don't know what fate will bring for us but I have made up my mind. There could never be any other man except you."

They slipped between the sheets and discovered one another for the first time. Emily was a virgin but soon became a generous lover, more concerned in giving pleasure than in taking it. The following weeks, while they waited for the ID papers to arrive from Mons, were the happiest in his life. He was addicted to her body and to her soul. He craved her almost innocent sexuality but adored this woman as his mentor and inner being. He could hardly take his eyes off her.

They made love countless times, in both his room and hers and walked together arm in arm in the grounds of the chateau. One afternoon they even had sex furtively at the lake they both adored so much. He was in a paradise and every sense within him was heightened by the feeling of security that at last she was his. He would never let her go.

There were also moments of high comedy in which Emily took great liberties with him. He woke one morning to find that while he was asleep she had shaved off his moustache which made his tanned face look odd because of the white patch over his mouth and lower cheek where it had been.

"My darling I couldn't do it before because it would have been too personal—but now it's different. You know I love you. I've always hated that pretentious Kaiser Bill moustache and the sight of you waxing it every morning was quite disgusting—so it had to go I'm afraid. I can't be kissed by a man with a thing like that!"

At first he was piqued that his moustache had gone but later he laughed because it was so typical of Emily. She did and she said what she thought was right and that was it. It was why he loved her so much. He could only pretend to be angry.

"You idiot, we'll have to get my ID papers done again with another bloody photograph don't you see? I bet the Princess will be furious!" he said in mock anger.

She laughed. "As a matter of fact, Marie thought your moustache was awful too—and while we're at it so did the Countess, so it's a fait accompli if you like!"

Their intimacy opened new windows into the other's personality. He told her that far from being the tall dashing extrovert that he sometimes appeared to be, he was in fact a quiet and shy man who preferred to remain in the background and not to assert himself.

"I hope that's not too much of a disappointment for you Emily. You ought to know if we are going to think seriously about the future that I am not really very ambitious. That doesn't mean I want a mouse of a woman—but someone who craves fame and success may find me entirely unsuitable as a partner. I have a suspicion they suspected a lack of ambition in me when I went for a commission in the Army—which is why they failed me. I think I'd rather take orders than give them.

"Give me a steady job I can do quietly, don't give me too many surprises in life or make me work too hard. I'd rather lie here on this bed with you, read a book, or go fishing or fill in my diary. I know my faults too. I think I have a gambling addiction and drink too much beer, not to mention smoking.

"I loved sport when I was younger and was good at cricket and rugby— but they were both team games. I suspect I'm a bit of a bore. You know, my mother would think it entirely out of character if she knew I was sleeping with a suffragette!"

"Well in that case we'd better call it off right now," she said laughing.

"OK—but they say that behind every successful man there's a strong woman. Why can't we have it the other way round? You go to work and become the first woman US Senator and I'll stay on the farm, harvest the apple crop and look after the children."

She kissed him on the cheek.

"You know I'm not what I appear to be either. To tell you the truth I don't like myself much—which is why when I was 16 my parents had to send me to hospital because I had an eating disorder. I just stopped eating. I soon got ill but I still couldn't keep anything down. It took me a couple of years before I could stop starving myself and I think it was only the challenge of passing my nursing exams that saved me.

"I had this view of myself of being a big clumsy girl with a wide ugly mouth and ginger hair. Whenever I met a guy of my age I always seemed to be looking down on him, which made me feel even more of a lump. I'd look at myself in the mirror and think 'yuk' what a loser.

"That inner view of myself has stayed with me all through the years and returns as an obsession every now and then—it then degenerates into deep depression which can last for weeks. I'm not very nice to know when that happens. I go quiet and reclusive. I just avoid people, even those close to me.

He took her in his arms, hugged her tightly and said gently.

"There are so many things you do not understand about yourself. You know, I think it's time I gave you an apposite description of Emily Horstmann. She's so stunning to look at that men stop and stare in the street, she's so strong in personality that people are infatuated by her—and she's so caring and compassionate and driven with energy that being in her company is addictive, if perhaps rather tiring sometimes. What's more she never talks ill of people unless they deserve it."

She laughed.

"Did you know that I had to keep on pinching myself to believe that someone as handsome as you would even think twice about a plain red-head with full lips and an ugly mouth that seems to spread right across her face?

"I had no concept of being sexually attractive to you and the most I hoped for was friendship. I still can't understand how you find me beautiful—but I'm very flattered."

She added with a grin: "Sorry about Gaston Quien."

"What do you mean?"

"I'm afraid I was guilty of manipulating you. I just needed to find out if you really did care for me and the only way I could think of was to try and make you jealous. The Princess thought it was hilarious."

Frank said laughing: "Well you certainly had me hooked long before then but I felt I could never possess you. I couldn't believe you'd find a semi-invalid with a hole as large as a saucer in his back sexually attractive."

She kissed him on the mouth and continued: "Don't you think I'm too bossy and pushy? I get so wound up in all my causes—and my feelings of right and wrong—that I guess I must be a pain in the butt. But I can't keep my big mouth shut. I just have to say things.

"I'm really worried, you know, that my over-bearing manner could make me a lousy wife and mother and that my depressions will get worse as I grow older. I look at other women sometimes and really admire their softness and femininity. They are happy for their men to dominate them— I've been engaged to be married several times and each time I have had to call it off when they started calling the shots in my life.

"That doesn't make me feel feminine somehow, which is why I don't like myself much and deep down I don't have the huge reserves of confidence and thick skin that people think I have. So what you see as typically me is usually just a front—I tend to talk a lot to stop people finding out too much about me. I force myself to be the big personality when I'm not."

She buried her head in his chest. "You see I'm really a mixed up and rather pathetic girl which is why a guy like you—who seems to have life under control—is everything I could ever hope for."

He kissed her again:

"We all conceal our weaknesses Emily—the important thing is to know what they are and to be able to deal with them. I think your strengths make you outstanding and I will always believe in you, whatever faults I find, including this so-called depressive nature which hasn't surfaced since I've known you. Your weaknesses will be addressed by having a partner who gives you every possible support.

"Let's say that all of your endeavours in the suffragette movement in Virginia are one day rewarded by political office. If we are still together when that time comes, I'll be right behind as your campaign manager in getting you elected to the Senate. Maybe I will become famous too—God help me."

She whispered: "Well, if we can get this darned war over we can go back and start work on that one. At the moment only 12 states allow women to vote and Virginia isn't one of them. There's going to be a lot to do and even though you say you're not political or ambitious, what you are is what I need. Can we make love now?"

The new ID papers delayed them for a few weeks and so extended their time together, for which they were both grateful. The papers arrived the day before the date was set for their escape. They were complete in every detail, even to the police stamp. Herman had gone so far as to forge signatures without ever having seen their handwriting.

They rehearsed their new ID roles and tested one another on the details in hilarious mock interrogations. At the start of her journey, she would be dressed in civilian clothes and carry a small leather suitcase in which would be her Red Cross uniform. He would be dressed as a Belgian mining engineer.

Chateau de Bellignies,
hiding place of Frank W Clarke

Prince Reginald de Croy was one of the key fig-
ures in the Edith Cavell escape network.

Edith Cavell
Organiser of an escape network for allied soldiers

20

ESCAPE

The next morning at dawn they left the chateau for the last time with the Prince as their guide and walked the forest paths to cross the Belgian border without encountering Landsturm patrols in the woodlands.

He was wearing a business suit belonging to Prince Reginald. He carried a battered brief case with a few technical papers inside it which he did not understand. He walked alongside Emily and occasionally they touched hands in a private demonstration of affection. They picked up bicycles in Montignies and cycled the several kilometres into Mons along the cobbled roads he had marched down in military formation the summer before.

There were many other people cycling and they did not attract the attention of the police or the Germans. Lorries and horse drawn wagons belonging to the Landsturm made up at least 50 percent of the traffic. They did not encounter any road checks, although several foot patrols passed them coming from the direction in which they were headed.

They were confident of their disguises and this feeling did not diminish when they boarded the tram for Brussels at Mons. Emily had changed into her uniform and they now sat apart. She was quite sure that her German would be good enough and that her appearance as a nurse would not arouse any suspicion. He was told to sit next to Prince Reginald and keep his mouth shut.

"Bury your head in these business papers, put your ID papers with them and when the guard comes hand them over to me and let me do all the talking. If you must talk French keep it very simple and straightforward and smile a lot. If the guard demands an answer to a question I will do the answering," the Prince ordered.

The journey passed off without event and without an unexpected ID check. They had to get off at one stop on the outskirts of Brussels because the Prince anticipated there would definitely be an ID check further on. They walked two stops and re-boarded another tram.

It had all worked well so far. At the terminal Prince Reginald walked away without saying a word, but as they parted he raised an eyebrow which was worth a thousand words.

They stood outside a shop window and communicated quietly without looking at one another. "Let me walk ahead of you and if you are stopped and questioned I won't stop because there won't be any point. If the same happens to me you must promise me not to try to intervene," she said and walked on immediately.

The couple remained 30 yards apart with Emily in the lead. Brussels was teeming with Germans, many walking on the pavement and even more in wagons and military vehicles. The constant clatter of horseshoes on cobbled roads—and the overpowering smell of horse manure—was new to them after spending so long in the forest around Bellignies. The walk to the Berkendael Institute, or the clinic as it was known, took an hour and a half.

They knocked on the door and were shown into Edith Cavell's ground floor office at the back of three houses that had been converted into one unit. The office looked out onto a walled garden. He noticed that there was a painting of Norwich Cathedral on the wall behind the desk. The way the matron conducted her escape network astonished him.

"You mean that most of your nursing staff, and the visiting doctors, have no idea that the Institute is being used as the main transit centre for allied soldiers trying to escape across the Dutch border? If so that's incredible," said Frank.

Edith Cavell replied: "Yes. Over the past few months I have kept the various affairs of the Institute in different compartments.

"The escape network is run on a need to know basis and the fact that I have 15 men currently in hiding in my basement is not the business of my trainee nurses. That is not to say they do not suspect that things other than the day-to-day medical matters of the Berkendael are going on. However, they are not expected to ask questions and those that do know are trusted to remain silent."

They liked Edith a lot. She was petite like the Princess but sat stiffly in her starched uniform at her desk and looked desperately tired. She became less formal and warmed to him discernibly when he told her he was a Norfolk man and had served as a regular soldier with the Norfolks at Mons.

"She explained her background and the fact she was a vicar's daughter. There was no trace of a Norfolk accent but it was clear her affection for Norwich and its county were pillars of strength in her mind at a time when all around her seemed to be crumbling.

Edith became very serious now and spoke quietly to them. "I fear the escape network will not last much longer. Please do not tell those on my staff who are part of the network—but when you get back to England I want you to tell the authorities that our organisation has been compromised by the enemy. It is only a matter of time before all of us are arrested. The Germans have started a new agency with the mission to catch everyone who helps Allied soldiers to escape through Belgium. It's called Section B.

"It's part of the German political police. Two fanatics run it, Lieutenant Ernest Bergan and Sergeant Henri Pinkoff. The two Germans are building up a dossier on us. I can do nothing to stop that and we will just go on until the end."

Emily interjected: "No Matron, we must get you back to England. Come with me and ask the Americans to make out papers showing that you are an American citizen.

"You are only well known here in Brussels—with the right papers you could board a train for Holland further along the line towards the border."

Edith Cavell replied sharply: "I would not consider that for one moment. It would mean deserting those who have worked with us so courageously all these months. No, I shall stay here, await arrest and face the consequences of a prison sentence. That way I will have done my duty."

He drew in his breath sharply, restraining himself from making any crass comment. He was looking at the bravest and most courageous woman he had ever met. A woman whom he felt sure would somehow make history. He felt humbled in her company.

"Besides," she continued, "my work as matron goes on here. I have a succession of nurses to train, lectures and talks to give, assist the surgeons at operations and keep the school accounts. On top of all this we are moving shortly to the Rue de Bruxelles and we are all extremely excited about that."

She told them that a group of soldiers from the Munster Fusiliers were occupying the basement rooms at the Institute. She intended to send the two of them to Madame Ada Bodart, the Irish widow of a Belgian who would be happy to accommodate the couple.

"You will find her kind and generous. Although food is becoming desperately short here in Brussels she will make sure that you have enough to eat. I suggest Emily that you make haste to leave Belgium the moment you get your new papers from the American Mission. It is getting more dangerous to be around this network every day and if the Germans are able to collect any evidence of your involvement with it then you too could be arrested. I don't want that to happen because I am sure you will have vital work to do when you get back to the Front."

"We will retain your identity as a French mining engineer, but you will need new permits to be travelling North of Brussels in the vicinity of the Dutch border. It could take a week or so and during that time we will decide who will go with you and who will act as guide.

"You will have to walk from here to Holland, and travel mainly at night away from the main roads. It will be a long and exhausting journey but I'm sure you have the mental strength for it. We will meet back here when all the plans have been made."

21

FAREWELL TO EMILY

They met Ada in a café run by Oscar Meyer situated at the junction of the Rue Emile Max and the Rue Victor Hugo. Emily had dressed down, arranged her hair into a plait and wore no make-up. Her long black dress folded elegantly around her full figure and it would have taken a blind man not to notice her natural beauty.

She took a risk going out, especially at night, in civilian clothes. Her height and long auburn hair would attract the attention of any man, German or otherwise. Fortunately, Oscar's was not a haunt of the German military—although informers and collaborators were known to use it.

No bars in Brussels were free of risk and Oscar's was no exception, but he knew his clientele well enough to warn them when to take care. The bar was the habitual rendezvous for some of the members of the escape network. The atmosphere was relaxed in the crowded bar.

Ada Bodart, a woman in her late 30s, was seated at a table talking to the patron Oscar. They were drinking pastis and she was laughing a little too loudly at his humorous banter. Ada had dyed black hair, heavy eye shadow and pillar box red lipstick. Edith Cavell had given them an accurate description of her.

They approached her table and had no need to use the password Jack, after Edith's beloved dog. Ada greeted them in her broad Irish accent and introduced them to Oscar. They all fell into conversation and the topic soon got round to their recent past. She told them she was a widow and had been living in Brussels for 10 years. Her husband had died in 1913.

She said she was a trained actress having been on the stage in Dublin, but any hope of further advance in her career in Belgium had been ruined by the war. Now she lived on what she could, by taking paying guests into her modest home where she lived with her two children from her first marriage. He decided to be entirely upfront with Ada about his relationship with Emily and took out his wallet to show her he meant to pay for his double room.

"She nursed me through the early stages of treatment for my wound and without her I wouldn't be here now. We've been in hiding together since Christmas. We're now engaged Ada. We'll be getting married as soon as we get back to England but I'm sure you can appreciate that these are not normal times because none of us can guarantee the future."

"Ah c'est la guerre!" she exclaimed in her Irish French.

She added firmly: "War or not, I won't be permitting an unmarried couple to rent a double room in my house. I have a reputation to protect—as a woman of strict morals."

Oscar then winked at him.

"That's not to say that after she goes to bed at night she'll be wandering around the house knocking on doors to check up on people. Not after drinking a bottle of Pastis anyway!"

Ada gave a shriek of demented laughter and kissed Emily on the cheek who looked embarrassed for the first time since Frank had met her.

Oscar said in a broken accent: "Best not to tell the matron Cavell that you intend to sleep with your girlfriend. She might hand you over to the Boche."

Later that night a group of fugitive soldiers from the Munster Fusiliers dressed in civilian clothes but wearing distinctly British army boots arrived in the bar having already had a few drinks elsewhere, to judge by the noise they made. The inanity of the soldiers' loud conversation, and their sheer disregard for any kind of security by speaking English at the top of their voices, both horrified and terrified Emily and Frank who left immediately.

"Christ, those fools are going to compromise the entire network," he told Emily as they made their way to Ada's house.

They checked into separate bedrooms but took advantage of Oscar's advice and he followed Emily into her room and locked the door after them. The following morning after breakfast Emily put on her Red Cross uniform and took a tram into the centre of Brussels to visit the American Mission. When she got there she identified herself as an American citizen, said she was in a situation of some distress and needed to talk to Brand Whitlock himself. Nobody else would do, she insisted.

"I remember you Miss Horstmann. Have you been with the Princess de Croy all this time?" asked the United States minister.

"Yes sir, I've been treating a wounded British sergeant in a hidden private hospital ward and it has taken him nearly seven months to get fit enough to go down the escape network. Now that he has started his journey I thought it was time to get myself out of the occupied territories and onto the Allied side of the line.

"So I have come to you today to see if you can fix me some papers that will get me clean away out of here."

The minister looked down at his desk, folded through some papers, rubbed his chin and then looked up again. "You're fortunate Miss Horstmann. There's a delegation leaving this mission by train tomorrow morning bound for Rotterdam, where they will board a passenger steamer for Harwich.

"We can include you in that party, using your real identity papers I think, with documents explaining that you have been undertaking a study into the effects of the .303 calibre rifle bullet upon the human body—and best nursing practice.

"If the German authorities demand to see your written work you must tell them they have been carried ahead in the diplomatic bag and you do not have access. If they question you as to why you did not leave Belgium when ordered to do so last year, argue that you have been in residence under diplomatic protection since last August doing your work.

"Wait here at the mission for an hour and the papers will be completed for you. Good luck and well done for your contribution. Your dossier of atrocities in Leuven has been read at the highest levels in Washington."

The interview was over. They shook hands and she waited in an outer office for her papers. When she got back to Ada Bodart's house she found him in the downstairs lounge reading *La Libre Belgique*.

The magazine, published by an underground organisation, upheld the country's press freedom and was virulently anti-German. "So do you want the good news or the bad news?" she asked.

"Give me the bad news first," he replied.

"Tonight's our last night together my darling. I'm leaving early tomorrow on a train with a group of junior and senior American officials headed for England via Rotterdam. The good news is I'm travelling with diplomatic protection. The chances of me being arrested according to Brand Whitlock are minimal because of that."

He felt a feeling of dread in his stomach, a sense of threat, but he managed to smile and kissed her on the mouth gently.

"Oh Emily my darling I am so pleased that you are going to be safe. It's marvellous news that you will have diplomatic protection. It takes all the threat away and I can't tell you how good that makes me feel. Your safety is everything to me and of course I will be joining you in just a week or two."

They embraced and spent the entire afternoon and evening in the bedroom, except for a quick dinner and a shared bottle of wine in Ada's kitchen. Their last night together was spent passionately—the conversation never turned to the dark side and its possibilities.

"You will marry me my darling won't you?" he asked.

"Yes my darling, as soon as we can and we'll do it in that little village in Norfolk that you come from, with all your family there."

She whispered in his ear: "Darling, we haven't been taking any precautions since we started having sex. What shall I do if I've fallen pregnant and something happens to you?"

He replied: "Well, I don't intend to be going anywhere my love except with you—but if anything does happen to me and you fall pregnant then you will both go back to America. That's where I would want any son or daughter to grow up."

She kissed him softly on the lips. Despite his inner dread of losing her through his capture, he reasoned they had good grounds for optimism. Edith Cavell's escape network had operated successfully for several months and the majority of men going down it had succeeded in getting across the Dutch border and then home to England.

Later they even tempted fate by setting a date for their marriage in September 1915, while the weather was still warm. He calculated that he would not be sent overseas again with such a serious wound and would probably be involved in training fresh recruits at the barracks in Norwich. There would be plenty of nursing work for Emily and they could set up home together in Norfolk.

The night turned to morning too soon. One last embrace inside the front door of Ada's house, then as she turned to go he kissed her on the back of the head, breathing in for a last time her familiar fragrance. She opened the door and walked through it into the early morning light. Then she turned and smiled, giving him a long lingering look.

"I love you Sergeant Clarke. Stay safe and come to me soon," she whispered.

She walked through the latch gate of the front garden, turned one last time and gave him a little wave. He knew it was supposed to be unlucky to watch her departing but he could not resist it.

She gradually became a distant figure as he watched her walking further away from him up the street. He choked back a sob, tears ran down his face and he was tempted to run to her and embrace her one last time. It would be too dangerous and also upsetting for her, so he restrained himself. Then she was gone.

The next few days were agonizing. Emily had been his total support for more than six months. He had not realised how much he had come to depend upon her. Her cheerful disposition, which never altered, was irreplaceable and he sank into a sense of gloomy pessimism.

That sense was heightened when the men with whom he would make the run to the Dutch border appeared at Ada's home with the guide Philippe Baucq. Among them was Gaston Quien, to whom he had taken a strong dislike at the Chateau de Bellignies. The Frenchman sensed Frank found him contemptible and avoided eye contact. To make matters even worse he had heard—while in conversation at Oscar's bar the night before— that Quien was suspected by some members of the escape network of being an informer.

They had wanted Edith to get rid of him and indeed she had tried, but he always returned to the Institute begging for help. Edith had grown to dislike him intensely because of his flirtatious attitude to members of her nursing team and domestic staff.

He wondered how long it would be before he administered a good hiding to the effete Frenchman. The party was made up of Gaston Quien and four private soldiers from the Munster Fusiliers. He recognized them from Oscar's bar. They introduced themselves as Gerald Fitzpatrick, Tom Murphy, Phil Jackson and Mick Smith. Each had been given an identity and papers which, at a cursory glance, would provide them with jurisdiction to Northern Belgium.

The fact that none of the Fusiliers could speak a word of French or German would mean that if they were stopped at any point they would risk capture—especially if the guard was able to speak French and started to ask questions. It did not look good.

Philippe said they would leave at the end of curfew the following morning. Each man would take sufficient rations for five days which consisted of beef lozenges, malted milk tablets, cooked sausage, water biscuits and tea. Philippe said he would also carry a small solid fuel stove in his backpack.

They would use it to boil water and any vegetables that they could scavenge. Ada would provide them with the food and Edith had arranged for each man to carry currency worth in the region of £10. Philippe said he would walk ahead on his own and the remainder should follow in pairs at intervals of 200 yards. The journey, he told them, was in the region of 70 miles to the point at the border where they would cross into Holland east of Turnhout.

In the second part of the journey as they came closer to the border they would be travelling across country at night during curfew avoiding all the main roads and villages en route. During the daytime they would hide, except for when they would have to pass on foot through Aerschot. At the half way point they would stay at the Monastery of Averabode for food and shelter and eventually make their way towards Turnhout, a town close to the Dutch frontier and then go into deep cover before crossing the border at night.

He listened carefully to the plan and decided that if this escape attempt was going to work he would have to ensure that he was the dominant personality in the group. He decided to insist upon regimental discipline.

"OK, I want to say a few words as the senior NCO. Regimental discipline will be maintained at all times and my word is law. I witnessed what happened in Oscar's bar the other night and there will be no repeat of that kind of bloody shit—is that understood?

"No going into bars or restaurants, no engaging the locals in conversation in English, and although we will look to Monsieur Baucq for guidance, you are all under my command. That goes for you too Gaston. You will call me Sergeant and I will address you by your surname. So it will be Privates Fitzpatrick, Murphy, Jackson and Smith. Those are my conditions and unless you accept them this trip will be aborted. Is that clear?"

The Irishmen and the Frenchman had not been expecting this intervention but none of them appeared to take issue with the sergeant's demands and they all nodded in agreement at his terms and conditions. He decided to stay slightly detached from the other escapees because he was determined to remain the symbol of authority. He couldn't care less whether they liked it or not.

He was helped by the fact that he was nearly 10 years older than most of the other men and much bigger than any of them except for Gaston Quien—who was also a tall man.

22

ON FOOT ACROSS BELGIUM

Frank decided he would accompany Quien to keep an eye on him. The two of them hardly exchanged a word. They set off through Brussels at 0800 hours the following morning on the Leuven road and made good progress all day until the curfew hour at 2200 hours when darkness was beginning to set in. Somehow they managed to avoid any checks although there was heavy German traffic on the roads. Philippe had planned the route and on the first night finally led them to a thick wood into which they walked for several hundred yards before hiding under the cover of dry foliage.

The Irishmen were all fit enough to cope with the ordeal of covering up to 15 miles a day, but Gaston Quien complained continually about his foot which he maintained had been injured during the Battle of Landrecies the year before.

"Look here Quien, don't expect any sympathy from either myself or the men. If you weren't fit enough to do this you shouldn't have bloody well come. If you fall behind the pace you're on your own—is that clear?" said Frank who could see the look of hatred in the Frenchman's eye. He was glad about that.

In the next three days they passed without incident through several small towns including Aerschot and reached the mediaeval monastery there on the late afternoon of the third day. They were well treated by the monks, slept in the laundry at night and the next morning they retired to a room at the top of the building where they passed away the time by playing cards.

Philippe came to them and said: "I am leaving you now. A new guide called Alphonse, who knows the countryside around here and how to cross the border, will be taking over. He'll collect you tonight at dusk. The monks will supply you with additional food for another five days in case you are held up in the border area.

"Just remember you must have patience when you get near the crossing point. Follow the advice of the guide at all times and do not try to rush things. Bon voyage."

Alphonse carried a compass but seemed to be confident with the route. He told them he was a locomotive engineer and because of that had not been called up into the Army. The Germans had replaced him after the invasion, having brought in their own work force to run the rail network. He expected, however, to get his old job back in the near future. In the meantime, he wanted the help the Allied cause in any way he could to defeat the hated Boche.

He was as fit as the men and warned Quien, who continued to complain about his foot, that they would have to maintain a walking speed of about four miles an hour. Frank got the feeling that Alphonse didn't like the Frenchman either. It took them a further two days of walking to reach Turnhout by crossing the Belgian countryside at night and lying up during the day in woodland and in one case a remote barn full of hay.

The journey included swimming and wading across three small rivers. Alphonse warned them that all the bridges were guarded and to try to cross those at night during curfew would be disastrous. The network must have assumed they could all swim. It was just as well they were all able to do so. Alphonse made them take off all their clothes, except their underwear and hold their rucksack above the water as they swam. This presented problems for Frank whose right arm was still weak—but he used it to hold up the rucksack while his left hand paddled. They crossed the rivers using a downstream route which meant they did not have to fight the currents.

On some occasions it was possible to pick a spot to cross where they could wade. Even then, it would still take at least half an hour to get all the men across one at a time. A shot ringing out in the dark or excited shouting coming from the opposite bank would denote to those on the other side of the river that their mates had been captured. This made river crossing a particularly tense time. The water was cold and muddy but they found it exhilarating.

Alphonse took water from the rivers and later in the daytime when in hiding he boiled it in a can using his small stove—before pouring it into the small containers carried by each man. They would not stop for food during their night march, but were able to drink the water when they needed it. Fortunately the weather stayed dry and the air temperature was warm. The clear night sky was well lit by the moon which bathed the countryside in an eerie silver light—which Frank knew may have been beautiful, but did not help them as fugitives.

Dogs barked frequently, especially as the group passed farms and small villages, but they soon learned that people in Belgium took no notice of the barking. At dawn on the third morning of the second leg of the journey, they reached the outskirts of a village and Alphonse led them to a barn packed with hay.

He told them that the farmer was friendly and had accepted a small offer of money for them to sleep in his barn. There were unlikely to be any patrols in the village that night and they could brew tea before sleeping but should speak only in whispers. If a patrol approached the farm the dogs would start barking and that would be their signal to dig into the hay.

The border, once they had crossed Turnhout during the following day, was only a two hour walk away. If everything was OK they would attempt to get across it.

"Christ, I do think we've got a bloody chance of doing this," he thought to himself that night. He could sense the excitement among the men, but Gaston Quien remained an enigma.

He was quiet, almost sullen, when Frank was around him, but became extrovert and quite boastful when he was out of sight. He knew he was being watched carefully by the British Sergeant, and his ferret brown eyes were always darting around looking for him. The other men were not aware he regarded Quien as a serious security risk and now he decided to have a whisper in the Frenchman's ear. He crawled over the hay to where he was lying.

"Quien, I won't beat about the bush. I don't like you and I don't trust you and I suspect you are a collaborator. The next 24 hours are going to reveal whether you are or not. I just want you to know that if you do betray us I'm going to get you personally. In fact I'll swing for you. So watch your back you bastard and sleep on it."

Gaston Quien did not say a word but looked anxious because he sensed that the British Sergeant was a violent man—capable of carrying out his threat—and more than a match for him physically. The Frenchman did not sleep much that night because for the first hour Frank lay there glaring at him. There was something creepy about the Frenchman.

They left the sanctuary of the hay barn the next morning after a cold breakfast and a cup of tea and made their way along the cobbled road towards Turnhout three miles away. When they got there they found it was packed with Germans at every corner who took no notice of the fugitives in their country clothes, disconnected by walking in pairs at intervals of 200 yards.

These soldiers on the narrow streets were not elderly enlisted Landsturm—whose mission was to be suspicious of every civilian—but men from the front line who appeared to be on some kind of rest and recuperation. Many of the Germans carried scars from wounds and some were wrapped in bandages. They talked loudly in groups on the street corners and seemed to be happy.

Suddenly, as the scattered group approached the market square, Quien left Frank's side and before he could stop him the Frenchman walked into a large café. There was nothing he could do about it and he felt that to follow him inside the café would be taking an unnecessary risk.

He was unable to see what Quien was doing inside the café or whether he had spoken to anybody. He was enraged by what had happened. Quien came out of the café after three or four minutes and signalled that he had only been taking a pee.

"In future if you want to take a piss you tell me first you bastard," said Frank grimly.

Alphonse led them past the mediaeval castle and towards a bridge over the canal. They discovered that to cross it they would have to go through a security check for the first time since their journey had started. There was no alternative to using the bridge in the daylight because wading across the canal would attract attention and certainly lead to them all being shot. The tail end pairs, although 200 yards apart while walking the streets, soon caught up the queue that was waiting to cross the bridge and included Dutch and Belgian traffic. They stood in silence as Frank had ordered.

After half an hour the sentry looked briefly at the papers carried by Alphonse and waved him through. The first pair of Fusiliers was also waved through. Things were going well so far. When the second pair presented their papers the German seemed to show more interest in them and paused. Tom Murphy anticipated there might be a problem and dropped a bank note out of his pocket which lay alongside the guard's boot. The German covered it hurriedly with his foot and waved them through. This left Frank and Gaston still to pass through the checkpoint.

"I've got a knife in my pocket Gaston and if you say one word to that guard I'll stab you straight in the gut—do you understand?"

Frank had no knife, but the Frenchman did not know that. Frank decided to follow Tom's example and he dropped a note close to the guard's foot. Once again the guard stood upon it and waved them through after a cursory glance at their papers.

They followed Alphonse out of the town for about a mile and then saw him turn left into the forest. He was waiting in a clearing where hundreds of logs had been stacked and beckoned them to conceal themselves among the timber.

"OK. Well done, getting through Turnhout was always going to be risky, but we've made it. We cannot walk directly to the border because there are patrols at several places along the road and also some on the move in the countryside. We'll leave immediately darkness falls and that means hiding up in this woodland for the rest of the daylight."

He handed over to Frank.

"You will remain in deep cover because I can tell you there are German troops all around. Eat cold food, brew coffee or tea now and then that's it. No eating, no shitting, no smoking, no talking. If you must pee do it lying down. I want each pair separated by at least three hundred yards and if you hear a disturbance hop it fast while you can—no heroics.

"Dig a pit deep enough with your hands well away from the nearest path and use the pine needles to cover your body. If there are German shepherd dogs tracking us we've had it—but I do not think we are being followed, unless. . . . ."

He looked at Gaston but said nothing.

"We will rendezvous here at 2230 hours. Is everyone clear?"

Alphonse continued: "There will be some moonlight so each man will be able to remain in visual contact with the person ahead. If any of you get lost remember that we are heading directly east rather than north from Turnhout because at the point towards which we are heading the canal actually runs alongside the border. The waterway will be the last point to cross before you reach Holland. We will not be sticking close to hedgerows or sunken roads because of the number of German foot patrols about.

"Their usual tactic, if they hear men approaching them, is to lurk out of sight and carry out an ambush. To lessen the chances of that happening, we'll keep to the middle of the fields and the open common—so that if we are seen and we attract rifle fire, we will still have a chance of getting away. If we are challenged by a patrol we must disperse in different directions singly. Do not go in pairs, it is every man for himself. Remember the border is to the east—even without me leading the group you will have a chance of reaching it by dawn on your own.

"When you come to the thick wire that marks the border, find a point where you can wriggle underneath it. Safety should be no more than half a mile beyond the wire, but I should warn you that German patrols sometimes sneak around at night over the border to nab those who show themselves too soon."

The Belgian added: "It's important to be patient when we reach the canal. The bridges are all manned with double sentries and the towpaths are patrolled on a constant basis all night. If you try to break out to cross the water too soon, the chances are you won't make it. You'll be shot while you are in the water. You will cross one at a time—at intervals that I shall decide.

"The best time is usually about five minutes after a towpath patrol has passed by. It usually means there will be no return to that point for 15 minutes—in which time we might get two men across the canal. If we can't all get over tonight the remainder will have to return here to the forest and wait for another 24 hours."

The journey that night went ahead as smoothly as any night exercise, except for when they heard rifle fire less than a mile away and the distant sound of shouting. He was pleased. The patrol that might have intercepted them obviously had discovered another group of fugitives somewhere out there in the darkness. He felt sorry for whoever it was, but relieved that the pressure might just be slightly relieved on his party.

They walked across fields of corn and wheat about to be harvested, potato fields, bean fields, tall maize and meadows where dairy cows were lying on the grass. Dogs barked all around them and sometimes searchlights probed the sky in the near distance. At one stage they crossed a deep brook and found themselves on what appeared to be heath land—over which they trudged for two miles before tall pine trees offered them greater sanctuary in a small forest.

Suddenly the group found themselves all together once again. They had come to the edge of the forest and encountered a 10-foot barbed wire barrier that looked several yards wide. Alphonse motioned them to lie down and disappeared. When he returned he had taken off all his clothes except his shirt, under-pants and boots, and told the assembled group to do the same.

"This will make it easier for us to crawl through the wire. Make sure your kitbags are done up tightly, put your clothes inside it and throw them with all your strength over the top of the barrier.

"My guess is that the barbed wire will be about 20 feet in width. A patrol passes here every 30 minutes so we must wait for the next one to come past and then start work."

He was correct. A patrol of two soldiers passed along the other side of the wire just under 10 minutes later. The wire was thickly meshed and close to the ground. Each of them then selected a spot and started to crawl through it in the pitch black. They had to lie flat on their stomach, stretching their arms at full length, grasping the wire and pulling the body forward two or three inches at a time. It took each man about 20 minutes to reach the other side. Frank's underclothes were seriously ripped and his bare skin had been cut by the barbs.

Alphonse was a small man and extremely nimble. He was waiting for them fully clothed on the other side of the wire and motioned them to keep well away from it because although the searchlights 200 yards away appeared to be switched off for some reason, they could not rely on it being a power cut. Any disturbance might mean the searchlight being reactivated.

He beckoned them into the shadows and said: "We will rest for a few moments, then we'll go at the double at 10 second intervals heading east towards the lights in the distance. Do not overtake me. The canal is only 200 yards away from here and we must approach it quietly. Immediately ahead of us is a small copse of Oak and Elm trees. We'll meet there in the middle of it. Lie on the ground and do not say a word because you will be less than 20 yards from the towpath which is constantly patrolled."

They all made it and he crept with Alphonse to a fence that bordered the canal and the towpath. The Belgian beckoned to him to look left and whispered: "There is a lock and a bridge guarded by three sentries and a machine gun only 150 yards up there. You can't see it in the dark but it is very close which means the crossings have to be done quietly and slowly. Tell the men that once they are over the canal they should be able to find a large haystack 500 yards further on by a crossroads.

"Technically they will be in Holland and there should be Dutch sentries about. You will know you are in Holland when you see the lights blazing in the villages. On this side everything is dark expect for the searchlights probing the major crossing points.

"The men are still at risk however and they should wait until shortly before dawn when they should come out of cover singly and run as fast as they can towards the north—until they reach either a Dutch village or a meet a Dutch army patrol. Once you have all crossed the canal I shall make my way back into Belgium."

Frank spoke quietly to the assembled group as they lay under the cover of the oak and elm trees.

"Alphonse and I will crouch by the stile—listen for the hoot of an owl. Creep on your stomach and do not make any noise. Come in alphabetical order—so it will be Privates Fitzpatrick, Gaston Quien, Jackson, Murphy, Smith and finally me. Is that clear?"

The two men returned to their position by the stile and waited for the patrol of eight armed men on foot to pass them—which it did in casual file with the German soldiers telling one another jokes and roaring with laughter. They waited for five minutes until the sound of the patrol had subsided and then he called Private Fitzpatrick. He lay beside them and he tapped Fitzpatrick on the shoulder—the signal to move—with one final instruction.

"The water's cold, but it's not deep. Wade as quietly as you can and if you somehow go into a hole in the mud just glide forward and swim quietly. Hold your kitbag above your head. If you make a noise the chances are they'll switch on the searchlight at the bridge. Remember, the haystack should be only 500 yards from the crossing point but go carefully when you are looking for it."

He repeated the same instructions to all the soldiers except Quien, who he just could not bring himself to speak to. The patrol returned, going back towards the bridge after Quien had crossed the canal and they decided to wait until it had gone past them. He estimated correctly that the soldiers would stop for coffee at their hut on the bridge and it was 45 minutes before they returned again, looking and sounding like a rabble rather than soldiers of the Kaiser's Imperial army. Some had been drinking. Drunken soldiers would be trigger happy even if their aim was not good.

Ten minutes later, after Private Smith had crossed the canal, Frank turned to Alphonse and said: "Well done and thanks for helping us. We are in your debt. I will cross now. Give me no more than five minutes before making your way back to the wire. If anything goes wrong I believe it will be because Gaston Quien is an informer. Please convey that back to Philippe and ask him to tell Edith Cavell. The best thing they can do is to arrange for his assassination otherwise he will give evidence against them in court."

Alphonse nodded and said he would speak to Philippe. Frank crept over the stile onto the towpath and then stepped into the water a few yards from where the other men had crossed. He nearly tripped twice on debris that lay on the bottom. He moved steadily, but as he reached the far bank he heard the German patrol approaching once again. He heaved himself up onto the bank with his left arm and dived for cover. They passed by on the opposite side of the canal and he waited in silence for another five minutes.

Then he started moving cautiously away from the canal. He crossed two fields with quite substantial hedges to crawl through, before spotting the haystack in the corner of the third field. Beyond it were the lights of a village about a mile away which he guessed must be well inside Holland.

He reached the haystack. Gaston Quien appeared in front of him. He was smiling broadly. There was no sign of the other men.

"Ah, Sergeant, I am so glad to see you. I was worried you might have changed your mind because of me and returned to the forest. You were right all along. I am an informer, but I'm afraid that's not going to do you much good because you won't be meeting that American bitch of yours any time soon."

Four German soldiers appeared out of the shadows from the haystack behind Quien and aimed their rifles at Frank's head. He could also see the gleaming steel of the bayonets. There was no thought of escape, just revenge. He was filled with an uncontrollable anger and a desire to kill.

He smashed Quien's nose with a devastating left which flattened his face. Then he kicked out with his right foot towards the Frenchman's genitals using all the force he could muster. Quien fell to the floor moaning in a high pitched voice of self pity. It served to enrage Frank even further and he managed to get in two solid kicks to Quien's rib cage and a third into his mouth. He felt a terrible pain in his ribs and then the world went black.

23
CAPTURED

They beat him about his face and body for two hours when they got him back to Turnhout Prison. He kept hearing what Edith Cavell had said and her words echoed in his head time and time again as he endured the violence of the physical assaults.

"Two fanatics run it, Lieutenant Ernest Bergan and Sergeant Henri Pinkoff. These two Germans are building up a dossier on us and are in the process of collecting evidence. I can do nothing to stop that and we will just go on until the end."

Now he sat in a chair in the interrogation room with a strong light in his face and the nasal tones of Lieutenant Ernest Bergan asking the same questions over and over again. He was covered in bruises and cuts and looked as though he had been in a long boxing bout. He did not care. He had hurt that bastard Quien who would not forget him in a hurry.

Bergan continued: "The wisest thing for you to do would be to give me the name of every person you have met in Belgium and France since you were parted from your regiment. We already know who is running the escape network but there may be other people on the fringe that you can help us to find.

"It will be worth your while sergeant—your comfort levels are going to be very important to you until the war ends and you go home. You were at large for nine months in occupied territory and that is an extremely serious offence. You are lucky we are not treating you as a spy—we have the right to do so because you were not wearing uniform when you were captured.

"We are reasonable men—we know it is your duty to try to escape. If you help us we will make sure your prison sentence here will be a light one."

Bergan hinted that his compliance would also affect the decision on where he would be sent after he had served his sentence in a civilian jail. Some camps, he said with menace, were a joyride compared to others.

He wanted Frank and the other soldiers who were caught with him to sign a confession implicating all the patriots who had worked with Edith Cavell and Prince Reginald. They wanted the role those names had played in the escape network. Frank had been nervous that one or more of the Fusiliers might be prepared to make a statement implicating the courageous Belgians. There was nothing he could do about that. He would give only his name, rank, and number.

At last Bergan grew frustrated and snarled at him.

"You are a swine. Now we'll hurt you some more!"

The beatings on his face and body with a rubber tube stuffed with solid material continued until after midnight. Every time he repeated his name, rank, and number he found himself the victim of another round of beating.

He gradually lost consciousness. Finally they dragged him into a tiny cell with a folding bed on the wall with only a bucket to piss in. Lieutenant Bergan spent the rest of the first week at Turnhout prison trying to extract confessions from the escapees but eventually he gave up.

The fugitives spent the next three months in the civilian prison in Turnhout. It was a tough regime: one man to a cell, half an hour's exercise in the yard, a cup of coffee and a piece of bread for breakfast, but a small meal of sausage and sauerkraut at midday. In the second week they were marched off to a local aerodrome where they were given the job of building hangars.

He was overcome with a desire to escape as soon as possible and find his beloved Emily. The opportunity never seemed to arise. Escape would not be easy he told himself—perhaps he should concentrate on learning how to survive. It was the first time he had been incarcerated in his life and for him religion, patriotism and love of family would not be enough to carry him through captivity.

He would have to guard against depression, indolence and the feeling of resignation to his fate. That would represent surrender of the spirit and for him could lead to insanity. He thought a lot about Anna and Emily's absence caused him physical as well as emotional pain. He had never been in love before and separation from her was tearing his heart out. During their confinement in Turnhout Prison none of the prisoners received a letter from home.

The British authorities had no knowledge of them, or where they were. He imagined Emily had given up hope of ever seeing him again. It made him want to scream out in the middle of the night. When she responded to his call in the dreams she always came to him and snuggled into the tiny wooden slatted bed covered by the louse-ridden mattress and thin blanket. Snuggling up with Emily gave him good dreams.

THE BARBEL—DIARY SEPTEMBER 1911

The way I am dressed nobody would guess I am just a corporal— and to be wearing expensive clothes will not endear me to the more senior NCOs who regard it as the height of presumption to impersonate an officer.

The green tweed suit is a 'hand-me-down' from Georgie who was a similar size and shape to me. This particular suit has always been one of my summer preferences because it seems to bring me luck at the river bank, especially when I fish in Ireland.

I also wear sturdy brown brogue shoes and carry a rod holder, a whicker basket, an expensive retractable landing net. On my head is a wide brimmed brown trilby to keep the sun off my face. The guards at the barrack gates salute me and imagine they are acknowledging the departure of at least a Captain.

As they watch me walking away at a leisurely stride down the road they cannot not see that I am chuckling to myself. I am off for a day's fishing on one of my favourite English rivers. I take the express train to Reading from Aldershot and change to the Newbury line before getting off at Aldermaston in Berkshire. There I meet my friend Charles Rimington who is waiting at the station in a pony and trap.

Together we are to spend a day fishing a famous beat on the River Kennet. On the way Charles stops at a small-holding to pick up Alfred, who introduces himself to me. Alfred is a professional bait supplier and the approximate equivalent of a coarse fisherman's ghillie.

Men such as Alf do the tiresome preparations necessary to ensure good bags of fish. These include activities such a ground-baiting a swim, digging bait, procuring grubs, par-boiling small potatoes, or even catching live bait.

The suppliers also usually have a canny knowledge of the rivers they call their own and are particularly popular with well-to-do fishermen wanting specimens for the glass display case.

Alf brings with him a jute sack that smells of horse dung and contains several hundred earth worms together with grenade-sized balls of ground-bait whose consistency has been hardened by the inclusion of clay in its ingredients.

'Have you done what I asked you to do this week Alf?' asks Charles Rimington as the pony and trap trots towards the mill on the outskirts of the village.

'Aye Mr Rimington Sir, I have. There are good barbel in the weir pool and the mill pool and you can hear them feeding actively in the runs and glides for 200 yards downstream of it. We ain't had rain Sir, but there be a plenty of fast flowing water, with healthy ranunculus (weed) growth in most of the swims.'

By 'active' he was referring to the loud sucking noises made by feeding whiskered barbel as they hunt for food at the bottom of the river's deep running swims. They thrust their nose into the loose gravel and suck out nutrients and insect life.

'Well, I reward results Alf, you know that—and if we do have a good day then I shall be pleased to pay you the full two guineas that we discussed,' said Rimington.

It is early September 1911 and I am stationed in Aldershot. The 1st Battalion has been taking part in the summertime Brigade and Divisional manoeuvres. They are always held on Salisbury Plain and are the precursor to full Army exercises in late September and October. Being stationed in this part of the world provides me with the chance to make fishing expeditions to top rivers like the Kennet.

Charles Rimington and I regard it as one of England's most important chalk streams. The 45-mile long Kennet is the largest tributary of the Thames and in summer contributes half of its flow. It runs unhindered through the North Wessex Downs and flows into the Thames near Reading.

The upper reaches, which we fished earlier that season, are more famous for dry fly trout fishing and have been a fashionable venue for wealthy game fishermen since the 1890s. Today Alf will help us in our quest to catch big barbel in the lower reaches of the river.

We intend to bag them at Aldermaston Mill, which is looked upon as one of the best stretches of barbel water in the country and which can be fished by purchasing a day ticket from the landowner. At Aldermaston, the mill pool and the series of runs and glides below it on the gravel river bed, hold shoals of barbel of 10lbs or more.

In summer the fish are often visible in the clear water, which is of excellent quality and well oxygenated. We start our day's fishing on the deep glides beneath the mill.

Alf starts ground-baiting the runs with his groundbait 'grenades'—and also by throwing large quantities of worms into the water.

We unpack three-piece rods of 11 feet with whole cane bottom and middle joints and a sensitive split cane top joint. We use metal trotting reels mounted with greased silk braided 10lb breaking strain line. These reels are free running and sensitive to finger control on the smooth edge of the drum. The check can be controlled either by finger or a ratchet button.

We each attach a six inch paint varnished cork and quill float and 15 lead shot arranged in groups of five down to a 6lb breaking strain silk gut and a size nine hook. It is light gear for the size of fish we are seeking to catch—but we regard ourselves as sportsmen. Alf inspects the tackle before we start fishing.

"With all due respect gentlemen I think you're both light," he warns us as he ties a large worm at its exact centre on each hook. The worms wriggle furiously and are highly active, having been kept in damp moss.

'OK Alf," laughs Charles Rimington. "I think we can both change our line if we get broken—but chance would be a fine thing!'

I am positioned on the higher run just below the mill on a slight outcrop which juts out into the fast-flowing river. I squat behind a bush which obscures me from view and I set the float to eight feet. I cast the tackle upstream with my long rod, allowing the bait to sink and drag along the bottom as it races past me.

I trot the tackle downstream for 40 feet through a gap between the weeds. At the end of the swim I hold the rod up so that the bait wavers in the play of the current. I repeat this action three or four times but there is no result. Thirty-five yards below me Charles Rimington is already into his first barbel and Alf is standing by him with the net. The next thing I hear is 'you bastard' and then Alf saying 'well sir, I did think you were a bit light.'

I chuckle, remove the gut leader for a stronger one, then hear myself saying: 'Come on Clarkey get stuck in, there must be fish here!'

The float is moving quickly down the swim with line trotting out after it. Suddenly it plunges boldly under the surface of the clear green water. I feel my heart racing.

I count to three and strike—vertically and firmly. It is as if I have hooked a locomotive. The barbel is enormously strong and the top joint of the rod dips sharply, taking the strain off the line.

The fish runs headlong down the river at enormous speed. I have hooked my first barbel.

'Dammit this fish runs as fast as a salmon!' I shout to Alf who walks swiftly upstream to my side.

'Careful Sir, he's big and he's strong and when you think you've got him tired he'll be off again—you see,' says Alf. After 15 minutes the fish does tire and I bring the barbel to the bank carefully, where Alf nets it.

He weighs it at just over eight lbs. Thanks to the constant intervention of Alf throwing in large lumps of ground bait and clusters of worms, we catch 10 fish each, none of them under five lbs. We even try the old fashioned Victorian method of barbel fishing by using a float and ledger tackle on heavily ground-baited swims in the mill pool.

Results are obtained by Alf attaching a ball of ground bait the size of an orange around the lead weight and with me casting it gently to the head of the barbel swim. We each catch two fish using ledger tackle but agree we prefer to trot for barbel, which offers a more exciting approach.

The biggest treat of the day is yet to come. Just as we are tiring of the barbel, Alfred points to a smaller river which flows into the Kennet a short distance from the mill.

'That's the River Enbourne gentlemen and it's another fine fishery. How do you feel about trying your hand at catching some large perch? There are shoals in the Enbourne with fish up to 3lbs or so and the tackle you have brought with you will suffice,' says Alf.

'Alf, you're a champion,' I laugh. I regard the perch as Britain's most notable coarse species with the exception of the grayling. I've caught them on the Derwent and the Norfolk Broads and on rivers like the Liffey and Boyne in Ireland. The handsome perch with its black stripes, sturdy green body, and spiky dorsal fin, possesses magnificent fighting qualities and is of high quality for the table as a gourmet dish.

'I have one or two spots in mind about half a mile up the river and I think it will occupy your attention for a couple of hours. I've also got some red worms in my sack that I thought I'd bring along in case we ventured onto the Enbourne,' says Alf.

'You don't happen to have a couple of bottles of beer in there too do you?' I ask pointing to the sack.

At that moment I am partial to a cheese and onion sandwich on coarse grain bread and some liquid refreshment. However, the sport turns out to be so good I forget my appetite.

'This is where I suggest you set up Sirs,' Alf says. He has brought us to a bend on the river where the foliage from two willow trees provides a screen from the bright afternoon sun and the water looks dark and deep. It is out of the main current and the bend forms a natural eddy. It looks good. Dark and forbidding water, together with man-made structures like tumble-down bridges or piers are natural haunts for the perch. Charles takes up a position 20 yards downstream of me.

I use a plummet to ascertain the depth of the hole, finding it to be six feet deep. I set the red quill float two inches from the bottom, put on a number six hook to five lbs breaking strain gut, and thread a red worm on the hook half way down its body, so that it wriggles furiously.

I cast the line and am glad to see the float is low in the water—which indicates there is sufficient weight taking the bait down to the bottom of the river. I now crouch down to minimize my visibility to the shoal, stay rock still and watch the cork and quill float circling slowly around the eddy under the shade of the willow trees.

After five minutes the float starts to bob as a fish takes the bait in its mouth and then playfully blows it out. It is exciting to watch because I know that at any moment the float will plunge down. It does so and with a gentle upward strike I connect with my fish. The perch seems to be momentarily stunned by the strike and I feel a dead weight. Then it springs into action using all its strength and dash—heading for the roots of the willow trees.

I check its rush for sanctuary and bring its head round. The perch tears off towards the middle of the river with all the dash of a wild trout. Five minutes later I bring the fish to the net and Alf weighs it at just below two lbs. He says: 'There'll be more in that hole for you because they swim in shoals—but the strange thing is that if one of them smashes you, then you might as well pack it in and move on. That shoal will stop feeding.'

That is exactly what happens when I hook the next fish under the willow trees. The fish bores deep and gets under a submerged log or something. The line snaps.

'Where do you suggest we go to next Alf?' I ask laughing—confident now I will catch a large bag of fish, despite this one mishap.

'There's a derelict landing stage with wooden piles that stick out across the main current and form an eddy. We normally get perch there,' says Alf.

In the next hour we catch 15 perch in various spots along the Enbourne. None of the fish is less 16 ounces and the largest I catch—in a deep hole close to a tumbledown pier—is two lbs 12 ounces. The baked perch is one of the few English coarse fish that is suitable for the table and Alf takes a bag of them home with him and says his family will be eating well during the next week. He earns his two guineas that day.

We have agreed we will return to the River Enbourne again as it is the most prolific river in England for the sheer variety of the species that populate it. It is a fisherman friendly river and Alf says that next time he will instruct us on the use of the pole which he makes from bamboo cane.

These are 20 feet long and enable the angler to fish otherwise inaccessible dark and deep perch pools under dense low-hanging trees and bushes. Alf shows us one—he has placed metal rings on the top six feet of this enormously heavy pole and through these he threads strong elastic to enable the tapered silk line to provide sufficient "give" to a fish when playing it.

I have never been a devotee of the latest angling technology and think I will find the act of having to "dismantle" the pole while playing a fish extremely irritating and ungainly. I am an old-fashioned purist who believes there should be a point at which the balance stands fairly between the fish and the angler.

Too much technology alters that balance and diminishes the

sporting chance that should always be afforded to the quarry. After all, angling is a sport devised for gentlemen and should be a personal hunt by one man for one fish. George Printer believed that the best river fishermen were those who understood—and were therefore able to exploit—the natural conditions around them.

Knowledge of nature is something that takes years to learn and it is why—without too much technology—the wisest and canniest fishermen are usually the eldest.

24
SENNELAGER CAMP

He slipped into fitful sleep continually as the train rattled and shook at a snail's pace through Belgium towards the German border and into Westphalia. The haunting vision of Emily's face and her irresistible smile was etched in his psyche and every time he woke and thought of her he experienced almost physical pain in his lower stomach.

They were unceremoniously bundled out of the carriages at Paderborn and ordered to fall in for the march to Sennelager which was not only a prisoner-of-war camp, but also a major training base for the German army. It had been built by the Kaiser for his elite cavalry regiments at the turn of the century and it lay upon a sandy plateau overlooking the railway.

The omnipresent sand, blown about in the stiff morning breeze, also soon permeated under clothing and those with inadequately dressed wounds experienced the agonizing pain of hot sand chafing insidiously on raw flesh.

Reaching the camp many of the men in the column dropped to the ground in a state of semi-collapse. They lay on the sand, their belongings strewn around them, with utter dejection written upon their face. German soldiers came bustling up and forced the fallen to stand. The guards then lined up the column and ordered the British prisoners to remain at attention.

They stood outside the camp for three hours, by which time the sun was high and the heat was stifling. The pitiful column was directed eventually to the barrack building within the main compound, where they were allowed to drink water. There was no food.

The identification process began for official records and with it the dispersal of each prisoner to either the camp hospital or into accommodation in one of the huts. He stood to attention before a grey haired Feldwebel with spectacles and a drooping moustache who sat at a desk holding a pen which hovered over a pad in front of him.

"Name?"

"Frank Clarke, Sergeant, number 7852."

"Nationality?"

"British."

"Age?"

"Thirty-two years five months."

"Wounded?"

"Yes, a bullet wound just below the right shoulder. It is bleeding and needs attention."

The Feldwebel ignored him. "Unit?" he continued. Frank remained silent. He had probably told the old man too much and was certainly under no obligation to reveal any further information.

He was damned if he was going to reveal anything else. The Feldwebel placed the sheet of paper bearing his name upon a pile and looked up with a smirk on his face. He scrutinized Frank for several moments before he spoke and the smirk changed to a look of contempt.

"There is a form I must give you to fill in for the Red Cross which will alert the British military authorities of your capture and location. If you do not give us the name of your unit it is likely your papers will not get processed and neither your regiment nor your family will ever know you are alive. It means you will not receive food parcels. So which is it to be—heroics or common sense?"

He decided discretion was the better part of valour, especially on the matter of food parcels. He filled in the Red Cross form and then said politely: "Sgt Frank Clarke, 7852, 1st Battalion Norfolk Regiment, wounded at Elouges, near Mons, on August 24th 1914."

The Feldwebel looked him in the eye again: "Ten months as a fugitive behind enemy lines eh? Now there's a story for Major Bach if I ever heard one."

There was another smirk and the elderly NCO waved him away after retrieving the file and writing something on it. He had been told on the train that nobody wanted to end up in Sennelager—it was run by a madman and climatically it was the toughest camp in Germany.

The NCO's sleeping accommodation comprised of wooden bunks, in two tiers, with a sack as a mattress but no pillow. The summer heat during the day was intolerable, but during the night it was freezing.

He saw that between his block and the 12 foot high electric wire fence were a dispersed line of sentries with rifles and fixed bayonets. There was a wooden tower with a machine gun post every 150 yards around the perimeter and a second barbed wire fence on the outer rim which was not electrified.

He started to make the acquaintance of the men living in his block. A broad-shouldered senior non-commissioned officer with the insignia of a warrant officer class one on his sleeves offered him his hand. He was older than Frank but several inches shorter. His grey face, which looked pinched with hunger, suggested he had been a prisoner for some months, but he had kept himself immaculately smart, considering the conditions in which he was living.

"Good evening, I'm RSM Percy Hodges–who do I have the pleasure of addressing?"

"I'm Sergeant Frank Clarke Sir, of D Company, 1st Battalion the Norfolks."

"It's OK—call me Percy when we are here. We all use our first names inside these four walls but retain regimental standards while among the other ranks. Were you wounded at Loos or Ypres?"

"No Mons, 24th August last year. I managed to evade capture till three monhs ago. I was caught near the Dutch border with a party of fugitives who were making their way down the escape network run jointly by a British matron in Brussels and a group of Belgian aristocrats. Their network appears to have been penetrated and we were betrayed by a French traitor."

The RSM looked grave. "Have you been interrogated yet?"

He replied: "No, just a few questions from a Feldwebel earlier today who seemed to think a Major Bach was going to be very interested in me."

"I fear the German sergeant may be right," he said.

Percy told him that Major Bach, the camp commandant, was an officer with strong psychopathic tendencies. He ran a regime which even his officers were terrified to criticize.

"The problem's made worse because Bach encourages the guards to hate the British more than the other prisoners, including the Russians. The German press is in a lather of hatred about Britain because we killed so many of their soldiers at the start of the war and those of us who fought at Mons are at the top of Major Bach's hate list.

Although we British are the main target for Major Bach, the men are under orders to retain regimental discipline. German officers have to be saluted at all times. Disputes about any matter—and it's usually about food—must be settled by the committee of non-commissioned officers. On the working parties the men have been ordered not give the Germans reasons to punish them for slacking. That's easier said than done because many of the men should not be working because of their poor physical state.

"Oh yes, and I must tell you that the committee has agreed that full compliance with the Germans means that for the moment escapes are forbidden, even if they were possible . . . and the committee doubts they are . . . because of the constant military activity going on all around us 24 hours a day."

Percy could see that Frank didn't like what he'd heard about no escaping. Another sergeant called Freddie Osborne chipped in.

"I know this might sound like we've given in to Fritz—but we're doing this for the sake of the men. Major Bach runs a brutal and illegal regime and men are tortured for the slightest infringement of their crazy Prussian rules, some of which are invented on a whim."

Percy warned him that he was likely to be questioned at length by Major Bach and it would be better to co-operate with him—if he valued his own skin—and wanted to avoid long term solitary confinement in the prison block, or worse the pole, which few men survived for too long. He was told that men were tied up and suspended by rope to a pole—then left for hours on end in agony. It was entirely against the rules of the Geneva Treaty, but Major Bach did not give a damn about the rules.

That night he slept for short periods thinking about the story he must concoct for his interrogators.

He kept waking as Emily drifted across his mind and then Percy's words returned to him about how he could best avoid compromising the courageous people who had helped him. He saw images of the people in the escape network and had nightmares in which they were executed because of what he had told the Germans.

There was a parade at 0600 hours and Frank stood to attention along with the other NCOs from his hut. They were faced by a bull-headed overweight Prussian officer on horseback who carried a leather whip which he cracked periodically. He began spluttering with rage.

"You damned English swine! Yes! You English dogs! You caused this war and we will not let you forget it while you are prisoners. We could punish you severely. But that is not the civilized German way. While your Government has stopped at nothing, we Germans will fulfil our honourable traditions. We respect the laws to which all civilized nations have subscribed. But remember! We are going to bring England to her knees. Aren't we, men?"

"Ja! Ja!" was the wild singing reply from the excited guards.

He was standing next to Percy and asked quietly: "Is that oaf Major Bach?"

Percy laughed: "No, that fat fool on the horse is just a pussycat compared to Major Bach. He always comes out with this nonsense like this on morning parade."

On the second day he reported to Dr Ascher. He was the official medical attendant to the camp and Frank grew to like and respect him in the coming months. He was told by the elderly doctor that his condition was not serious enough to warrant being detained in hospital, but he should clean the punctured wound every day himself and dress it in the paper bandages with which he was provided.

"I lived in Cambridge before the war and so I know the British well— and from the way you speak I get the impression you are an educated man. Come to the hospital once a week. An orderly will examine the wound and keep it free from infection. After that report to my office and we will talk for a while. In the meantime I'm afraid you are in for much continuing pain but you will have to put up with that. The important thing will be to avoid re-infection."

It was a friendly meeting and Frank felt strengthened by it. The key now, he told himself, would be not to catch the virulent flu virus that was sweeping across Germany and try to avoid dysentery and typhus, the deadly disease carried by lice.

25

THE STENCH AND THE FLIES

He had been aware of the awful stench around the compound but did not know just how poor the sanitary conditions were at Sennelager. The camp's sewage system consisted of an open cesspool within a stone's throw of the barracks. The smell in the heat of summer was worse than anything he could describe.

No disinfectants were used in the latrines which were emptied every three days when the stench became even worse. In fact, the conditions were so revolting that the outbreak of an epidemic was expected, not only by the prisoners, but by the authorities as well. The primitive sanitary arrangements caused a pestilence of flies both inside the huts and within the perimeter of the barbed wire compounds.

They looked like domestic houseflies but were much larger, extremely aggressive and tormented the prisoners. The severity of their sting created a maddening irritation. Within a few days he had lice on his body and clothes and these remained a feature of his life for the next three years. Every evening he would use a lighted match to burn them off his clothes, but by the next day the dead would be replaced by another generation. So far the camp had been unaffected by Typhus which remained a threat to the entire prison community, including the Germans. Dysentery however remained an increasing problem.

Each day started at 6am with a parade. If a prisoner wanted to have a wash and a shave he needed to be up and about by 5am to get into the washroom. After parade, there was breakfast consisting of a mug of lukewarm coffee made from ground acorns and a hunk of black bread. The ersatz coffee was hot but neither milk nor sugar was available.

Frank was shocked on his first Sunday to discover that the general public was invited by the Commandant to enter the camp to have a look at the British prisoners. The civilians wandered about the camp in much the same manner as they would have strolled through a zoo looking at animals. The men countered this by staying indoors until the German crowds had gone.

By now he was consumed with grief at what was happening to him. He did not know what had happened to Emily and continued to worry that she too might have been arrested near the Dutch border and subsequently maltreated. He missed her warm presence so much at night that he felt pain in his stomach and frequently wept for her.

After a few weeks he opted to join the agricultural field parties as an overseer which would take him out into the fresh air and into the countryside away from the stench. The countryside was also a place, except for the deep depths of winter, where food might be obtained. From the start he was looking at things from the long-term. It would be a battle to survive imprisonment lasting several years and he could tell from the way his clothes fitted that he was already losing weight. An escape plan had to be his number one priority.

The day's work started at 7am and continued without respite until mid-day. He decided that the fate of the men on the working party, of which he was in charge under the watchful eye of the armed guards, would depend on everyone getting stuck in. So he was hard on slackers unless the men were very sick and at this early stage in the war most were capable of work if they were not ill with dysentery.

Meanwhile, he decided he would attempt to ingratiate himself with the guards in order to win their friendship and inveigle subsequent small improvements for the working party. It did appear this was successful in the case of some of the Bavarian guards.

He collected cigarettes from those prisoners who were receiving food parcels, which for the moment he himself was not. The guards loved British tobacco. The Prussians were still implacably anti-British, but the southern Germans seemed to be entirely different and he began to get on friendly terms with Manfred from Munich and Hugo from Frankfurt.

They were prepared to talk to him, especially the fat one Manfred. Hugo was less willing to talk but listened with patience to what Frank had to say. They were both in their mid-30s, family men, who just wanted a quiet life away from the Front.

In the middle of the morning, after a wary look around the large potato fields, they would accept a cigarette from Frank and ask him if the men would like to rest for 10 minutes to snatch something to eat. Slices of black bread would be shared out and if there was anything edible in the field the men could help themselves. After a few more weeks Frank was able to bring a Tommy's stove with him hidden under his coat.

The Germans would hand him a sufficient quantity of solid fuel to light it. The prisoners would boil potatoes and any other vegetables they could scavenge. At midday the detail returned to barracks for lunch. They would pick up their basin and run down to the cook-house for their rations. This was invariably red-cabbage soup scooped out of a big cauldron of boiling water.

Alongside the cauldron was a table on which the cabbages were cut up before being dumped into the water. The main meal of the day was a bowl of boiling water—upon which floated shreds of largely uncooked red cabbage—and a slice of black bread. On rare occasions, a few potatoes or a bone would be found in a prisoner's basin under a piece of cabbage leaf.

Men would soon starve to death on these rations. The third meal was a repeat of the breakfast ration—a mug of lukewarm acorn coffee without milk or sugar with a further portion of black bread.

At 10pm the lights in the huts went out and the men were ordered to extinguish their oil lamp. Any who hesitated for too long were punished severely by the guards and faced the possibility of solitary confinement. The punishment cells were tiny, about seven feet square and were housed within a small brick building within the compound.

Each cell was fitted with a tiny grating on the outside wall otherwise it would have been in pitch darkness all through the day. There was a straw sack crawling with vermin on the floor. To sleep a prisoner had to either accept the lice—or stretch out on the cold stone.

A small bucket in the cell was provided for toilet and emptied every third day, which meant the cells stank of shit. Bread, water and soup once a day was the diet and all exercise denied, except for a brief chance to stretch the limbs accompanied by the sentry to fetch the mid-day meal from the cook-house.

Conversation with a fellow-prisoner was forbidden but inside the solitary confinement cells that rule was unenforceable and there was a babble of conversation between the prisoners which the guards grew to accept.

However, as Percy had warned Frank, solitary confinement in a tiny darkened cell was considered a privilege compared to the dreaded "post" as it was known, at which as many as six men at a time were literally strung up in rope and left in agony. It was something to have nightmares about.

SEA TROUT—DIARY JULY 1901

We assemble our rods at the bridge before descending onto the footpath by the river. I use the light of an oil lamp to tie a sparse Red Butcher onto a seven foot silkworm gut cast. George Printer has told me never to use a bushy one.

I make my way along a rocky path beside the River Bandon in County Cork on a hot July night. An owl hoots and a vixen calls her cubs. There are sounds of flapping wings from the trees lining the bank. Low clouds and the quarter moon ensure there is no silver light to guide me to the deep pool that lies 150 yards below the weir nearest to the Castle.

The fourth Earl of Bandon is not in residence and I have no fear of his lordship's gamekeeper stalking me—for the Earl's man walks just a yard ahead in the dark, treading the path with a confident step.

Walter could walk this path wearing a blindfold. King Edward VII has recently been crowned at a spectacular coronation and so far it has been a wet summer, with sufficient storms to bring the river frequently into spate and with it the fish running up in large numbers from the Estuary.

'It's a great night for the sea trout,' mutters Walter breathlessly. I fancy a sack full of them tonight. Best watch out for poachers though Frank. They can get nasty if they are disturbed.'

'I'll not be thinking of those buggers," I laugh.

At just 18 I care nothing for poachers and feel myself man enough to square up to anybody. We come to the pool, arriving at its head and stand looking downstream as the dark water tumbles past us. It is pitch black apart from the moon's glistening reflection upon the racing stream.

The gushing water beneath the bank creates a magnificent sound and fills us with a primeaval sense of expectation. We are hunters in the wild. Motionless we listen in tense anticipation for two or three minutes.

At length we hear what sounds like a door flap being pushed open. I count . . . one, two, and three. . . . as the sea trout leaps into the air. There follows a magnificent crash from the middle of the river—like a man executing a "belly flop" into a swimming pool. A large sea trout has propelled itself out of the water three feet into the air.

Some say they do this in an irritated attempt to throw off the freshwater mites that cling tenaciously to their gills. The mites are attracted to the trout's silver body by the brine that still inundates its scales.

'At least a six pound fish I'd say,' exclaims Walter, who knows his onions as far as sea trout are concerned but enjoys exaggerating every possibility. He then leaves me, disappearing into the darkness to fish the next pool upstream about 40 yards away.

I am alone in the night experiencing the greatest thrill any angler can expect from the sport. There is nothing to match the excitement of fishing a pool teeming with wild migratory trout—long after midnight—when they are leaping out of the water setting the pulse of the angler racing in anticipation of a take.

It is a wonderful privilege to be alone with nature and her nocturnal creatures on a hot summer night on a sea trout pool and those who have never experienced it have not tasted the ultimate test in river fishing.

I reconnoitred the pool in daylight this morning and know that granite boulders across the river create a partial dam through which a large body of water cascades into a deep swim 20 yards long—on the right bank looking upstream.

The gravel bed of the river slopes gradually downwards from the shallows of the left bank where a man can wade. Walter advises me never to enter the water unless absolutely necessary because even the largest sea trout patrols into the shallows at night, swimming in a few inches of water.

The presence of a man disturbing the current with his feet spooks the shy creatures back into the deepest reaches of the pool, where they will lie on the bed of the river, unresponsive to attempts to coax them up.

I estimate the breaking strength of the cast to be somewhere around eight lbs and the fly's number eight hook is large enough to embed itself sufficiently in the bony mouth of a large fish. I douse both the cast and light green silk fly line along a trail of mud left by the cows from the Earl's herd.

This ensures both will sink immediately as they land on the

water and are carried downstream towards me by the current. The first cast in the darkness is unnerving because it can only be governed by guesswork—based on an estimation of the length of the backswing that can be made by the fisherman from the bank of the river.

I have paced the length of my backswing this morning and I reckon I have at most 10 yards before the leaves on the branches of the trees on the sloping bank will foul the cast and hook. It is best not to be too ambitious. I begin fishing the back of the pool with short casts, building a rhythm before attempting to reach the neck and deeper water.

I take care to minimise the number of preparatory swings, reminding myself over and over again that in the dark, in pursuit of the sea trout, it is usually stealth that counts more than distance. It is now my fifth cast and the Butcher lands on the surface of the water before being dragged down by the current. I estimate it is halfway up the pool—about 30 feet—and in the deeper area where the current is strong.

I allow the line to travel with the flow and draw back line at the speed I guess the current is carrying the fly towards me on the current. I feel a gentle tug and soften my grip while slowing the process of gathering line. I wait for the second tug before striking gently to set the hook.

The startled trout, a wild creature unused to any constraint, responds by leaping out the water, before tearing off upstream into the deeper reaches of the pool in an enraged attempt to escape. I whistle loudly to alert Walter to bring his landing net and begin to play the sea trout, which is a big fish.

There are no serious snags along the far bank, but the important job will be to keep the sea trout in the immediate vicinity and not allow it to escape through the cascading front of the pool and away upstream. Similarly, I must stop it getting behind me downstream. The skill is in applying just enough pressure to prevent either eventuality.

The greatest virtue here is patience and self-control—to stay in charge and feel that you are in charge. A sea trout fighting for its life is a wild and unpredictable creature that will use its great natural strength in any way it can to disentangle itself from the hook lodged in its mouth. Even when it seems exhausted and its strength spent, its head being pulled inexorably towards the net, the sea trout is game for one more battle to save itself.

'My God, he's gone again Walter,' I say as the fish suddenly springs to life and surges off up the pool, covering 30 feet of water in a few seconds and boring deep into the rocky right bank of the river.

'No, he's yours Frank, just be gentle with your hands my lad and draw him in, he's well spent now,' advises Walter.

It is true. The fish finally succumbs and now appears indifferent to its fate as I draw in line carefully with my hands, keeping the rod high. I bring the 6lb sea trout to the net.

Catching a sea trout from a fast running river in the middle of the night surpasses the thrill of catching a much larger salmon during the day. The flesh is better too.

26

EMILY MEETS ANNA CLARKE

Frank's mother Anna had received a letter from Emily out of the blue in the autumn of 1915 requesting a meeting in Norfolk, shortly after the American landed in England and presented her credentials in London to the Mary Borden Red Cross Ambulance and Hospital Unit.

The letter just said that he was alive, having been wounded in August 1914, but that he may have been betrayed by an informer in the escape network that tried to get him back to England via Holland the previous month.

This letter from a complete stranger contained both good and bad news as far as Anna and the family was concerned Since the previous summer she had heard only once by letter from the Regiment. It came from the Commanding Officer of the 1st Battalion who said that Sergeant Clarke had been reported missing during the fighting at the Battle of Mons, shortly after attempting to carry out a highly dangerous undertaking for which he had volunteered.

He went on to praise him as one of the Battalion's most capable and courageous senior non-commissioned officers and said he was regarded highly by both the officers and the men. Sgt Clarke had not been reported killed in action, said the letter, because no body had been found or reported, neither were there witnesses.

He had disappeared while trying to carry an urgent message to the Commanding Officer of the Cheshires who were in a position adjacent to the Norfolks. Frank would have had to run in front of the enemy lines while carrying the message—and he would have been dangerously exposed to their fire.

Everyone in the family had by now, over a year later, come to assume that Frank was dead—and that the most likely explanation for the lack of a body was that he had been hit by shellfire. Anna was the only one who expressed any hope he was alive—and these hopes were rekindled by Emily's visit to Norfolk.

Emily told them everything she knew about Frank's experiences since his arrival in France and took them through to the moment of their parting in Brussels. Anna was deeply thankful for this insight, but at the same time she felt deep anxieties for her son's safety now that he was in the hands of the Germans—because of his involvement with the escape network.

In recent weeks there had been widespread newspaper coverage and subsequent international revulsion at the execution of the English nurse Edith Cavell—and now the family had learned from Emily that Frank was implicated in this case and therefore possibly at considerable risk of execution himself.

Anna, a reserved and rather old-fashioned person, typical perhaps of Victorian women of her class, was slightly ill at ease in the company of the American girl. She had not decided whether she liked her or not and then there was the matter of the German name which made her feel concerned that Frank might be getting personally and emotionally involved where he would be better off keeping his feelings to himself. The young nurse seemed not to be aware of the more formal manners of Englishwomen when they were getting to know one another. Anna thought Emily was too direct in her choice of words and just plunged straight in, without a thought that she might be embarrassing people.

"Frank and I have been lovers Anna since shortly after he was entrusted to my care. He had evaded capture for several months and was eventually placed in a secret hideaway within the chateau which I shared with him. As I brought him through a period of recuperation from his wound, we fell deeply in love—and planned to marry after getting safely back to England with the help of Edith Cavell."

"Emily was now tearful but Anna felt herself unable to embrace her. The girl was still a stranger—even if she did say she loved Frank. She ignored the weeping and continued to gaze at the oil painting of her son fishing on the beloved lake close to the chateau that Emily had painted the previous summer.

She said somewhat stiffly: "This is very good Emily and somehow it embodies Frank's great love of nature—and of course his fishing. I shall have it framed and placed in his room ready for the day he returns after the War. I am sure he will always treasure it."

She put it to one side and looked at Emily, who was still weeping silently. "My dear girl you haven't told me the nature of Frank's wound at Mons—how serious was it?"

Emily wiped her eyes with a handkerchief and continued: "He was wounded in the lower shoulder by a bullet shot at close range from the front—the exit wound in his upper back is as large as a saucer. It's a miracle the bullet missed his lung and did not shatter any of his ribs.

"He lay unconscious on the battlefield for several days after the British Army had retreated and was taken for dead by the Germans. Then, mercifully, a Belgian nun found him barely alive and she took him back to the small convent hospital. He had to be moved from there after preliminary treatment by the Sisters pouring salt on his wound, which definitely saved his life.

"He was then taken through an escape network and after many adventures ended up with me in a secret compartment at the chateau—where we spent six of the happiest months of our lives. Now I ache for him. I have pledged myself to Frank and want you to know Anna that there could never be another man."

More tears welled in her eyes.

"I dread to think how my poor dear boy is coping with the grief of our separation while he is inside a cold prison cell. I can't bear to think of his pain. It hurts me physically to even think about it."

This time Anna steeled herself to comfort the grief-stricken girl and she placed her arms around her shoulders, saying quietly:

"If he is in custody somewhere and this has not been reported, then he has no protection. We must make urgent enquiries immediately through both his regiment and the Red Cross. I shall also write to the War Office and our member of parliament.

"I know you are busy Emily and about to be posted to the Western Front and so you should leave everything to me. I have the time to devote to this matter and my youngest boy is also very precious to me. Don't worry too much about him—he's a tough one is my youngest lad and I'm sure you know that."

She added: "I give you my word that the moment we hear anything about Frank's whereabouts I shall write to inform you in France so that you can contact him and continue your loving relationship. Let us pray for that moment. Personally, if it's any consolation to you, I am not of the opinion that he will be linked to the planning and organisation of the Edith Cavell escape network any more than you were.

"After all, he was just one of hundreds of British fugitives who were using it to escape—and that of course is the duty of all soldiers whether they are German, French or British. I feel confident we will hear where he has been taken to very soon.

"In the meantime Emily, I am sure the whole of our family would want to thank you for everything you have done for Frank in nursing him back to health and strength. You are certainly a remarkable young woman, a credit to your country—and I can quite see why he regarded you with such love and affection."

Anna now kissed her on the cheek.

Emily caught the train from Norwich back to London that evening, and a week later she was serving on the Western Front with Mary Borden's Red Cross ambulance and hospital unit looking after wounded French soldiers.

It would be many months, however, before she heard again from her beloved Frank. Her letters went unanswered and without these letters of consolation and reassurance he would have to endure torture and solitary confinement without her. For her part she dreamed of him every night.

27
TORTURED

The call to attend the office of Major Bach eventually came one Saturday afternoon and he reported to the German officer with fear in his heart. It was winter and the ground was still covered in snow. He was kept waiting in the freezing outer office for two hours before the Commandant called him through.

Bach sat at a tidy desk and his office smelled strongly of saddle polish and cheap cigars. He was a tall man with a shaved head and small pig-like brown eyes. A file was laid out in front of the German and he studied it carefully, ignoring the British sergeant. Eventually Bach looked up and stared in a baleful manner at him.

He spoke in good English. "This report tells us that you were wounded in August 1914 but not captured until July 3rd 1915. I want a full account of what you were doing in the intervening months, the doctors who treated your injuries, who gave you sanctuary and who organized your attempted escape across the Dutch border.

"Unless you can give me a satisfactory explanation and provide me with all the names of those involved, I shall assume you were acting as a spy during those months and have you executed."

Frank was stunned into silence. He thought frantically of something to say but was unable to respond—except to reply that he had already provided the camp authorities with all the information to which they were entitled. Bach continued angrily.

"You are a spy. You were not wearing your uniform when you were captured and were moving about freely in German occupied territory. I intend to lay a formal charge of espionage against you—which I am sure you are aware is a capital offence.

"If you co-operate with us we may be in a position to offer you a lighter sentence and that might mean you avoid the firing squad. My job now is to collect evidence for a trial at a later date. Is that understood?"

"I am Sergeant Frank Clarke, 7852, of the 1st Battalion the Norfolk Regiment, wounded on August 14th 1914. That's all you are going to get from me."

The major looked extremely angry and summoned four guards who dragged him out of the office. He shouted at the top of his voice: "Give this man four hours at the post!"

He wrote on the file an instruction that any incoming mail for Sergeant Frank Clarke should be destroyed. Escorted by the guards with loaded rifles and fixed bayonets, he was led to one of six posts just outside the barracks, but in full view of the British compound.

Guards stood ready to bayonet him should he make an attempt to escape. Two of them uncoiled a length of rope. Frank's hands were forced behind his back and his wrists were tied tightly together and the rope drawn so taut that it cut deeply into the flesh.

He forced himself not to cry out in pain. The guards backed him against the post around which the rope was passed. His ankles were then strapped to the post.

Finally another length of rope was passed round the upper part of his body, lashing him firmly to the support to prevent him falling forward. Trussed and tied he was left to undergo the ordeal in the freezing temperature. He moaned softly but remained determined not to cry out or squeal—like a broken man pleading for mercy.

The ropes had been drawn so tightly around his wrists and ankles that the circulation of the blood through the hands and feet were restricted, while the flesh above the knots soon swelled up. He soon lost any sense of feeling in his hands and feet.

He knew he must not panic and must avoid writhing and twisting in attempts to secure relief. Each movement would only cause further pain. He let his body drop forward slightly so that his head fell down upon his chest. He would feign unconsciousness in order to give the minimum satisfaction to that bastard Bach.

The major was indeed watching, and felt a spasm of annoyance that the British sergeant was not screaming like a pig, which was the case with most prisoners who experienced this form of torture. In the case of the British victims it gave him a satisfactory sense of revenge. Major Bach had lost his only son at Mons.

"Wake the swine up," he called to the guards after an hour.

Buckets of icy water were hurriedly fetched and he felt the full force of the cold water upon his face and upper body. He refused to move an inch, and even though breathing was now becoming more difficult, he lapsed into further detachment. He had found a way to defeat pain and torture and fell into another deep sleep to dream of his beloved fishing.

A WILD WEST CITY—DIARY MAY 1901

Bert our butler at Amiens Street, Dublin is always interested to hear about my fishing adventures although not an enthusiastic angler himself. He listens with patience to my stories which he suspects are frequently embellished.

He says to me: 'I'm a Galway man as you know Mr Frank and I'd be pleased to take you there for a good day's fishing. If you come you'll have the privilege of being the only man not from Galway allowed to catch salmon on a sacred beat, although you may have to risk your life doing it.'

'Now there's a challenge Bert,' I respond. 'What exactly do you mean by that?'

'Well you'll see when you get there. You'll need a spinning rod, some hooks, cork floats and lead shot.'

Bert invites me to fish the River Corrib in the west of Ireland which flows from Lough Corrib through Galway and spills out into Galway Bay. It is only four miles from the Lough to the sea and said to be the shortest river in Europe. It is also among the most powerful and fast-running, especially after a few days rain.

People from all over Ireland come to the city seeking spring fish in the Upper Corrib, the part of the river that flows from the southern end of the Lough to the Salmon Weir. Few outsiders, however, are allowed to fish the April and May spring run of salmon below the Weir where the river runs through Galway city and out into Galway Bay. It is known as the Lower Corrib and three bridges cross it—the Salmon Weir Bridge, William O'Brien Bridge and Wolfe Tone Bridge.

The spring run lasts two months, the latter part coinciding with the Mayfly and presents a memorable spectacle when the water is clear. Thousands of fish gathering in the estuary move up the river in April—some years it is earlier—in their short journey to Lough Carrib.

The privilege of fishing for these abundant salmon in the lower part of the river is exclusive to anglers who live in the city—and any interloper who tries to fish there during April and May is inviting big trouble for himself from the locals who protect their exclusive rights to the river.

'So how am I going to avoid getting a good thrashing from the locals if I show up with my rod along the city stretch?" I ask nervously as we walk from Galway station to the river.

'You leave that to me Mr Frank,' says Bert. 'I am well known here.'

We arrive and glance down at the river. It is high but receding. Bert screws up his face.

'The tide's wrong at the moment Mr Frank. We'll be wanting to fish when it's on the incoming. I suggest we take advantage of some of the local hostelries for an hour or two. I can't tell you how much I miss the local ale.'

It is only 11am but Bert obviously feels the thirst and so I follow him into a succession of public houses in which he is continually greeted as a long lost father or son. Bert the family butler turns out to be a figure of respect in Galway who everybody wants to know and who appears to have taken on an entirely new persona since arriving in the city of his birth.

I ponder why a man who engenders so much respect and who is such a popular figure ever left the city. In Dublin he keeps himself to himself and few know him. The men who greet him with such enthusiasm here seem to represent every class of person from worker to professional.

Bert drinks quickly for a small plump man and rarely has to buy a pint. I am introduced with great enthusiasm to all we meet. By 1pm my head is spinning. I hear myself laughing a lot and I am not as steady on my feet as I usually am.

I perch my bottom thankfully on a bar stool. At length sandwiches are brought and having tucked into those, I sober up slightly—but the drinking continues and my head starts spinning again.

By 3pm I am seriously drunk and my words slurred. My enthusiasm for fishing has not waned and I tell everybody I encounter with a wide smile: "I'm gunna catch a big feesh . . ."

At 4pm I fall off my stool. Bert appears unaffected by all the beer he has poured down his own throat and we depart the last public house shortly before 5pm with me staggering after him. I have no idea where I am, where we are going to fish, how we are going to fish and for how long. I just hope that when we get there

I will be able to find somewhere to pee.

At least 20 people are fishing in an area of less than 100 yards and what astonishes me is that there is a drop of around 30 feet to the water. It does not appear to deter people.

The townsmen are all rigged up to catch the running fish with heavy pike floats, weights and a double hook. Upon their tackle is fastened a prawn attached to the hook by white cord to stop it falling off on the long cast that is necessary to get it across the river.

The fishermen cast out the heavy rig and drag it slowly back across the river which is rippling with menacing power as the making tide surges up the river carrying the salmon with it. It is an amazing spectacle because the running fish are visible in the daylight not far beneath the surface and there are thousands of them.

The watching crowd shouts encouragement to the fishermen— the local experts are catching for the spectators. Bert disappears into the crowd, having been greeted by all with great affection. It seems he does not have an enemy in Galway and a reputation of almost heroic proportions.

Suddenly, after an absence of at least 10 minutes, Bert reappears carrying a rod and a modern steel reel, already baited with a prawn. He hands the rod and tackle and a large net to me.

'Its better equipment than yours Mr Frank—got the right kind of reel they tell me.'

'Ish a very crude way of fishn' for salmon,' I say still slurring my words.

'So what—it's the way we Galway folk have caught our salmon for generations and it works. There are a lot of hungry people in this town. Anyway, I'm not asking you to use it,' says Bert sternly and takes the rod back.

'The whole point is that you can't fish but I can—but I'm too old and fat to scramble down that ivy with the net when the time comes, hang on to the branches and get it under the fish at the same time. That's why you're here. You're going to be my ghillie Mr Frank.'

I would have seen the amusing side of this had not one of the rods nearby hooked a grilse at that moment and started dragging it unceremoniously across the river. It struggles for a few brief seconds but is fastened to heavy tackle and soon the angler signals to a young man holding a net to get down the wall to retrieve the fish.

The fellow climbs over the metal fence, net in hand and gradually makes his way down to the level of the water showing an extraordinary degree of dexterity and confidence. He descends a few feet at a time placing his feet and arms into the Ivy branches that cover the wall.

In places the Ivy bulges under his weight but the young man does not remain in any one position long enough to break it.

The fisherman guides the grilse to the side and the younger man deftly dips the large net deep enough into the water to get under the salmon and retrieve it. He climbs back up to the railings followed by the flapping fish with the ease of a small monkey. Now the grilse lies on the cobblestones as the large crowd gathers around it cheering enthusiastically.

'Christ I've never seen anything so quick in my life," I say to Bert. 'You don't expect me to do that do you—because I'm pissed you know. . . . '

'Mr Frank I have every confidence in your ability to do just that. After all, you are a well known sportsman in Ireland. You wouldn't want to be taken for a chicken would you? And then you being a Dublin man. . . . it would cause me severe embarrassment if I had to call on someone else to retrieve my fish. Anyway I've got to catch one first haven't I!'

Bert is about to have a stroke of beginner's luck. He is casting with great clumsiness, sometimes hooking himself as he tries to throw the line out into the river. On the sixth of these clumsy casts the float soars through the air and makes it half way across the river. Unfortunately it is sufficient to attract a fish. The prawn lands right in the path of a grilse and it rolls over exposing its belly as a great arc becomes visible in Bert's rod.

'For Christ's sake play him Bert—or he'll smash you in a moment,' I shout and am sobering rapidly at the latest turn of events. Bert looks shocked and promptly hands me the rod. I play the fish and bring it towards the shore after about five minutes. At that point one of the other anglers puts down his rod and marches over to us with an angry look upon his face.

'There's no way this stranger is going to land that fish Bert—if necessary we'll cut the fucking line to stop it happening."' He peers into my face.

'Give that fucking rod back to Bert and do your own bloody job stranger.'

Bert looks sheepish and takes the rod from my hand and points to the net—and then to the river 30 feet below. I have never been so sober in all my life. I pick up the net and gingerly heave myself over the railings and start descending the Ivy.

It is as if the people in the crowd had ceased to watch others fishing and are now concentrating upon my progress down the wall.

The Galway folk are shouting and laughing—but now there is silence as I gradually inch down, somehow managing to retain my hold upon the net. When I am half way down I notice that closer to the water there were sturdy branches with which I can get both a hand and foothold.

'The cheeky sods—they don't tell you about that bit. It's all a bloody con,' I laugh. I am being over-optimistic. The branches are as slippery as soap and it is hard to keep a hold and concentrate upon moving the net into position under the fish that now lies prone upon the surface of the water.

For the first time I feel alarm about my predicament because the tide below is raging and I do not fancy my chances if I fall in. None of the idiots in the street would try to help me-I am sure about that.

'Come on Dubliner get a fucking move on,' someone shouts.

It stirs me into action and I plunge the net into the water and bring it below the grilse which fortunately is only a small fish of about 5lbs. I am suspended literally by my left knee and thigh which are embedded into a nook behind a thick branch.

As I pull the net clear of the water with the salmon deep within it I feel my body gradually slipping away as my grip weakens. I pull myself up just a second before I fall and scramble like a demented cat back up the Ivy as quickly as he can.

I heave myself over the railings and lay panting on the cobblestones with the net behind me. I expect to be jeered and taunted by the locals—instead as I climb to my feet I am patted and prodded in a friendly manner.

They come forward, lift me onto their shoulders and carry me into a pub where I spend the rest of the evening drinking at other people's expense.

'You do know you were set up don't you!' laughs Bert.

'That fisherman who threatened you is my brother so you didn't have to go over the wall at all. We just thought it would be a jape. Not many people who aren't locals can do it because our lads have been climbing up and down it since they were kids and they know all the tricks!'

'You old bastard Bert—I could have drowned.'

'Mr Frank if I'd have thought that you would have drowned, or been too pissed, I'd have stopped it. You might have gotten a soaking but that was all.

'Now, let's get you a soaking in another way young man.'

The day whets my appetite for the city and we agree to start going there every year for horse racing at Ballybrit. The Galway Races summer meeting is the highlight of the Irish racing calendar. Crowds of 60,000 watch Ireland's top steeple chasers racing over the mile and a half course.

Perhaps I'll have the chance to watch Tipperary Boy win the Galway Plate again. Bert drinks hard, plays hard and flirts with the ladies when he's in Galway. His behaviour bears no similarity to the meek man who returns to Amiens Street as butler.

I tell him: "Don't worry Bert. What goes on tour stays on tour!"

He woke up in the guardroom early the next morning. He had been lying on the floor and was wracked by pain. When the guard saw that Frank was awake he called out to another guard and five minutes later Major Bach appeared.

"So you think you can defy my punishment you English swine. We'll see about that!"

He walked over and kicked Frank in the ribs. He spoke quietly at first but his words became louder until he was shouting: "Yesterday I was being kind and spared you real agony. Now you have angered me. I don't care if you die before your trial—it is all the same to me!"

He was bundled outside again and tied to the same post. This time he was forced to stand on tip-toe while the upper rope was passed around his neck. This rope was left loose and then looped in the form of a double knot. Being on tip-toe he found that when he tried to transfer his weight his toes gave way and he was left in a hanging position.

His head fell forward, as he gradually lapsed into unconsciousness, until it pressed against the restraining slip-knot. He was now suffering the agonies of slow strangulation in addition to the searing pain in his hands and ankles, while the weight of his body dragged his neck more tightly than otherwise would have been the case against the upper rope.

His face went blue from his inability to take only intermittent small gulps of air. He felt that his eyes were half out of their sockets. His mouth was wide open and his tongue, which protruded, was becoming dry and swollen.

A voice within kept telling him not to panic. Periodically the guards threw buckets of ice water over him. At one point he thought he saw Major Bach standing a couple of paces away, his legs wide apart and hands clasped behind his back.

There was a look of satisfaction on the Major's face. He heard him shouting taunts to attract the attention of other prisoners. The guards were roaring with laughter. Frank then noticed—it was Sunday—that his torture was providing entertainment for the German crowds who were visiting the camp to gawp at the prisoners.

A group of civilians gathered not far from the post, but were prevented from coming within 10 yards by a sentry. He had no idea what they were saying, except that it was hostile. Some of his tormentors were girls and they squealed with laughter at jokes being made by young German soldiers who were doing their recruitment training at the adjoining military camp and had come to watch.

The delights of seeing someone undergoing torture was regarded by many Germans from Paderborn as good fun—like going to circus—and even more entertaining if the victim at the post was a Tommy. Some had been before and were expecting the victim to utter shrieks of pain.

On this day the victim suffered in silence—despite their jibes and jeers. The fact that this kind of punishment was being offered as an entertaining spectacle for the benefit of the German public was not lost on the

Sergeant's Committee, whose members viewed it with disgust and growing anger from the window of their hut. The fact also that Frank's punishment and other men like him, was driving the men in the camp to the point of mutiny was not lost on senior NCOs like Percy.

They understood this was precisely what Major Bach had in mind—a mutiny. He could unleash an ever more barbaric regime of terror against the British prisoners, even perhaps shooting large numbers of them. The punishment of innocent men infuriated the prisoners—who were unable to voice a word in protest. Frank was by no means the only victim of the post. Major Bach was aware it was having a restraining effect upon the British prisoners and so the slightest offence brought a sentence of two hours. Then, in stages of two hours, it rose to the maximum of eight hours.

On some days as many as three or four prisoners were under punishment at the same time. Their combined shrieks and cries of agony penetrated to every corner of the camp. Sometimes Percy and his committee of senior NCOs wondered whether compliance with the German camp authorities was the right policy after all.

Frank knew that survival depended upon his ability to stay calm and exercise self-control and patience. If he panicked he might choke to death. All those years as a fisherman had served him well and he would fall into sleep when the nature of the ordeal became too much to bear. He could always tap into a rich vein of memories of pre-war fishing expeditions on the great rivers of England and Ireland.

THE ABERDARE HIGHLANDS—DIARY JULY 1906

When my 12-month contract with the East African Protectorate Police Force ends I decide to undertake an expedition to the Aberdare Highlands with Charles Rimington. He is also leaving the Protectorate's police force after his secondment—to return to work as a senior detective at Scotland Yard.

While on patrols we have seen tumbling rivers running fresh from the mountains and sense there might be exotic fishing to be had. The Aberdare Highlands lie next to a large plateau overlooking the slopes of Mt. Kenya to the east.

In the Rift Valley we feel like pioneering explorers on horseback. We take Benjamin Amin and three Askaris for protection against an unlikely encounter with hostile tribesmen. Lions are also a threat in this part of the interior.

Our party is accompanied also by six native porters who carry supplies for the fishing expedition on foot. We have left the wagon at the last settlement,

We will remain in the wilderness for three weeks before our departure for Durban from Mombasa on the first leg of our voyage back to the United Kingdom. To reach the Highlands we ascend forest tracks which remind me of the recent military expedition. It leaves me alert with feelings of trepidation about being ambushed.

The exotica of Africa's abundant wildlife should be enjoyed without having to watch out for tribesmen armed with poisonous arrows and spears. The Masai, however, are herdsmen and said to be friendly. The nearest Nandi clan, now much depleted and confined to a reserve following the uprising, is 100 miles away.

Charles records and sketches several wildlife species in his notebook. These include waterbuck, suni—a rabbit-sized antelope—several large herds of elephants, zebra, Thompson gazelles and leopard. We see no lions.

It takes several days of slow and steady progress to reach the part of the highlands where the rivers are said to be stocked with brown trout and by the time we reach our destination we are in a state of excitement about what we might find.

The terrain becomes moorland above 8,000 feet. The spectacular slopes of Mount Kenya are clearly visible.

An earlier generation of white pioneers within the Protectorate's interior somehow stocked the small clear streams with trout. I asked several people in Nairobi, but none has been able to tell me exactly how they did it, or who was responsible.

Twenty years later the rivers remain full of brown trout, few of which have ever been caught by rod and line. There is no guide to what flies are most successful. This is part of the thrill of the undertaking. The rivers run in a succession of waterfalls and deep pools, between long shallow glides slowed by boulders that hinder the progress of the current. The water is clear and peaty when in spate.

It reminds us of the upper reaches of the River Dart on Devon's moorland, but whereas British moorland trout rarely exceed ten ounces because of the presence of migratory salmon and trout, these rivers hold an abundance of fish up to twice that size.

We finally come across a river that is at least 30 yards wide in some places and fish are rising briskly in the pools and shallow runs, even though we are in the heat of the afternoon. We decide to dismount, eat and wait for the shadows to lengthen in cooler air with the approach of the early evening.

We follow the river downstream on foot. It runs through a creek ending at a waterfall which falls about 50 feet into a deep pool over 35 yards in length. This is a fisherman's paradise and we wonder whether any game angler has ever been here to witness it.

The fast-flowing pool, with its cold water from the high altitude, gradually becomes shallow enough to wade. Rocks along each bank of the river enable a dry fly fisherman of reasonable agility to clamber over them.

I can cast upstream and cover the pool right up to the waterfall itself. It fills me with deep excitement just to behold what is before my eyes. Fish are taking fly on the surface everywhere in a prolific evening rise. I have a 10 foot split cane rod which gives me the ability to cast a reasonable length, also allowing the fly to drop gently to the water in the windless conditions.

I place my hand in the water and estimate its temperature to be about 60 degrees Fahrenheit. It is slightly brown with silt following a spate. Even though my initial approach to the pool is clumsy, the trout continue to rise in several parts of it only a few feet away.

I stand on a rock at the back in shallow water and cast a black fly—on a size 14 hook—gently over a rising fish 20 feet upstream in water about four feet deep.

The fly lands without disturbance 12 inches ahead of the rising fish which rises enthusiastically, feels the prick of the hook and is so startled it leaps two feet out of the water. It continues to leap as it dashes upstream towards the sanctuary of a large boulder just below the fall.

The fish is magnificently strong and its power resists all attempts to bring it to the net for several minutes. It dashes at a terrific speed from one side of the river to the other. When I bring the trout to the net I inspect it closely.

The trout is yellowy brown with the largest red and black spots I've ever seen on a river trout. I measure it at 14 inches in length and noticed it has a strong square tail—which accounts for the strength and speed of the fish in the water. I cover the pool with a variety of dry flies for half an hour and take a further six trout—none larger than 16 inches, but all full of fight.

Charles fishes the same pool from boulders on the other side of the river but decides against using a dry fly. He fished the hatch wet, casting upstream with a bronze nymph and enjoying equal success. We hand our fish to a porter who wades in the river to fetch them. Thirty yards from the bank Benjamin and the Askaris, armed with their rifles, keep watch for lions—from high boulders overlooking the river.

The African sergeant seems to enjoy the spectacle of fish being caught and roars with laughter and approval each time one is landed. He tells me that one day he will teach his sons how to fish like the white man. He has asked me to show him how to throw the line into the water and give him the skill to be a trout fisherman.

He confides in me that perhaps he and his sons could become guides for other white men wanting to fish the Aberdare Highlands. Maybe it would be better for them to do that, he says, rather than become soldiers like their father and grandfather. Benjamin says he has had enough of killing and wants his sons to own land and live long enough to become old men.

Having exhausted the fishing in the first pool and waterfall, we move north and come across two more rivers.

At the second a waterfall descends into a deep pool that darkens as the evening descends. Many more fish are caught.

The third river is the largest and remarkably similar to the first location—but the water here is clearer and from my vantage point I can see large fish lurking on the river bed, despite the human shadows on the water. They do not seem to be spooked by the presence of men around the pool—which suggests they have never been caught before.

The evening rise on the dying spinners continues as dusk approaches. I have gone right through my fly box and the fish have risen with gusto to anything that I cast to them.

I decide to try a Big Daddy although I see no insect resembling anything like it on the three rivers. I flick it a few yards up the river in an experiment and it rides the surface without looking unnatural—with its long legs spread wide.

I cast 12 yards upstream to an eddy below a granite cliff. It appears to be deeper than anywhere else in the pool and the water runs more slowly. The fly lands and loops around, after colliding gently with the face of the cliff.

I wait with a sense of anticipation. Suddenly, from out of the depths, the shape of a fish moving incredibly quickly flashes before my eyes and explodes upon the tranquility of the water.

I feel the force and the violence of the trout's strike upon the fly from the butt of my rod which curves dramatically into a deep loop. I raise the rod gently to set the hook.

This is a much bigger trout than anything I have caught previously and it bores down 12 feet to the bed of the pool, before turning and then ascending with awesome power, launching itself three feet out of the water.

The breaking strain of the silk cast is only 3lbs and I feel constrained from placing too much reliance on such a frail oiled silk line—against the strength of a big wild fish. I pray my looping fly rod will take much of the pressure. The fish responds to every tentative draw of the line with another surging dash. I need gentle hands.

'Christ, you are a beauty. I'm damn well not going to lose you,'

I hear myself shouting. This is a great fish, a wild African trout. It fights for its life for at least 15 minutes before I bring it gingerly to the net with whoops of joy from Benjamin. I gaze down upon this specimen. It is nearly two feet in length, a darker shade of brown than anything else I have caught before, but with the same large red spots.

It has sharp teeth but its head is in proportion to its long body. This is a specimen fish. Lovingly I lift the trout from the net, extract the hook from its upper lip and return it to the pool. It is too noble to die and anyway the party has sufficient fish for food that night and probably tomorrow.

Darkness has now fallen upon the water and Benjamin orders the porters to light a large fire close to the waterfall where we will eat dinner, drink bottles of beer and smoke cigarettes well into the night under the starlit sky—before descending into sleep under a military blanket, while the Askaris keep watch for lions. I will always remember this particular day of fishing on African rivers that have no name.

28

More solitary

At the end of his second ordeal at the post he was dumped in a cell for so long that time became meaningless. He would mark the wall with a scratch every dawn and knew he had already experienced eight days of this barbaric confinement.

The highlight of each day would be his walk under guard to the kitchens to collect his rations. They allowed him half an hour to stretch his legs before collecting his food. He would then return to the darkness and spend as long as he could chew the food very slowly—dire and incomplete though it was.

His triumph of being able to turn to dreams of fishing adventures from years gone by would also help him to retain a coherent mind. Panic was probably his greatest enemy. He found some comfort in being able to hear the everyday sounds of camp life in the distance but was frustrated that the small window of the cell allowed only a minimum of daylight into the tiny room.

The smell of his sanitary bucket did not bother him. He was getting so little to eat and drink it did not become full and fetid for several days. He tried standing in the cell and despite being more than six feet tall found he was able to do so. He introduced a regime of sit-ups, star-jumps and press ups—half an hour twice a day—to keep his circulation active and to remain physically fit for as long as possible.

As his stomach shrank, so did the hunger pains. He would eventually starve to death if his confinement continued indefinitely, but in the short term he must see everything in a positive light. He allowed his hatred of Major Bach to keep his sense of anger alive.

He had drawn great strength from his earlier conversations with Doctor Ascher who had told him that historically the most compelling insights into the human condition always came from those who were tested to their limits, often in prison.

He had reminded Frank that both the Old and New Testament scriptures were filled with the legends of those whose greatness bloomed under adverse conditions. The doctor recalled specifically the stories of Joseph, Jesus, and Paul. Socrates most moving speech to his students took place, according to Plato, from the prison cave where he awaited his death. Boethius, author of The Consolation of Philosophy, wrote his classic work while he was a prisoner of the Emperor Theodora in the fifth century.

The doctor told him that those heroes shared a common bond. They were each cast into a pressure cooker of a situation in which they were compelled to plumb the depths of their existence. The old man said that at times of great challenge which happened only to a few men - the soul could undergo, if it was strong enough, what was called "hermetic transformation."

Drawn from the great literature, thought and philosophies of the Middle Ages the idea of transmutation of one's deeper self in the spiritual sense could, said the doctor, be applied to wartime captivity. Frank spent hours examining the doctor's arguments.

After exercise and food on the twenty-eighth day he was marched by the guard to the Commandant's office where Major Bach sat at his desk once again in his immaculate uniform reading his file. The prisoner remembered to salute the officer and looked ahead of him, avoiding the eyes of the Prussian.

The Major gazed upon the prisoner with utter disdain but noticed with some satisfaction his grey and grimy face—and sprouting growth of beard. His thinning black hair had grown in greasy strands over his ears and face. Frank could actually detect his own rancid body odour. It was some consolation that it must be unsettling to the major, who seemed to prefer the more congenial smell of saddle soap.

Major Bach smiled thinly:

"I'm pleased to say that you look like a piece of shit. Indeed you are a classic specimen of your race. Now, I want you to sit down and start telling me all about your adventures from August 1914 until July 1915. I will listen and take notes. Sit please."

"I'm Sergeant Frank Clarke, 7852, 1st Battalion Norfolk Regiment, wounded August 24th 1914."

He stared ahead of him, ignored the order to sit and instead looked directly at a print of Kaiser Wilhelm hanging on the wall above the Major's desk. The Prussian was incandescent with rage.

He had subjected this impertinent British NCO, this nonentity who wasn't even an officer, to sessions at the pole—which broke most men—and then he'd had him spend weeks in the hell of solitary confinement. Yet the pig was still being defiant.

He clutched his pistol in his holster and considered strongly the option of shooting the prisoner in the head for his insubordination. He restrained himself just in time because he knew that any more bad reports of his irrational behaviour reaching headquarters might involve further trouble with the General—and a transfer to active service at the front. Instead of killing the Englishman, Frank was hit hard over the head with the weapon and was knocked unconscious.

ST PATRICK'S NIGHT . . . DIARY MARCH 1908

St Patrick's Day arrives and before the big fight I take the Johnsons to the haunt of Dublin's beau monde, Jammets Restaurant in Nassau Street, which more than anywhere else—for those who can afford it—exemplifies the unique village atmosphere of Dublin. The diners are all going to the title fight at the theatre.

The hubbub of conversation in the restaurant dies away to a murmur as Jack and Sophia arrive. I show them to the table where James, Charles and Sean O'Malley are already seated.

Jammets serves the best cuisine in Ireland. The cultural and ruling elite of Dublin, often from explosively different political ideology, sit down to eat alongside one another on St Patrick's Night.

Dublin is no different to any other Edwardian city in the British Empire. Privilege and desperate poverty live cheek by jowl. A humorist says that half the population of Dublin is clothed in the cast-off clothes of the other half.

A higher proportion of children here walk in their bare feet than in any other major British city. Only the priests and radical politicians care about the poverty.

There are local celebrities at Jammets on St Patrick's Night 1908. William Butler Yeats and his partner Augusta Gregory, who have established the Abbey Theatre, sit at a table with the poets William Orpen, James Stevens and Yeats' younger brother Jack, a painter.

Hugh Lane, the wealthy art dealer and entrepreneur, sits at another table with the actress Molly Allgood. The genial Doctor Gogarty and some of his sporting friends are seated at a third.

The Countess Markiewicz presides at a fourth table with a group of men and women who include Republicans such as the pacifists Francis and Hanna Sheehy Skeffington, the painter Sean Keating and the diplomat Sir Roger Casement.

The people at this latter table are involved in a heated argument and occasionally look in contempt upon those at a fifth table. This is occupied by group of uniformed Army officers who, from their insignia, appeared to be from the 2nd Cavalry Brigade.

They include a Colonel and three Majors and seem to be relaxed and

245

unconcerned being in the company of so many Republicans.

'I think the presence of a black man with a white woman just about completes the suit at Jammets tonight,' drawls my brother James looking around him in amusement. 'I think we're sitting upon a powder keg,' he adds.

'Yeah, certain subjects are taboo tonight and Irish politics is certainly one of them,' laughs Sean O'Malley. He smiles at Johnson. 'We'll refrain from talking about Jim Crow and American politics too.'

O'Malley raises a glass: 'Here's to a Roche victory over Burns later. They tell me our champion is fighting fit and ready for a crack at the world title. What do you think Jack?' he asks, winking at the others round the table.

'You know what I think! They're both artless bums, lumbering strongmen looking for a place to land their roundhouse punches. With luck one of them will land a good punch early on, knock the other out and allow us to get back to the Red Harp for the business of some serious drinking.'

He pauses and then continues in his Texan drawl: 'As I said, you could put both of the bums in the ring together against me—and if anyone wants to raise a purse then I'll cancel my shadow boxing demonstration next week and whip both of 'em in three rounds!'

The roar of laughter this engendered attracts the attention of other diners in the room—and out of the blue a tall slim dark-haired man wearing spectacles, who is seated at the table of the Countess, stands up and begins speaking.

'As someone born in America and raised as an Irishman I'd like to toast Mr Johnson.'

The room now falls silent as the Irishman continues.

'We welcome you to this country Jack. The Irish people here tonight regard you as a representative of a race also oppressed in their own land. So here's to Negroes and to Irishmen and to their freedom!'

The diners at our table and most of the restaurant stand up to drink the toast, a few out of conviction; far more out of politeness. Charles Rimington, a Scotland Yard detective, gets up only with reluctance—much to our amusement at his obvious discomfort.

I know the Irishman proposing the toast and lean over to James to whisper in his ear.

'You know who that is?'

James shakes his head negatively.

'Remember watching me play against Blackrock College for Monkstown earlier this season?

"I'd got the ball and only had the full back to beat inside their '25. I chipped the ball over his head and he tackled me as I went past on the outside.'

'Ah yes,' replies James laughing.

'I remember that. The referee, a Blackrock man, awarded a penalty try because he was so angry at what his full-back had done. He said that gentlemen didn't do that kind of thing on the pitch. All the spectators started fighting!'

I laughed also at the memory of it. 'The full-back came up to shake hands and apologise to me after the game. He introduced himself as "Dev" and said he'd had acted on the spur of the moment and regretted it.

'Other chaps in his team said after the match he was considering ordination as a priest but has a reputation on the rugby field for being a bit of a hothead. Apparently he played for Cashel RFC in Tipperary—and more recently at Blackrock College. I played against him several times. He looks as though he didn't study for the priesthood but has become a nationalist activist instead!'

Only the Cavalry officers remain seated during the toast. They sit in silence. I sense the tension caused by the refusal of the officers to drink to the toast, but no one scolds them. The evening continues with exchanges of banter, often between the tables. The soldiers are ignored.

Several people ask Johnson for his autograph, which he provides with a broad smile and usually an anecdote about one of his fights in America in recent years—and how he always manages to upset white society.

Jack Johnson appeals to the Irish that night. Sophia could hardly take her eyes off me and occasionally we touch knees in tenderness under the table. I feel guilty and become alarmed that Jack might notice the attention she is directing towards me, but the boxer remains oblivious to the feelings of his so-called *wife. Later, he leans across and says: "They tell me you are a fisherman, is that right?"*

I reply: 'Why, would you like me to take you salmon fishing? Good.'

More than anything else Major Bach hankered after a transfer to an officer's camp instead of presiding over these human vermin at Sennelager. He bellowed for the guard to return to his office.

"Throw this pig back into solitary confinement and deprive him of food and water for 48 hours!" he screamed after summoning Frank to his office again the next morning. He ignored the bruising on his prisoner's face and walked round his desk hurriedly coming up close to Frank's face, who felt the spit from Bach's mouth as he shouted in his rage.

"After, I'll put you back on the pole until you are screaming for mercy and ready to talk! Do you understand me?"

Frank continued to look straight ahead and made no response, except to say defiantly again.

"I'm Sergeant Frank Clarke, 7852, 1st Battalion Norfolk Regiment, wounded August 24th 1914."

Major Bach's face was flushed to a purple shade and he screamed at the guards to get Frank out of his sight. He allowed himself to be frog marched out of the Commandant's office. When he got back to the cell he was shaking from his ordeal. He managed a small smile as he recalled the expression of frustrated rage upon the face of the Prussian.

Major Bach sentenced him to the pole for the third time and chose a Sunday again. This time the public were allowed to stand much closer— within spitting distance. The women were the most vicious and he felt he would have been lynched if the guards had allowed them to get their hands on him.

"Why do they hate me so much? Am I responsible for their misery? Do they think that I started this awful war? Why can't they see the truth? It is their leaders who betrayed them and now their children go hungry."

The pain in his wrists and ankles was so excruciating that he wept, but he did so quietly with his eyes closed. He just got through the third ordeal at the pole by detaching himself completely from his predicament. He absorbed the excruciating pain into his self-consciousness, preventing fear and panic from overwhelming him and staying patient. Sleep gradually possessed him.

JACK THE ANGLER—DIARY MARCH 1908

All Dubliners have a love-hate relationship with the River Liffey. The river passes close to Dublin's slums and is a dumping ground for untreated sewage and rubbish in the early 20th century. Despite pollution the Liffey somehow remains a prolific river through Edwardian times, especially in its cleaner upper reaches.

The running fish put up with the slime and the stink as they dash through spring, summer and autumn on the tide through to the cleaner reaches of the river. It is a famous game fishery for salmon and trout as well as being a magnificent haven for perch, pike and roach.

The Liffey rises in the Wicklow Mountains 12 miles south of Dublin. From its source it flows in a long crescent for over 80 miles before entering the sea at Dublin Bay. The upper river meanders through the limestone plains of County Kildare where it is full of brown trout yielding wild fish up to five lbs.

The river has thick hatches of olives including sedges, midges and some mayfly during the early summer months when it is at its best. It attracts only a relatively small number of fishermen. I fish at Ballymore Eustace, Kilcullen and Newbridge and closer to Dublin, between Celbridge and Straffan.

I take Jack to Ryans, one of the city's tackle shops. The American is equipped with clothes for a chilly fishing expedition; waterproofs, thick Shetland pullovers, corduroy trousers, waders, two expensive split cane river rods, one for trout and one for salmon, fly-reels and lines and a box of flies.

I tell him: "We'll take a trip to Memorial Park on Saturday morning and then we'll fish to Leixlip Bridge to its confluence with the Rye Water. Both are good stretches for salmon and the early fish are already running.

'Most Liffey salmon are taken on spinner or worms and we'll try to get you a first salmon using that method to break you in. It means you won't be requiring your expensive salmon rod to start with—but I have a sturdy 12 foot Greenheart for you to use.'

Two days later we arrive in the Dion Bouton in the picturesque village of Leixlip. A mediaeval castle, it has a conical tower flanked by two smaller towers, standing sentinel on a rock overlooking the great river.

I tell him: 'You'll have your own ghillie, Padraig Quinlan, who once fancied himself as a heavyweight. He's a policeman and he knows more about how to catch salmon in the Liffey than any other man.'

We park the yellow automobile outside the police house in the main street. It stood alongside several tea rooms that catered for Dubliners enjoying the fresh air outside the city at weekends. Padraig Quinlan comes out of the house carrying a small jute sack of worms and a walking stick.

He is dressed like a game-keeper. Padraig is a tree trunk of a man, like most old fashioned policemen of the era. The art of being an officer of the law is to look intimidating to any potential law breaker. He stands well over six feet and has a long black beard. His ice blue eyes and swarthy complexion make him look fearsome, but these conceal a wicked sense of humour—which is manifested immediately as he offers his hand to Johnson.

'Now don't you upset me you great black bastard or I'll leave you hand-cuffed to the fence of St Michael's Church!'

Johnson laughs his loud laugh and a grinning Quinlan pats him affectionately on the back. The men are instant friends and the policeman sits in the front of the Dion Bouton as they drive upriver to Islandbridge.

On the journey Quinlan explains to Johnson that salmon flies are heavier than trout flies and have doubles or treble hooks. The choice of where in the river to fish is critical to success. The angler, he explains, has to cover places where salmon prefer to rest. He should make for the deep runs where they might be lying.

He said that salmon fishermen use a floating silk line, or a sink-tip line. The fly, or lure, unlike dry fly fishing for trout, is designed to imitate a small fish rather than an insect, so it is important to get the lure down in the strong current while it was still at the head of the pool.

To get the fly down in spring conditions on the Liffey, when plenty of water is running through, Quinlan advises using a fast-sinking braided silk leader on an oiled floating line. He recommends a 16lb breaking strain silk gut leader. We reach Islandbridge and I bait up the tackle on my 12 foot Greenheart rod before handing it to Jack.

'I told him we'd start him off with a worm to try to get him a fish quickly—to warm himself up and be off to a flying start,' I say

'I suspect he's an impatient man!'

'Yeah, that's a good idea,' says Padraig Quinlan, adding upon reflection: 'These Americans are so dumb it would take me an hour to show him how to swing a fly rod. I can soon teach him how to cast a worm.'

Johnson roars with laughter. 'We ain't so dumb as you think,' he says.

Less than 100 yards below Islandbridge, the river curves to the right and there is a deep pool where the swirling waters slacken below a group of rocks. Johnson shows remarkable ability in handling the reel and rod with its very light ledger tackle and from the bank he drops the bait deftly into the head of the pool in the middle of the river, where the depth approaches eight feet.

"Let it go down the river with the current, but don't hold it up, or the bait will look unnatural," orders Padraig. 'Give line, walk slowly down the bank after the bait, but don't stand on top of it. The water's still quite clear and you'll spook the fish.'

Johnson asks: 'If I feel a knock what shall I do?'

Padraig says: 'Well to start with don't imagine it's Tommy Burns on the other end. Let him take the bait and start moving off and then lift the rod firmly but gently away from him. Be ready to give line because believe me he'll take off like a racehorse!'

The routine up and down the long run continues for another 20 minutes and Johnson is beginning to lose patience. 'I could have whipped six bums' arses by this time,' he complains loudly. At that moment he gets the knock.

He screams: "Yippee! Hey man!"

The American does not over-react to the taking fish and displays the patience necessary to avoid losing the salmon in the opening seconds. The fish rushes off downstream to the end of the pool, but instead of continuing to fly down the river into shallow water it turns and headed back into the pool, seeking sanctuary in its depths.

'That's good. Get yourself downstream of the fish if you can

251

because that will put more pressure on him in the current,' shouts Padraig.

"Am I doing this right?" screams Johnson.

"Yes, you are handling it well, keep it in check, give it line when it wants it and stop it from leaping or splashing wildly on the surface,' continues the policeman. I am astonished at the calm dexterity of the boxer who shows all the skills it usually takes a fisherman many years to acquire.

He gives line and then retrieves it again as the salmon begins to tire. He is patient and does not try to rush the fish which is brought ashore after 15 minutes and weighs 8lbs. It is a fresh run fish and in magnificent condition.

'I think you'll be able to swap that for a few bottles of champagne back at the Gresham Hotel,' I tell Johnson.

'I can tell both you guys that catching this fish has given me more pleasure than anything else since I left California,' laughs the American.

'Well, you ain't seen nothing yet you black bastard,' laughs Padraig Quinlan.

'Now we're going to christen that fly-rod of yours and show you how to catch one properly—on the fly! Let's get up to my home village of Leixlip. I know just the place where you'll catch one.'

We drive to Leixlip and the policeman puts the boxer on a large pool which runs through a meadow outside St Michael's Church. It is a pool that has been legendary for hundreds of years—because it is where the Rye Water converges with the Liffey. There are no trees to obscure the back cast, no tall weeds for the line to fall away onto, or rocks for Johnson to wrap his line around on the forward thrust.

In March the pool is full of running salmon. In such a stretch of river in England a fisherman might wait to take his turn, or put up with crowds of onlookers, but even in this relatively well populated corner of Ireland the banks of the Liffey are deserted.

The Negro stands in the river wearing waders next to the familiar figure of the policeman while I watch from the bank. In half an hour Johnson learns how to cast the fly 30 yards with a two-handed 20 foot rod. The boxer has height, soft hands, precise timing and mighty power in his right wrist that causes the line to surge through the rings on the rod, ensuring a long and clean cast into the head of the pool.

The bushy yellow fly drops into the water with the minimum of disturbance. Padraig Quinlan is greatly impressed but has no intention of flattering the American.

'Remember, on the cast the fly is going to go in the direction your nose is pointing. You've got to stay in touch with the fly and stop the line dragging it downstream, because no small fish would move in such an unnatural manner with rapid accelerations. So you must keep 'mending' the line.

'Get into a rhythm and never rush things. It's like boxing—you should stay contained within yourself and be patient. Don't get excited!'

'It ain't easy man, my heart's racing and I'm sweating like a racehorse,' laughs Johnson.

'OK. Now lift the rod firmly and flip the line so that the downstream belly created by the action of the current becomes an upstream belly. Yes, that's it, you've got it. By doing that action, you can fish for the most part with a fairly straight line, and stay in direct connection to the fly by pointing your rod at it and keeping it low.

'Now, you've reached the tail of the pool, lift your rod slowly and let the bait rise to near the surface of the water. An irritated salmon might be following it.

'If you think you've connected with a salmon let the fish take line and then tighten into the fish and don't be too shy with it. In slow water like this pool the visual senses are more important than feeling your line. I have seen salmon take a fly and spit it out while the angler had no clue that it had taken his fly because he wasn't watching what was going on in the water.

'Man, I'm finding all this really confusing.'

'OK—just remember to stay in touch with your fly, keep a straight line and point your rod at the fly, keep your rod low, almost on the water to eliminate the bow that forms in the line when the rod is held high. Always look at where your fly is, if you can see it, or where you believe it should be.

'If you cannot see your fly in the water then make sure you use your peripheral vision. Concentrate and be sensitive to the smallest movement in the water or the line—there's a whole world happening under the surface of the water.'

Johnson continues to fish the pool for half an hour but catches nothing. He is becoming impatient and he hands the rod over to Padraig who, with the minimum of effort, covers with his first cast nearly twice as much water as Johnson had managed.

The fly lands in quite shallow water—and with a swirl is gathered into the depths. He hits a salmon immediately. It leaps out of the water and thrashes around the pool. Johnson might be forgiven for being mad. He has probably been teasing the same fish for several minutes and might well have caught it.

He is certainly frustrated, but genuinely admires the greater skill of the Irishman. He puts back his head and roars with laughter.

"I reckon I could 'whup' you in the ring too," cracks Quinlan as he brings the 10lb fish ashore into a large landing net. Johnson fishes on in two other upstream pools at Leixlip but it is not to be his day. He has to be content with a fish caught on the worm. He tells us that afternoon is the high point so far of his visit to Europe.

Certainly the fight between Tommy Burns and Jem Roche isn't the high point of Jack Johnson's visit to Ireland. It turns out to be the shortest heavyweight title fight in history and thousands of Dubliners who turn up at the Theatre Royal feel they've been cheated. Some demand their money back.

It is all over in one minute 28 seconds and Roche doesn't even land a good punch. Burns hit him with a left and then with his right—and the Irish champion goes down like a sack of potatoes.

Jack had been right—we were back in the Red Harp by 10pm. In fact, Jack has a mischievous grin on his face for most of the night and announces he is already the de facto heavyweight champion of the world.

The Johnsons depart for France early in April after a succession of parties and wild nights of drinking which never include Sophia. I spend as much time with her as I can in her hotel room during the day without arousing Jack's suspicion.

Sometimes I wonder whether the American knows about our

illicit relationship but just doesn't care as long as it remains a secret. We make love once more in the hotel room when Johnson is taken to the Curragh by his friends from the Red Harp, but our relationship becomes more anchored in genuine friendship than in lust. I become her mentor and advise her to leave Jack before he sails for Australia. She says she will.

I feel miserable and guilty for weeks after Sophia has gone because I wonder whether I should have eloped with her to somewhere in Europe to free her from a life she loathes. I do not think Jack would have pursued her—he had other things on his agenda.

I treasure the memory of the sensation she caused when she moved briefly in our circle. Her life is a tragic one. She is really just a simple Italian girl caught up in events entirely beyond her control and she deserves better than to live in such violent circumstances. I wonder what will happen to her.

SANITY SLIPS AWAY—DIARY JANUARY 1916

Gradually my sanity is slipping away. I cannot think in a rational manner. This has kept me strong earlier in my confinement. Now the darkness is beginning to terrify me, to confuse me and worst of all the restraint of the four walls has at last become so overbearing that I feel I cannot cope with it.

The acute problem is in knowing that I cannot under any circumstance leave the tiny space and walk out. It causes an almost hysterical panic that eats away at my mind—panic attacks come in surges without warning and I notice my body twitches in a manner entirely detached from my own self control.

I am covered in sweat—yet the temperature is hardly above freezing. This must be an ominous sign because it means that my body is no longer responding obediently to the remaining logic in my prevailing thoughts. It is going its own way, perhaps sensing and forecasting the bigger picture that foretells my eventual descent into madness.

A voice within is telling me to let go, to stop resisting and allow myself to be totally subjugated by the regime of the psychotic Major Bach. The cell walls in the gloom begin to waver and move towards me, they are becoming my ultimate jailer threatening to squeeze me into a straightjacket.

I cry out as tears stream down my face: "God if you are there save me from this hell."

I am frightened by these attacks—by the cell walls—because when they come I find I cannot move, yet they move inexorably towards me. I cannot breathe when I feel their inward march to compress me.

The walls are living creatures, malevolent and ugly beasts that mock me and take satisfaction from my gradual surrender and surging fear.

The only sanctuary is sleep and I know I will retain my sanity only if my dreams remain sweet. Once they become the ugly demons of nightmares or relentlessly recurring tiresome thoughts suffered by those in fever I will soon become a lost soul incapable of resistance.

I must not lose this battle against Major Bach and I must

manage gradually to arrest this descent into insanity. I must keep bringing through my feelings of hatred for the German officer.

"You fucking bastard, you fucking bastard," I call out time and again in the darkness of the cell. I still have a coherent mind and imagine how triumphantly the Prussian will react if I allow myself to be dragged into his presence a broken man, a nonentity pleading for mercy and release. Whatever happens, I know I must not compromise any of those heroic men and women who put the well being of others before that of their own in the Edith Cavell network.

I decide I have reached a stage when I need something more than thoughts. I need the strength that can only be provided by having access somehow to the greater knowledge and wisdom of educated men who have also endured similar predicaments to those of my own.

I wish I had paid more attention in my earlier life to education and reading books. In my cell I continue to day-dream of the past and find I am taking myself further back into time.

Yes, I think a lot of Emily, of Dublin and Norfolk and of fishing adventures, but I am beginning to get snapshots from my childhood. Curiously Emily appears in these with me and becomes a playmate in my adolescent world.

Physically, I remain reasonably strong despite the appalling diet, but my bodyweight is in serious freefall and I know it is only a matter of time before my debilitation will have serious consequences.

I begin to make the acquaintance of other prisoners in solitary confinement. We are able to talk to one another despite efforts by the guards to stop us. We knock on the walls of the cell and soon find ourself communicating with those suffering a similar horror. I have a conversation with an Australian private called Mick O'Connor who is in solitary for the fifth time in just a few months. We meet to exchange a few words when we empty our toilet bucket in the yard.

Mick is huge both physically and in temperament, with dark eyes and greasy black hair that covers his ears in an unmilitary fashion. He is regarded by the Germans—to Mick's great amusement—as a wild and violent man who is dangerous and unstable.

Mick tells me proudly that he is a serial thief—he is in the slammer not for stealing from his comrades but for helping himself to vegetables and the fruits of the countryside while on working parties, often under the nose of the guards. He comes from Sydney and was in a machine gun section in a New South Wales infantry battalion before being captured. He is two or three inches taller than me, of massive build, with huge hands and fingers like bananas.

Mick tells me he worked on sheep farms in the outback of New South Wales. We agree to meet up in the camp when both of us are released.

I have come to the conclusion early in the confinement that I will need a ritual to follow and stick to rigidly each day. If I want to be able to measure time without losing my mind and avoid becoming an animal, ritual will be the single feature beyond the ability of my captors to deny me.

I work out that this ritual will need to be built around dreams of fishing adventures, intense concentration, prayer, exercise, clandestine communication with the cell next door and imaginary conversations with Emily in which I must learn to speak aloud.

I have never been a regular churchgoer but the prayers I say, during these days of solitary confinement, must be prayers of quality presenting ideas of substance passed on to me by the old doctor. I remember Descartes and how in his philosophy he separates mind and body. I find the body decays the mind with its desires and functions and these are capable of eroding established sets of principles. Body and mind are inseparable and I understand I am in physical decline and might not be able to fight the system forever.

One of the more positive aspects of ritual in confinement is the discovery of vast mental resources within the human brain and mind for storing new information and producing through sheer concentration from its recesses, memories that have been long forgotten.

I learn to draw the past out of hidden consciousness with remarkable recall by easing slowly toward the event I seek and not crowding the mind too readily. My mind goes back to the house in Islington where I grew up in a large family and the dominating figures of my father Henry and grand father George. I recalls going with the older man to the Caledonian Market where his livestock had been driven from Liverpool Street Station.

Memories also take me back to the vast market at Norwich and my cousins selling their cattle on Saturday mornings. I recall the overpowering stench of horseshit, a smell that also pervades the whole of London and every other city and town in Britain. I try to remember certain events like birthday parties, who got invited, what was on the table to eat and what games were played. It is possible to get there after days of concentrated effort; to break the locks on the filing cabinets of memory and open the drawer. Time and solitude are required.

A lot of this stuff is futile, bloody stupid and pointless, but when I get there, when I remember things I didn't even know I'd forgotten, it doesn't half make me feel good—they are little victories that make me feel strong for days.

The jubilation energises the human spirit and the will to resist is strengthened. I am becoming insane but for the moment I understand that. I recall the adventures I enjoyed as a young man when I was free to roam the countryside. One day I wander back further to unlock from my memory my first ever angling experience on a river with my grandfather George Printer.

My recall has not visited this day for more than twenty-five years and it astounds me how I am able to piece it all together again like a jigsaw puzzle. I will write it down in the diary sometime in the dim light of the cell.

MY SIXTH BIRTHDAY—DIARY FEBRUARY 1916

It is my sixth birthday. There is a party and I remember a girl with auburn curls that fall below her shoulders—she is wearing a white fairy dress, a silver paper tiara and silver dancing shoes. I ask her to marry me as we sit at the table sharing sponge cake covered in icing sugar. She agrees of course because it is love at first sight. Her name is Emily.

I am wearing a sailor suit that my mother Anna has given to me and which Victorian children wear on special occasions in the 1880s. Then I see the tall dark bearded figure of grandfather walk into the room carrying something under his arm wrapped in a linen cloth.

"Happy birthday Frank my dear old boy. This is my present for you but we'll wait till the party is over before you open it because I have a few things to say." My mother and father stand by his side beaming.

"You shouldn't have been so generous George—I'm not sure that the lad will appreciate such a thing at his young age," says Henry Jocelyn Clarke whose full shock of red hair seems to light up the room.

For over a year George has read fishing stories to me most nights before falling asleep, to dream about the days in the future when I will be a master angler myself. I know the gift is a fishing rod with a reel attached and wonder whether it is one of the beautifully varnished cane rods with a cork base and brass rings for the reel that grandfather showed me in the window of the shop in the Burlington Arcade.

Later we go into the study of our house in Islington and I open the linen holder. It is the rod I had hoped the old man would give me—together with a small varnished wooden reel onto which a silk line has been coiled.

George also gives me some quill floats and shot and hooks from his own collection—and a bait tin for worms or grubs. Then father comes into the study and presents me with a small wicker creel with shoulder straps which has also been fashioned into a box seat. In those few moments on my birthday in 1889 I become an angler and I hug both adults in joy.

George says: "This is the start of a lifetime's journey Frank. You'll learn to think in the ways of the master angler. First you must start learning about nature, the cycles of the season, the creatures that inhabit rivers and streams, and their place in the food chain.

"You must get to know the habits and peculiarities of the fish species that inhabit the rivers. Then you must learn the inner qualities of the master angler—patience, introspection, determination, ingenuity and self-belief. One further piece of advice—in all your lifetime never stop reading about the art of angling, there is always something to learn from others, especially old men like me."

Father adds: "Grandfather will take you to Norfolk when the season opens in June to fish in the small rivers around the county, but first you are going to have to learn to swim. As soon as the weather is clement, I shall take you to the ponds on Hampstead Heath where you can master that without fear. We don't want to lose you through drowning old boy—believe me, rivers can be dangerous places.

"For now, you will only be allowed to go fishing with your grandfather or older cousins, but by the time you are eight we will allow you to venture out unaccompanied provided you are by then a proficient swimmer."

During the third week of June that year on a humid overcast morning that threatens rain, grandfather takes me in a trap laden with fishing tackle and picnic food—after a train journey to Norwich from North Walsham—to a tributary of the River Waveney.

It is a famous fishery which forms the border between Suffolk and Norfolk for much of its length within the Broads and flows to the East and the coast through Diss, meandering on to many haunts such as the famous Bungay Cherry Tree's water below the weir at Wainford Maltings.

This is George Printer's eventual destination as he steers the trap through the country lanes before halting at a tiny tributary of the great river—which many would have judged to be hardly larger than a ditch.

"We'll have a go for some roach and dace here in this tiny stream old chap and if we can't catch them in this brook then we will still have time to move on to other spots I know. I think this will serve us well though," he said, pointing to the stream which is largely free of weed and less than three feet deep. He knows it holds roach, dace, gudgeon, and minnow.

"Just as the dog is man's best friend and his faithful companion, so the roach is the angler's constant and reliable companion, living his life modestly in even the tiniest waterway.

"I guarantee that in your life Frank the roach will continue to give you as much pleasure in the catching as any other fish.

"Rutilus rutilus is a species of carp but he is silver with large scales, a deep body and forward facing mouth, red eyes and reddish pectoral, pelvic and anal fins. He spawns in shallow areas in the spring—like in this small tributary—and the tiny eggs are sticky, clinging to mosses or other submerged vegetation.

"The hatch of fry each year varies widely, particularly in rivers and this can result in marked variations in the adult population. That's not necessarily a bad thing because too many small fish in a stretch of river can lead to a stunted population . . . so nature has her way of maintaining the balance in the interests of the angler.

"The roach is a long-lived fish—some survive for up to 20 years. Smaller roach feed on zooplankton and other small invertebrates and the larger fish typically feed on larger invertebrates and filamentous algae. In Norfolk and elsewhere they have been known to gorge themselves on spilt barley so there are all sorts of possibilities on the subject of baits for our friend the roach, which beg experimentation.

"They are a shoaling fish, living contentedly even in mediocre water quality—and so they have always headed the angler's list as a popular target for coarse fishers. Nearly all are returned alive to the water and I should not like to think that you would deliberately kill one Frank.

"Poor men, who have no other choice, must eat them and I do not discriminate against poor men as anglers, but the roach, although edible, should not be a popular food on the table of a gentleman."

I have heard all this before on the dark evenings in Islington when grandfather reads to me about angling. I am only six but feel I know enough about the roach to catch them.

I peer downstream to see if I can see any shoaling in groups close to the surface of the stream. I look hard and eventually train my eyes to see them. There seem to be some fish—all around six or seven inches long—and they do not remain motionless in the slow current but moved across the flow from one side of the stream to the other on patrol for food.

While grandfather talks I assemble the rod and reel and draw the silk line through the rings. I do not need to be shown how to fix the float, tie on the tiny No 16 hook with a loop-to-loop knot and affix two small shot to the line.

"No need to fish too deep in these light waters. Our friend the roach has sharp eyesight and a keen sense of vibration created from human footfall. He will see the grub floating downstream several feet ahead of him. We should not approach him any closer than 20 feet so we'll crouch down behind this bush to stay out of sight."

I have practiced casting endlessly in my bedroom for three months and even from the squatting position am skilful in using the six foot miniature rod, which is at least foot and a half longer than me. George is impressed by my dexterity and the unhurried rhythmic way in which I cast the rod and line slightly downstream—and to the far bank. He watches with interest as I give line, but not too much, so there is no interference with the downstream progress of the float.

I feel the excitement rising within me as I guess when the grub has reached the place where I have seen fish. The float suddenly dips and seems to dive below the surface in a crazy manner so I can no longer see it. It must be a huge fish I think to myself and lift the rod in a gentle strike. Instead of a thumping response I feel only the slightest resistance—a barely perceptible tapping. I reel in the line and pull out a tiny minnow.

"Oh no, Grandpa, it's a minnow and I was hoping my first fish would be a good roach," I laugh.

George Printer laughs too. "We'll throw in some grubs and bread to bait up the swim which will get our roach shoaling in bigger numbers. Then they'll chase off the minnows so you won't have to bother about them. Just stop fishing for a few moments and let me do that."

In the next 20 minutes after grandfather has baited the swim thoroughly I catch several small roach—and a larger one that is almost eight inches long. I bring each fish carefully to the bank and my grandfather shows me how to remove the tiny hook without harming the creature.

"OK old boy you've done your schooling on this small brook. Now, after our picnic, we'll move on to the big river to see if we can't find you a good roach of a 1b or more to give you a really smashing thrill."

Over our picnic lunch the old man explains that some anglers of his generation in Norfolk prefer to spend their time on small rivers not much bigger than the one before us. They are lightly fished because few bother to venture to them—yet if an angler got to know a river really well—then over time he would be able to select largely undisturbed places that would yield large fish of many species.

"In wet autumn conditions I have taken bream and chub from this little brook up to 20 ounces, and even the odd trout in one really wet September. Yet most anglers in these parts, because of the fantastic fishing on the Broads, want to catch either big bags of roach, bream and tench—or one-off specimens for the glass case.

"Of course, it's important to be able to do that but for my money exploring a small brook looking for holes where a big fish in a small pool might lie in wait is adventure indeed—and it is on streams like this that you will learn more about nature and the cycles of the season old chap because things are more visible.

"OK old boy you've done your schooling on this small brook. Now, after our picnic, we'll all move on to Bungay to the big river to see if we can't find you a good roach of a 1b or more to give you a really smashing thrill."

Emily joins us and tells us she and her brother Pete have fished the mighty Shenandoah River from their canoe and caught fish to cook on a camp fire. An hour later, we are sipping ginger beer on a seat outside the Cherry Trees in Bungay—while grandfather talks with other anglers inside and enjoys a mug of ale.

We join a group of local lads playing cricket in the sun on the dusty surface of the main street, using a soft ball and ancient bat—but I long to get back to fishing.

"What is cricket?" Emily asks in a bewildered tone but within ten minutes of playing in the street is capable of smashing the ball to the other side of the street.

Eventually George emerges from the bar and calls us over to the trap. Soon we are on our way to the common and my first excursion to a big river. We come to a bridge, tie the pony to a post and venture down the slope to the banks of the river. I am surprised how clear it is. George has had this swim baited in the previous few days by the local bait supplier.

"First let me prepare the swim and see if we can get the shoal feeding in the heat of the afternoon. While I'm doing that, tie a couple of grubs onto your hook and set the float at six feet which means the grub will trot down near to but above the river bed. Then we'll cast into the swim under the bridge where the current runs slowest."

It was a thrill and experience I will never forget. In 20 casts we two children pick up six fish all around the 16 ounce mark and are whooping with delight.

For the first time in my life I feel the contact through the rod with the thumping resistance of a roach as it fights courageously to escape capture.

We learn quickly, without losing our quarry, not to rush—and let the fish have its head in the dash to the depths. The disturbance in the swim caused by several of the dashing fish eventually puts the shoal off the feed. It is time to move on.

29

THE KINDLY DOCTOR

Dr Ascher called to see him at the prison. He had bribed the guard and in doing so risked severe punishment from Major Bach, who was not in the camp but visiting his superiors in Berlin. They sat down in one of the rooms reserved for the guards and Frank took off his shirt so that his wound could be examined. The doctor brought with him a razor and soap and told the guard to give them a pale of water. He felt deeply touched that the old doctor should think of him and take such risks on his behalf.

After giving him an examination, and helping him to shave, the doctor said: "I cannot stay to talk with you for long but I wanted to say that I have been worried for you. They have punished you too severely. I am being sent on a short term transfer to another camp tomorrow to replace a doctor who is ill and so there is nothing I can do now to intervene to get you an early release out of this camp, except to say that the military authorities are going to get a full report from me about what Major Bach has been doing here.

"He has made Sennelager a living hell for both his own staff and for the prison population—and even if it costs me my career I am going to try to do something about it."

He handed him a book: "I think your body is still reasonably strong but your mind might be at risk and so try to conceal this book from the guards. Although the light is dim in your cell make sure you read it over and again because I believe a chap of your intelligence will draw strength from it. It's a book of military ethics but its ideas date back two thousand years."

The old man added: "When I return to Sennelager we will find an opportunity to discuss it—and having this book will also give you something to remember me by and help you to understand that not all Germans are evil. Try to remember the miseries being inflicted by upon the civilian population and understand the reasons for their anger."

He took the book to his cell and started to read it straight away. He had never heard of it before. It was titled Enchiridion and based on the work of the philosopher Epictetus, who had been the son of a slave and who lived shortly after the time of Christ. It was a "manual" for the Roman field soldier. At first, when he began to read its dry and high-brow text, he thought he would neither understand it nor be capable of reading it.

"Does the old doctor really think I'm going to draw lessons for my life from this thing?" he asked himself after reading the first dozen pages.

"I'm a regular soldier, a non commissioned offer, not highly educated. I know how to get people to follow my orders but I am not a scholar.

"I do not question the intellectual rationale behind an order. I am taught to obey them. My self discipline comes from the code of military training and ethics.

"I am a sportsman, a fisherman and I know what I want from life . . . just to get the hell out of here. I am deeply wounded physically and emotionally now that I am parted from Emily. I ache for her touch and her voice and the feminine scent on her skin. And what does he hand me? A book with bullshit such as- 'It's better to die in hunger, exempt from guilt and fear, than to live in affluence and with perturbation.' Affluence-for God's sake I'm living in a cell not much more than six feet square!"

During the early weeks he read Enchiridion in a state of continuing irritation. Its essence made him feel uncomfortable as it countered his spirit of hatred and resentment against the Germans and captivity. He forced himself to read it several times and gradually a new light began to dawn in his comprehension.

The book was the key for him to enter the world of true wisdom inhabited by the old Roman Epictetus, who had risen to greatness from being the son of a slave.

He became aware that the world of Epictetus was one that few prisoners, whether they knew it or not, were never far away from. He would pick out key phrases and repeat them over and over again until he was indoctrinated by the ideas.

He came to understand that these thoughts served to underline what he had come to feel and understand about his own captivity in early spells of solitary confinement.

'Men are disturbed not by things, but by the view that they take of them.'

'Do not be concerned with things which are beyond your power.'

'Demand not that events should happen as you wish, but wish them to happen as they do happen and you will go on well.'

He discovered that this was the essence of the philosophy of stoicism, and he gradually came to accept it in his confinement as the best way to fight depression, alongside ritual. It was not the last word, but it was a debatable viewpoint that was appropriate for many circumstances that were beyond his control.

'Lameness is an impediment to the body but not to the will.'

That was significant for him because he was troubled with debilitating pains which shot like electric currents from the wound and affected his mobility. Other statements of Epictetus took on added meaning in the face of the bullying attitude of the guards. So much of what they said was implied threat with implications of physical violence. He had to cope with the humiliation of being made to feel weak and cowardly, because there was no tangible way he could resist against men with loaded rifles.

What he could do was feel detached and a superior being in every respect. Accordingly, the best defence of course was to keep his conscience clean.

He must keep his honour and self-respect intact, even if it came to something as trifling as not accepting the offer of a cigarette.

If he didn't lose his integrity he couldn't be possessed by the enemy-and thus he couldn't be hurt. Time and again he returned to the notion that everything came down to retaining his profound sense of patience and he thanked God that he had been introduced to fishing by his grandfather all those years ago.

Patience could not insulate him, however, from the sudden unexpected turn of events that were borne with malevolence—such as products of the evil and twisted mind of Major Bach. One morning he was dragged from his cell and frog-marched to the commandant's office, where his adversary was seated at his desk holding a white order sheet. The major looked at his prisoner with both anger and contempt.

"I have in front of me a notice from my superiors in Berlin who have considered your case carefully. They have taken into consideration that you were at liberty behind enemy lines for a period of 10 months in which time you were treated medically and provided with sustenance by unknown enemy agents.

"Your refusal to provide the military authorities with any information about these agents has been taken to mean that you are in possession of secret information. Furthermore when you were captured you were wearing civilian clothes, you were in possession of Belgian and German money and maps of the border area between occupied territory and Holland.

"You have been found guilty of espionage by the military authorities and consequently will be executed by firing squad here at Sennelager. The sentence will be carried out at 0700 hours tomorrow morning." He paused.

"Guards, get this English scum out of my office!"

He'd been awake since well before dawn. The guard opened the door of the cell at what he guessed was about 6am and brought with him a plate on a tray which contained two thick chunks of black bread, a piece of German sausage and two spoonfuls of sauerkraut. There was also a steaming mug of coffee which had milk and sugar in it. He had not tasted anything like it for many months.

The guard said nothing and departed. He guessed he had an hour to live and sat with his back resting on a cell wall slowly digesting his food and deciding how he should spend his remaining minutes of human existence. He missed his diary and the ritual of filling it in. There was a feeling in his stomach that felt like it was weighed down by a large stone, but no signs of approaching panic or self pity. He did feel angry that he'd never be able to get his revenge on Bach. The Prussian would go on living and he wouldn't.

He still felt strangely detached, as if the death sentence had not been pronounced upon him, but another person called Frank Clarke. He had been brought up to be a Christian and had sufficient faith to believe in the hereafter.

He'd been shot before and clung to the belief there was insufficient time for the body to react to the entry of several simultaneous bullets by feeling pain.

There would be no pain, not even the sound of the rifles being fired—all he would hear would be a command from the captain of the guard and then there would be darkness.

It began to be obvious to all the prisoners in the British camp that the Germans were making as much of a drama as they could about the execution of the sergeant from the Norfolks. The sense of tension was palpable and some of the men in the cells began banging on their door with their spoon, beating a rhythm. Past experience had shown that agitated prisoners would soon upset German guards, who did not understand how to cope with expressions of individuality.

"Thanks for the send-off chaps," he roared.

There was a loud cheer from within the cell block that must have been heard all over the British compound. It continued for several minutes and gradually spilled out of the prison block and into the three compounds. They came for him during the morning. He was ordered out of his cell and marched between four guards to the inner courtyard of the prison block. His hands were tied and his eyes blindfolded.

He still felt detached, although a deep sense of fear manifested itself in his lower stomach. The lack of bowel control worried him. If he shit himself now he would have failed to die like a man. His legs were shaking, but he managed to conceal this from his captors, determined not to give them the satisfaction of seeing him terrified by his predicament. He accepted he was going to die and wanted the moment to come soon. He was ready.

He heard Major Bach's voice. The bastard wanted the satisfaction of seeing him slaughtered. Bach ordered him lined up against the wall facing the firing squad of eight soldiers.

"That pig does not deserve to live for another minute," he shouted.

The captain of the guard screamed out his order: "Take aim!"

He new the command to fire would be the last thing he would hear on earth. There would then be darkness and silence. It seemed like 10 seconds between the order to take aim and the order to fire, whereas it was just a second. A fusillade of shots rang out.

He did not understand why he had heard them. He felt no pain, he remained standing and then he heard the sound of laughter. It was the sound of a man beside himself, uncontrollably amused, so that he might fall over. He recognized the laughter and at last understood the truth. The bastard had stitched him up.

Major Bach had thought of yet another triumphal way to find amusement in torturing Frank—the mock execution which he had conjured in the past, but never before at Sennelager, nearly always had the victim at least pissing in his trousers.

It was also seen as great entertainment by the guards. This English pig, however, just stood there in his blindfold, standing to attention but not too rigidly and almost detached from the whole circus, except to repeat what Bach had heard so many times.

"Sgt Frank Clarke, 7852 1st Battalion the Norfolk Regiment. Good morning."

He could not see what happened next, but he felt the tension in the air. Major Bach's face went crimson with rage. He pulled his pistol out of his holster and raised it slowly towards the prisoner's head. The barrel remained pointing at him for at least 10 seconds before the Prussian lowered it.

"Get the pig back into the cells. Tomorrow if he doesn't talk he will face his real execution—that I can promise him," shouted Bach. He was still in his blindfold but could not avoid grinning in the direction of the German. It cost him a crack across his face with the Major's riding whip but he decided it was worth it. Once back in his cell it took several hours for the effects of the adrenalin rush to subside but he gradually fell into a deep sleep.

LOUGH CARRIB—DIARY JUNE 1913

The angler rises with the sun and therefore has frequent opportunities of beholding the various beautiful phenomena which attend the advent of that glorious orb; he hastens with buoyant spirits to his favourite stream, wending his way through flowery meadows or to some lone mountain glen, where the congregated waters of the hills find a devious passage through rocks and woods to the calm bosom of the expansive lake.

T. C. Hofland Esq

The Art of Angling 1839

I have always been passionately fond of Munster but the closest to heaven I ever ventured in my life is the west of Ireland and my fishing expeditions there. Lough Corrib in Galway is the largest loch in the country covering over 100 miles of water. I frequently visit the western shores of Lough Corrib near the village of Oughterard in Connemara.

I am taking a few days off in late June 1913 to celebrate my promotion to Sergeant, and trying my hand at trolling for trout on Lough Corrib. Since being here I have witnessed a mayfly hatch and been astonished at the vast numbers of these insects which literally create a cloud over the water which is so thick you cannot see through it.

The conditions today are flat and windless and I have taken up the offer from a tall dark-haired young ghillie called Desmond Keaney for a day's trolling after Ferox trout. The young Irishman shows considerable strength in rowing the skiff along the edges of the shore but does so unobtrusively, leaving no ripples in the water from the blades and little wake behind him. I am very impressed with the ghillie's enthusiasm and knowledge.

'Purists look contemptuously at trolling Frank, but it's a fine way to fish for specimens when nothing else is going to work," he tells me as he mounts a dead six inch parr onto a two x treble mount and what he regarded as the correct amount of weight to fish at a constant depth of 30 feet below the surface of the Lough.

'What's the biggest trout you ever caught Frank?'

'I should say it was a wild fish of just over 6lbs from the Kells Blackwater in the Boyne Valley—spinning with a spoon on high spate water.'

'Jesus that's a good fish for the Boyne Valley Frank—but I'd place a bet you'll exceed it today, these conditions are perfect," laughs young Des.

I have brought a 10-foot spinning rod and a large wooden star-back reel—it is all I have at the time—with a 15 lb breaking strain silk line.

Des tells me to let out 80 yards of line while he continues rowing with an accomplished rhythm—sometimes building up pace and then "freewheeling" on the glass surface of the Lough.

After half an hour of trolling south along the shoreline where Des knows there is a deep channel, the rod in my hand arches down and I know I am into a powerful fish. The tackle is strong and in my experienced hand the big fish will not prevail. After 15 minutes Des nets my first ever brown trout in double figures, a wild Ferox of just over 10lbs.

'Do you want to keep him for the glass case?' Des asks and smiles in approval when I tell him I always return specimen fish for someone else to catch. A smaller fish of just over 7lbs follows and after that Des pulls the boat rapidly across to one of the myriad of small islands for lunch and a glass of beer.

'So do you think it's boring?' asks Des in the middle of the afternoon after a quiet period of fishing the depths well out in middle of the Lough.

'I have never been bored while fishing in my life Des. The angler that gets bored has chosen the wrong hobby and lacks the passion for it. I count myself lucky just to be here—this is real freedom and the catch comes second. Mind you I'd like to net one more fish today—and bigger than the first one!'

The fishing continues for several more hours and Des shows no signs of fatigue at the oars; nor does my enthusiasm wane. It is still daylight at 9pm with the sun only beginning to sink below the Western Atlantic horizon. As we pass over a deep channel I feel the familiar tap-tap-tap on my rod tip.

Thirty feet down a monster Ferox trout is head-butting the dead parr to try to knock it off its course through the water. I sit ready and as the fish finally gorges the bait I lift the rod sharply. Des whistled in appreciation when the huge fish surfaces and porpoises along the surface 30 yards behind the boat.

The long battle is on. First the trout dives away and runs off making the reel sing like a magpie. Then it heads in a mad headlong rush towards the skiff.

'Damn, I think maybe it's off,' I say as I reel in nearly 40 yards of line.

'No it's just clever,' laughs Des.

'It wants you to think that. Keep taking line. I contact the fish again a few yards from the rowing boat and the fight continues for a further 15 minutes with me applying steady pressure on the head of the fish. It is close to the boat's side now. In the clear water we can see it is hooked by a single hook of the treble only.

I take great care but do not panic and feel an inward calm—even if my heart is racing in my chest. Des slides the net under the fish in the lengthening shadows of dusk. It is in perfect condition and we allow it to rest in the landing net to recover before we lift it carefully into the skiff.

Des weighs it—and it is an incredible 15lbs. It is returned to the deep of Lough Corrib to live perhaps for another 20 years.

30
THE IRISH BRIGADE

The next day the guards dragged him out of his cell and he was taken back to Major Bach's office. To Frank's astonishment the major smiled at him and spoke quietly and without anger. He felt instinctively that the Prussian had not had a change of heart and sensed danger.

"I understand from information we received about you that you have spent much of your life in Ireland. Don't bother to answer me because all this information comes from someone with whom you have had conversations."

He was baffled and wondered what was coming. Surely Emily had not been talking to them? Did it mean she had been captured and tortured? He felt a deep sense of foreboding and anxiety for her.

No, she would not betray him at any cost—but perhaps she had talked about him unknowingly to an informer? He looked directly at Major Bach who continued talking.

"We know that you have a great love for Ireland, went to school there and have many Irish friends. We also know that you are aware of, and indeed have met, Sir Roger Casement, the former diplomat who was knighted by the British some years ago for his consular services in South America and Africa. You have read his admirable report on slavery in the Belgian Congo.

"He is of course now a wanted man in England because he is an ardent supporter of the movement to free Ireland from British rule. Sir Roger is now in Germany visiting prisoner-war-camps where there are Irish soldiers. His mission is to recruit an Irish Brigade that will return to Ireland with the intention of supporting an uprising.

"I have decided that in exchange for your life—and the commuting of your death sentence—you are going to help Sir Roger raise at least a company of men for his brigade from the Irish prisoners here at Sennelager—and that you will yourself be volunteering to serve with him in the fight against British rule. The Irish Brigade needs to recruit senior NCOs from the British Army who will, after training, be commissioned into its officer corps.

"While I would not say for one moment that you would be officer material in any other army, I think you will be suitable for commission in this one because they are not looking for gentlemen but men of lesser social rank."

He found it impossible to conceal the look of horror upon his face while noticing the look of amusement upon that of Major Bach.

"You will be released from solitary confinement tomorrow morning and later in the day you will address a parade of prisoners who are either Irish or have strong Irish connections.

"You will ask them all to listen to what Sir Roger Casement has to tell them when he visits Sennelager next week and to follow your example in taking up the opportunity of repatriation back to Ireland by joining the Irish Brigade.

"You will tell them that by enlisting in Sir Roger Casement's force they will be entering into a righteous cause. You will say that you see it as your duty to help free Ireland from British imperialism—even though you were born in England. You will persuade these men to join the cause of Irish Republicanism and proclaim yourself publicly as a believer in this cause of independence against your own government. I you fail to persuade the Irish soldiers you will be shot."

"I can't believe this is happening to me!"

He spent the early hours of the following morning in his cell examining his predicament. The cunning bastard Bach was trying to set him up. He was giving him a choice. He could either be shot by the Germans, or shot by the British for being a traitor. He'd worked out how Bach had come to know about his connections with Ireland—and to his relief it had nothing to do with Emily. It was Gaston Quien. The collaborator would have been expected to file a report on the escape attempt going all the way back to Bellignies.

He remembered the dinner party at which he had first encountered the Frenchman. He had talked about Ireland then and that bastard Quien must have been taking mental notes of everything he said. He knew about Sir Roger Casement who was an erudite man and a poet.

Casement was the son of a British army officer but he opposed the old British establishment in Ireland that was loyal to the Crown. In July 1914 the British papers reported that he had sailed to New York to promote and raise money for the Irish Volunteers.

Rumour had it that the renegade Casement was by then involved in gun-running to build up a stockpile of ordnance for an armed insurrection. When the war broke out in 1914, the papers reported that Casement had gone to Germany to secure the Kaiser's help for Irish independence.

He now viewed himself as an ambassador for the Irish nation—the British regarded him as a traitor who would be executed when he was caught. Now his attempt to form an Irish Brigade to fight the British in Ireland would seal his fate with certainty.

Casement's was a lost cause. An uprising in Dublin at a time when the British Army had so many troops at its disposal to put it down was madness. Irish soldiers at Sennelager would be running a grave risk if they listened to the former diplomat and joined the proposed Irish Brigade. It could end in the firing squad for all of them. He knew he must do his duty to stop it happening, whatever the consequences for himself. He could not stand by and allow good men to die because of their ignorance.

There was plenty of time to sleep on it in his cell—but his opinion remained steadfast. He lapsed into a dream of Ireland and an incredible and unexpected adventure he had not long before the War.

GIANT CHAR—DIARY JUNE 1912

At first I think my drinking companion is joking when he talks about giant char over three lbs and two feet long. Nobody catches char much over 16 ounces in Ireland.

I'm on long weekend leave from Hollywood Barracks in Belfast. I pack my fly-rods and tackle, stuff a rucksack with clothes and a Tommy stove and take off by train via Dublin into the hinterland of Ireland. I'm in pursuit of brown trout on the many small rivers of County Waterford.

I end up in the Nire Valley, which forms part of the northern border between Co. Waterford and Co. Tipperary on the main route from Dungarvan to Clonmel. The Nire tumbles down through the valley from its source high up in the Comeragh mountains—eventually joining the smooth flowing Suir near Newcastle.

As a youngster I fished the Munster Blackwater, which flows through West Waterford before entering the sea at Youghal. It is my favourite salmon river offering spring, summer and autumn fishing with rich stocks of sea trout and brown trout.

Occasionally I have left behind the game tackle and gone coarse fishing for roach and tench at Lismore. I always prefer smaller rivers, however, because of the many mysteries and unexpected things they offer up as I wander upstream.

In this part of Ireland an angler can walk 10 miles up a river and not see another human being. My particular favourites are the Tar and Nire, where Ballymacarbry and Newcastle offer suitable Inns to stay.

A fisherman is really spoiled for choice with the Suir, Colligan, Finisk and Brickeyto to choose from. The brown trout in these rivers are in immaculate condition, rise to the fly with enthusiasm and are incomparable in their fighting qualities. Now that I am back in Ireland and stationed in Belfast I can revisit old haunts.

I hitch-hike on a number of lorries from Waterford—where I get off the train—and end up on the Saturday evening standing at the bar of a pub in Ballymacarbrywhere I fall into conversation with two tall and thickset ginger-haired brothers called Pat and Sean. They talk initially about nationalist politics but soon brush the subject aside to indulge in more interesting chat about fishing.

They come to the conclusion presumably that I am an adopted Irishmen who once lived in Dublin. I don't tell them I am a soldier. They provide me with a few tips—not knowing I am familiar with rivers in Waterford. There is a lull in the conversation and Pat swigs down his beer, puts his pot on the bar expectantly and says in a quiet voice: "What about Char—have you caught many of them?"

'They're good eating, good sport, but don't really grow large enough to excite me too much,' I reply.

'Well now, there I can prove you wrong. Have you been high into the Cummeragh Mountains?'

'No, I must admit I have not.'

'Well this is not known to many people—but high up in the those mountains are the two Cummeloughs, and two Stillogues, all quite small waters of four or five acres, which are so remote and far away from the mountain paths that few have ever been there—and even fewer have fished them. You won't find them on any ordnance survey map.'

He continues in a confidential manner as if in fear of being overheard.

'In these loughs are several kinds of trout—and char more than two feet long. The cock is grey blue with a red belly and the female is yellow bellied. When you cook them the flesh is red and eats better than a salmon.'

I am now listening intently and say: 'Pat, have you caught these monster char or are you just relating what you've heard from others?'

'Sean and I fished one of the Cummelough waters last season and caught four char each over three lbs. No one else fishes there but we don't want to hit the stocks of char too hard—so we confine ourselves to a couple of expeditions a year. We know exactly how to find the four loughs and will be delighted to take you to one of them early tomorrow morning in exchange for a night's drinking and a guinea each.'

'What on earth makes you think I've got that kind of money?' I laugh. 'I'd rather take my chance on the Nire early tomorrow morning. Thanks all the same though—and I promise you that none of what you've told me will be passed on.'

We carry on drinking, eat mutton and potato pie at the bar and by 10pm are all in a merry state. I take a quiet look at my wallet while in the gents and decide I can afford to spend two guineas on what seems like an interesting and once in a lifetime expedition.

I break the news to Pat and Sean, who pat me on the back in delight as if I have made some extraordinary decision that will change my life.

'OK Frank, now listen to this. We trust you of course but we can't afford to give out on exactly where these loughs are in the mountains. So be outside here tomorrow at 5am with your tackle and we'll have a trap to take us to the point where we'll start climbing the hills. We are going to blindfold you for the first hour and a half so that you won't be able to recall any of the landmarks en route. Once we reach a fair altitude we'll remove the blindfold.'

I study them closely. 'This isn't some stupid caper is it? An Irish joke to make an Englishman look a right fool? Or are you intending to shoot me in the back when I can't see?'

Pat and Sean roar with laughter. I know it is going to be worth the risk.

I cannot see a thing, but we leave the trap a mile outside the village and start by ascending the steep slopes on the right hand side of Lough Coumfea. My military training enables me to keep up with the rapid pace set by the two Irishmen.

Sean says: 'Gaelic speakers refer to the Nire Valley in our language as the land of the yellow / brown stone because of the stones along the river bank in the valley down there. It's a pity you can't see it!'

He roars with laughter and Pat adds: 'By the way Frank did you know that your rucksack has Hollywood Barracks, Belfast, inscribed all over the back of it?'

They rock with laughter even louder.

'So you know I'm a soldier then?'

'Yes Corporal Clarke, 7852, we know all about you. You are a regular soldier and a member of the 1st Battalion Norfolk Regiment. That's not on your rucksack by the way—someone had a quick look in your room last night while you were getting pissed up with us.'

I feel my heart sinking and fear I have walked into a trap. Pat and Sean continue to laugh as they watch me stumbling along the path blindfolded.

"So what are you going to do with me?" I ask.

"Well, we're going to take you fishing of course," says Sean.

Pat adds: "We've done a deal and that's that. If you were an officer we might take a different view of things. So you can count yourself a bit lucky that you're not!

"We're not assassins by the way—we're members of Sein Feinn and don't like the way the English lord it over the Irish in our own country.'

I relax and feel confident enough to sound light hearted and certainly am not going to mention that James was an officer in the 4th Royal Dublin Fusiliers.

'Well you blighters have certainly done your homework I must say!'

They remove my blindfold after a further half an hour so I can enjoy the walk. We cross the Nire at the end of a long pool where trout are rising and from the Coumalocha make our way across to a crag that overlooks the upper Mahon valley, before climbing down to the Sgillogue Loughs.

Trout are rising here too as the air warms and the sun rises—and I really want to start fishing. Next we make our way across a valley called the Coumlara. There is no lake along the valley floor, but I consider its tranquillity makes it one of the most memorable places I have ever encountered. Finally we start the rocky ascent to Knockanaffrin and soon run into fog.

Forty-five minutes later, after nearly three hours of walking and far from any path, we climb a steep ascent to the lough that Sean and Pat assert hold giant specimens of char.

It does not strike me as being a place of great secrecy because we have been off the mountain track for less than an hour. However, the climb has been extremely steep and even being at the peak of physical fitness I feel exhausted. The colour of the water is astonishing. It is a dark, almost inky blue and very cold.

It looks deep and as I gaze across its four acres I realise it is enclosed on three sides by sheer rock face. Nothing is rising on the surface and a stiff breeze causes rivulets to race across the surface. I wonder how we should fish it.

Pat stands beside me: 'Forget about the dry fly my friend. There is rarely a rise at this altitude throughout the season, except perhaps on a hot June evening and even then the char is not as enthusiastic as a native brown trout, so you'd probably catch them instead. Let me tackle you up for what we call wet fly long lining.'

'I'm happy to do exactly what you say,' I say.

'We're going to fit you up with three dropper flies all on size 12 hooks—that's a point fly at the end of the line, a middle fly and a bob fly which will fish just below the surface.

"This is a Black Pennell which will go at point and this is the Blue Zulu, which will be the bob fly—it is usually bushier than the point fly.

People often find the middle dropper is the least productive fly on the cast and give it much less consideration than the others. Sean and I think that's the wrong approach.

'We'll use a Solicitor, a Scottish fly, which is quite bright. It can be very productive when the char are feeding on small fry—I think the shine gets it taken for a little fish. I see you've got an 11 foot rod so we'll be able to use a 12 foot five lb silk leader with the droppers spaced equally along its length. We'll attach the droppers with a water knot which helps make them stand under the water rather than limp along too close to the leader.'

We stand at a spot where the stiff breeze is behind us which helps with casting—I propel the line at least 60 feet and pause for the best part of a minute to let the line sink before beginning a slow retrieval. I fish continuously for nearly two hours, walking round the lough to cast from different places and at different intervals tying on Green Peter, Invicta, Grey Wulff, Claret Bumble and Kingsmill flies of different sizes.

There appears to be no interest in what I have to offer and neither Sean nor Pat has any better luck on their kit. I am beginning to wonder if I haven't spent two guineas too rashly. Perhaps I am the butt of their joke—I certainly would not put it past them.

A few minutes later Pat puts down his rod, walks over and

surprises me with what he has to day.

'Sean and I think we're going to catch bugger all today on the wet fly. It's time to go coarse.'

'What do you mean?'

'We think that for two guineas you've got to get at least one fish in the bag and we propose to use the same method as our pals on Lough Eske up in County Donegal. Don't worry—we've got the tackle and you can use it.'

Pat produces an 11-foot rod and a centre pin reel mounted with an oiled five lbs breaking strain silk line and kits it up with a small cork float, a lead shot pinched on the line just beneath it and a number ten hook—upon which he attaches three maggots at a depth of just 12 inches. He hands me the rod and says: 'Cast it as far as you can with the wind and we'll throw in a handful of maggots after it.

"Don't wait for the float to disappear under the water—strike gently at the slightest twitch or movement.'

I laugh. 'So it's come to this has it?'

The first three casts produce nothing, but the impact of the handfuls of maggots thrown in by Pat has the required effect upon the fourth cast. Ten seconds after the float lands quietly on the water it rises slightly and cocks to the left.

I keep a taught line and flick my hand upwards in a gentle strike to set the hook. There is a sudden explosion on the water as the char leaps out of the water exposing its length of well over 15 inches. It then bores down into the depths of the lough and I let it run for as long as it wants for 40 yards. There is nowhere for it to snag the line.

'OK, he'll come to the net now,' says Pat and within a further five minutes the char, a female with a yellow belly, is in the landing net and on the bank. She weighs in at just below two lbs.

'I think we can do better,' laughs Pat. 'Let's move along the bank 20 yards but stay with the wind behind us.'

I look at my watch. It is now after midday and the air temperature is climbing. I detect a slight drop in the wind and the rivulets have diminished considerably on the surface. Now there is just a slight ripple on the surface of the dark blue water. I feel my luck might be in—and yearn to fish the fly again. I am even more inclined to do so when a fish rises with a mighty splash just out of casting range.

'Ignore that, it's just a big trout!' says Pat.

I cast the float and maggots again, this time achieving more distance and almost reaching where the fish has risen. Within three seconds of the float landing it disappears abruptly beneath the surface and I strike again. The char flies out of the water and this time I have hooked a much bigger fish. It jumps three times, exposing its silvery shape and then tears along the surface of the lough before turning its head to double-back in my direction.

The char then seeks sanctuary in the depths of the lough and seems to descend forever before flattening out and beating a heavy response to every effort to retrieve the line. I bring what turns out to be a cock fish to the surface when its strength is spent—after a long fight of 20 minutes. As I reel in the line the char becomes aware of the net below it and takes off again at terrific pace towards the middle of the lough. It obviously senses the sight of the net means the end of its life.

Finally, in a state of exhaustion, it is reeled in and brought to the shore.

'That's a bigger fish than any of us have ever caught,' says Sean excitedly.

We weigh the char and it is three lbs eight ounces, a magnificent specimen and possibly the biggest caught in Ireland on record.

"It's going back," I say and hold its red belly gently in the water as it recuperates slowly—before darting back into the depths of the lough.

'I've had my money's worth,' I tell them. 'Let's go!'

He was bundled into Major Bach's office the next day having worked out what he was going to do in this dangerous situation—which on the face of it would lead to the firing squad, or the noose for treason, depending on the way he handled it.

He knew it was rotten luck for a mere sergeant to be faced with such a responsibility but he had grown used to shouldering such burdens. He understood where his duty lay and that was all that mattered.

Major Bach surveyed him with triumph in his eyes: "So, have you decided to co-operate with us and speak favourably of Sir Roger Casement to the Irish prisoners?"

"Yes sir."

Did he detect a glimmer of surprise, and perhaps even disappointment upon the face of the Prussian?

Bach continued: "Good. The Irish prisoners will be mustered in the British compound at 1100 hours today and you will be brought out of the cells to address them. Remember, if you fail to do exactly what we are asking, you will be executed."

He was escorted back to the prison block, but instead of being flung into his cell was taken to the guard quarters and given a razor blade and shaving cream with a cold bucket of water. He was also handed a clean British army uniform complete with the three stripes of a sergeant.

One of the guards told him: "You will also wash your hair thoroughly and I have been instructed to cut it when you have finished washing."

It was clear they wanted him to look clean and smart as the first representative of the Irish Brigade in Sennelager Camp. He caught a glimpse of his face in a mirror while washing and what he saw depressed him. He certainly looked smart, but the face of the thin man that peered back was nearer to 45 years-old than his real age.

He guessed there were around 150 men mustered on the sand in the British compound and they stood at ease waiting to hear what he had to say. He did not detect any warmth towards him. They seemed to suspect he was trying to save his own skin.

Frank did not know it but most Irish soldiers in the British Army were indifferent to extremist politics before the 1916 Dublin Uprising when British atrocities caused many to change their view. The windows of all the barrack blocks in the compound were crowded with other prisoners hoping to witness what was said.

He heard himself begin speaking and knew he was walking a tight-rope. He needed to be able to talk for long enough to make a significant impact before the guards dragged him off the rostrum upon which he had been made to stand.

"Sergeant Frank Clarke, Norfolk Regiment, number 7852. I am not an Irishman but an Englishman brought up in Ireland—and I regard it as my home.

"Next week you will be receiving a visit from a gentleman called Sir Roger Casement who is also an Englishman brought up in Ireland, and who also regards it as his home.

"Sir Roger is the son of a British army officer and he served with distinction in the British consular service in South America and Africa, for which he was knighted some years ago. Now this Englishman with a passionate love of Ireland has become totally immersed in militant Irish Republican politics and he has put it above his loyalty to the King.

"Indeed he is prepared to die for the cause of a free Ireland by revolution. Sir Roger, along with other Republican leaders, has become attracted by the potential of an Irish-German alliance as a means of securing full Irish independence.

"Traditionally, Irish revolutionaries have looked to England's enemies for aid and Sir Roger Casement has been the central figure in developing the rebels' relations with the Germany. The Kaiser believes Britain's power could be broken by exploiting unrest in Ireland.

"Volunteers will be transported to Ireland to fight for independence—together with thousands of rifles and rounds of ammunition supplied by the Germans. The uprising will come soon but only the Irish revolutionary leaders know exactly when it will take place.

"You as trained soldiers will be given the opportunity to fight in the Irish Brigade and those of you who agree to join may be commissioned as officers to lead the various militias that have already been formed and are under training in Ireland.

"So you now have the chance to go and fight—or remain here and perhaps play a role in the democratic process in bringing Home Rule or Independence to Ireland after the War.

"I predict the whole enterprise involving the formation of the Irish Brigade will end in fiasco. The uprising will fail and men like Sir Roger Casement will be arrested and tried for treason. Every man who joins the Irish Brigade will be tried for treason. Do not die in vain!

"I urge you all to reject Sir Roger Casement and have nothing to do with his German-inspired Irish Brigade . . ."

Spontaneous cheering broke out. He knew what was coming. The guards were ordered to drag him off the rostrum by an English-speaking officer on horseback. They frogmarched him across the sand back towards solitary confinement in the prison block. He didn't go there. He found himself inside Major Bach's office.

The Prussian stood at the door. His face was crimson with rage and he was holding a riding whip. He brought it hard across Frank's face and kicked him simultaneously in the groin.

The Englishman fell to the ground and as he lapsed into unconsciousness was aware of being kicked all over his body. He had fainted long before the Major was restrained from killing him by Dr Ascher.

The old man had been told what was happening and rushed over just in time from the hospital to stop his friend's murder. Bach, paradoxically, was on the point of arrest for murdering Russian prisoners but had been determined to kill Frank before he was.

Now, well away from Bach and back in solitary, Frank slept deeply and was with Emily as they rode together on the banks of the Shenandoah River followed by their two children on ponies.

BLACKWATER SALMON-DIARY MAY 1899

The river is usually tea-coloured caused by its percolation through peat which has a lot to do with its origins. The Blackwater rises in the Mullaghareirk Mountains in East Kerry and makes its way through Cork and Waterford before reaching the sea at Youghal.

It stretches for 75 miles, is the fourth longest river in Ireland and one of its most important salmon rivers; second only to the Moy. It is a large and mature river not subject in the 19th century to agricultural abstraction, or to the whims of the weather and spates, so it provides good fishing consistently—even in low water.

There are extensive and quite narrow tidal reaches, stretching for approximately 20 miles from the estuary mouth at Youghal to Lismore and these provide a unique haven for salmon and sea trout in low water conditions before they run the main river.

The best salmon fishing—and my frequent beats—is between the tidal limit below Lismore Bridge up to Mallow, a distance of 45 river miles. I particularly enjoy the stretches below Fermoy with their variety of fly runs, glides and deeper pools. I return there every season for my best summer fishing.

The English aristocracy own most of the river—but there is so much available fishing in Munster that a poacher like me can walk for 20 miles along the bank, up or downstream and not be troubled by another living soul, whether fisherman or bailiff.

The Irish seat of the Duke of Devonshire, Lismore Castle in County Waterford, is regarded as the most spectacular castle in the country. It overlooks the Blackwater River and seems to scan the valley, serving to remind the natives of the enduring power of England's great families. I walk past it many times with a sack of salmon on my shoulder but never come face to face with the Duke—and would not care if I did.

I catch more salmon on the Blackwater than any other Irish river and it has been my top water in the early years of my life. The casting distances required to catch active salmon often vary from 40 to perhaps 100 feet using a two-handed rod.

The speed of the fly in the run and the instinct to know where the fish might be lying are more important factors. On this extraordinary river, which offers up some of the biggest salmon in Ireland, the fresh running fish are sometimes close to where the angler can wade. I have to take care not to get so near that I spook them.

All of this means the Blackwater is a fisherman-friendly river—worth every penny of the Duke's money. My best rod is 20 feet in length. I learned various casting techniques from friendly locals such as the Snap-T, Snake Roll, and the longer ranging Single and Double Spey casts.

I present the fly across and downstream using a floating line. Fishermen expect the salmon to come to the fly rather than the other way round—and presented not much more than two feet down in most conditions.

Small highly coloured number eight triple flies are used with bushy tails—although canny fishermen turn to a sparse black fly shortly before dusk to double the chances of catching a salmon or a sea trout.

The best lines are braided and oiled with care by hand to give them drive and flow through the rings of the rod. Only on or after fierce weather or high water do I use spinning tackle, metal spoons and plugs—although sometimes on the lower tidal stretches I try my hand at Harling, where a local boatman and I shuttle on the making tide between each of the riverbanks, letting the wobbler, spoon or fly at the end of each of our two rods move downstream towards the upriver-moving fish.

Harling, which originates on Norwegian rivers like the Nansen, was much favoured by English gentlemen in the 1860s on expeditions to that great river. The technique sometimes catches fish where no other method on a high river will work.

This day in late May 1899 the beat I choose is above Millstreet, a favourite drinking town. It begins with a narrow fast section and a longer broad pool that is overlooked by a large turreted house where dogs bark continually.

I am accompanied by my oldest brother Georgie, who like me has been schooled in the art of angling by our grandfather George Printer in Norfolk.

The latter never enjoyed the opportunity to fish for salmon in Ireland but as a game fisherman on many of England's salmon and trout rivers George was convinced that the angler must go to the water initially to observe.

He believed strongly that an understanding of nature was required and therefore what was going on around him in the countryside—the better to register in his mind what, in terms of insect life, was happening in the river to be fished.

Both of us always heed George Printer's customary approach. We never walk straight to a river, assemble our tackle and start fishing. Sometimes we will spend half an hour walking the bank—watching and seeing. We might not even start until we know the whereabouts of half a dozen fish.

Access to the top of the beat is from a meadow where a herd of cows are grazing. We make our way quietly through the cowslips down a high bank to the head of a fast flowing run. This comes out of a very deep pool which meanders powerfully between two cliff faces. The pool is entirely inaccessible without a boat but is packed with fish.

In the centre of the run below the big pool there is a small deep hole of about nine feet in depth before it diminishes to less than four feet and here the flow heads across to a high bank on a corner. We are not short of time and pause to "get the feel" of the river. We enjoy a cigarette before setting up our tackle.

I tell Georgie: "I came here in September once in low clear water after an exceptionally dry August and used the floated shrimp. I cast the shrimp as far as I could and let the current take the float under the far bank—connecting on the first cast.

'It was a grilse and I think it had been there for a week or two. It went absolutely crazy and with my short rod I had a hell of a job bringing it to the net. This is a river that never seems to go dead even when the water's low in a drought.'

'Not spinning conditions today though Frank. This is perfect stuff for fly fishing. I'm going to have a crack at the tail of the pool which they say is an excellent lie when salmon are running the upper river in high spring water,' says an excited Georgie. He is not such an accomplished fisherman as me even though I am the younger sibling.

'Good thinking old chap-see where the pool shallows up as the trees begin on our side? From there, down to just above where the barbed wire protrudes into the river, there's a deeper run, which I was told in the pub last night is another excellent spot to take a running grilse. I'll try my luck just there.'

'What are your preferences in flies today, old man?'

'I don't know Georgie and I won't until I look inside my box. I'll just go by instinct when I turn them over—but I'll start with one of the popular and traditional fly patterns such as Thunder and Lightning, Silver Grey and Green Highlander. If those don't work for me I'll move on to something like Sunray Shadow, Rusty Rat or Black Doctor.'

A quarter of an hour later, I wade into the water through shallows over a gravel bottom until I am up to my thighs and tie on a Silver Grey. I cast out to the deeper water around six feet in depth towards the high bank opposite.

The gravel and rock bottom are clearly visible but I can see only shadows lurking. The fly races downstream and I keep the rod down pointed towards where I believe it to be, following its progress to keep an absolutely straight line from the tip of the rod.

Every few moments I mend the line to eliminate any belly shape that forms as a result of current variations. I always finish the drift allowing the line to fully complete its swing and pause for a couple of seconds at the end of it.

Experience shows me that a salmon often takes the fly when it has stopped, after following it across the pool. It moves to the fly, takes it in its mouth and turns. The hook should set automatically if there is a good current and I have kept a straight line; all I have to do is raise the rod when I feel the fish.

As the fly races downstream I alternate between dead drifting and twitching the line to create movement. I believe the speed of the fly in the swim is more important than the simulated action and indeed is even more crucial than fly selection.

Blackwater Salmon seem to prefer flies that travel at a slower speed. Of course it varies from place to place and requires constant experimentation on the part of the fisherman who cannot afford to be lazy or complacent.

The speed can be controlled by mending line to slow the fly, stripping line to speed up the fly, or lifting the rod tip to hold slack line off the water to slow the fly down. To cover the maximum amount of ground at the end of each drift I take a step or two down stream and cast the full length again, repeating the procedure until I am at the end of the pool.

It is why I always prefer the larger pools because I can cover greater expanses of water. My thoughts are interrupted suddenly by a large fish that rolls at the surface 30 feet below me. Common knowledge suggests that leaping salmon tend not to take a fly—while salmon that roll are more likely to move on one.

I feel a thrill of excitement as a second fish rolls at the back of the pool. I can tell by the disturbance that it is a very large fish.

Some days I fish for hours without moving a salmon; on others a large fish comes to the fly on the first or second cast. It is why novices sometimes catch salmon on their first few expeditions to a river—without having a clue what is going on beneath the surface of the water.

I allow the fly to drift to the back of the pool having pulled off a further 20 feet from the reel. As soon as I do so I accidentally lift the rod and the response is a gigantic pull that rocks me forward so hard on my feet that for a second I fear I am going to fall forward. I regain my balance and the strong tug is replaced by slack line as the salmon charges up the pool towards me.

'Christ you are an awkward one you sod,' I shout in excitement. I regain connection and the fish rages about the large pool out of control. Somehow I manage to stay on the end of it and Georgie comes to my side with the large net. It is a monster.

We only realise how big it is when it briefly comes to the surface and dives in and out of the water in shallow formation like a porpoise for 10 yards or more.

'Good God Frank this is no grilse,' laughs Georgie.

'You're right and if it gets out of this pool then I'm completely mucked up," I say looking up at the high bank on both sides of the river.

'There's something majestic in the way it's fighting—its initial rage has gone and now it wants me to know that it is infinitely more powerful than me,' I tell him.

I move back to the middle of the river where there is a shallow run. Being there might just help to stop the salmon getting above me. I am putting an enormous amount of physical work in controlling the fish which rushes for sanctuary in every part of the long run but finds no rocks large enough to provide itself with shelter.

'Just keep in there brother,' says Georgie in encouragement.

'We eventually net the fish, but not until after it sulks on the bottom of the deep swim and remains motionless for five minutes. I start to believe I have lost it, but then it explodes back into action. She turns out to be a hen fish and weighs more than 20lbs on the scales. She is silver, bears the marks of lice infestation and is probably no more than a few days out of the sea.

'You're going to do it aren't you? I know you're going to do it because you are a perverse young sod!' laughs Georgie.

'I always do it with specimen fish,' I say as I disgorge the treble from the side of the Salmon's mouth, guide its head upstream to take the flow of the current and hold it gently until it is ready to swim slowly away.

31

THE RUSSIAN TUNNEL

Frank woke later in the day in great pain. He had been woken not by the pain but by the sound of the sirens and of rifle fire close at hand. There was trouble in one of the compounds and the prisoners in the solitary block were all banging on their cell door demanding to know what was happening in the main camp.

The guards who had remained at their post ignored the pleas for information but they looked tense. The shooting continued and with it came the sound of an angry crowd. The prisoners inside the cell block could see nothing, but only speculate on the cause of the noisy activity outside.

"I reckon that bastard Bach has done something to start a bloody mutiny—you mark my words mate," speculated Mick.

Suddenly, without warning the guards came to each cell and dragged out the prisoner inside until they were all congregated in the walled yard. They were ordered to stand to attention in line. At first some of them were worried they were going to be shot. They presented a ragged sight, all of them bearded and with grey faces.

"You are being released immediately and each of you will go back to your hut in the main prison compound," said the Feldwebel in charge of the guard detail.

"None of you has served his full sentence and so you will all be brought back here later to complete it. If you are found guilty of misconduct in the meantime you will be sentenced to the post," he promised.

As the Feldwebel was talking a group of 20 dishevelled Russian prisoners were herded violently into the prison compound and slung into the cells—which a few minutes before had been occupied by the British prisoners and one Australian.

Most of the Russians were hit by rifle butts even though they did not look likely to cause trouble and were cowed. The Russians were thin—like a group of old men—yet most were still in their 20s.

He winked at Mick as they were both marched separately under armed guard back to their respective hut and indicated to one another they should get in touch. He was literally slung through the front door of the NCO block but he received a standing ovation from the men inside, who crowded around him to give him a pat on the back.

Percy spoke for the NCOs: "Nobby have provided an excellent example to the men in the dignity and resolution you showed under both punishment and torture.

"We are proud of you for the way you managed to stay so calm under such provocation. You have earned the admiration of every non commissioned officer in this block."

"Thanks Percy and thank all of you. I tried hard to keep going but I'm not sure I could have held out for much longer. What is it that has intervened to save my bacon?"

Percy continued: "It seems the Russians were building a tunnel out of one of their huts but they didn't get their engineering right. They weren't deep enough and didn't use sufficient wooden props to stabilise the underground shaft.

"The poor sods must have been short of wood. They had burrowed all the way under both wire fences and the end of the tunnel had reached the perimeter road. They literally had another 10 yards to cover to reach a screen of trees. This morning a supply lorry was coming down the road and as it was driven over the tunnel the road collapsed and it fell into a large hole.

"The guards went crazy and started firing all over the place. Then that bastard Major Bach arrived on the scene and literally exploded in rage. The Germans soon traced the hut where the tunnel began but couldn't identify either the men who'd been doing the tunnelling, or the guys who were going to escape down it.

"Rumour has it he shot the two senior men in the hut and ordered his guards to arrest at random the Russians who have now replaced you and the other prisoners in the cell block. There has been uproar all afternoon in the Russian compound over the shootings and arrests. A revolt was only avoided by the Germans bringing in a company of crack front-line troops who were on leave in Sennelager barracks.

An infantry colonel has replaced Major Bach who hasn't been seen around the camp since earlier this afternoon. While we're sorry that tunnel didn't quite make it and for the loss of life, we're just hoping that this incident will mean the replacement of Bach by someone with decent human values.

"I think if he does go, you'll be off the hook too Nobby. You look bloody awful mate and obviously haven't had anything decent to eat in weeks—so I've got some good news for you.

"Your first food parcel arrived here a couple of days ago from your regimental headquarters in Norwich via the Red Cross. You won't be able to collect it until tomorrow but we've had a whip round. Tonight you are going to have tinned braised beef and potatoes, a proper cup of tea with condensed milk, and tinned peaches. And here's a packet of 20 cigarettes for you. How's that then?"

That night when he climbed into his bunk in the NCO block and onto his straw mattress he felt as if he could have been in a suite at the Ritz. It was the height of luxury and comfort after weeks of deprivation in a dark and dank cell and he soon settled in a deep and long sleep.

Emily had climbed into the small bunk with him and they held one another tightly all night without moving. Every half an hour he would wake and kiss her on the cheek. She had saved his life—always being there for him.

32
LIFE IN A NEW REGIME

It was now the summer of 1916 and Germany no longer reaped the harvest of earlier successes on the Western Front. Morale among German soldiers at the front line was high, but at home shortages of all kinds—caused by the Royal Navy's blockade—meant that the German people were going hungry.

There were queues for everyday food and in some cities there were even riots. Fuel was rationed, homes were cold and dark, larders were empty, soap was unobtainable and the country's newspapers portrayed Britain as the perpetrator of all Germanys misfortunes.

Sir Roger Casement's attempts to recruit an Irish Brigade had sputtered out miserably. He never came to Sennelager because it was clear from the response of the prisoners to Frank's speech that he would find no support there. A disillusioned Casement was able to recruit only 50 men—mainly from Limburg Camp—and many of them later reported they'd only signed up so they could get back to British territory and rejoin their unit. They were trying to double-deal the Germans.

The inability of the former British diplomat to raise a brigade among prisoners-of-war contributed to the eventual failure of the 1916 Uprising in Ireland, which was managed so ineptly that some of the participants did not even realize they were taking part in an insurrection.

Casement was tried and executed. Paradoxically he had already decided before Easter 1916 that any uprising was going to fail—and had returned to Ireland to try to prevent it happening. Major Bach had been gone for several months and the regime change created a completely different sense of order at Sennelager.

It had been one of Germany's horror prisoner-of-war camps. Now it was one of many large camps that were relatively well run on civilized lines in accordance with the terms of the Geneva Treaty.

Most prisoners received two parcels a fortnight and those that had somehow been excluded from the system received help from other prisoners. The men received new tunics, boots, socks and underwear to replace worn out or tattered khaki. Blankets and fabric were sent from England for the tailors in the camp workshop to fashion for the men into shirts and overcoats.

Parcels included chocolate, cocoa, tinned milk, tea, bully beef, luncheon meat, sardines, biscuits, cheese, butter, dripping, Crosse and Blackwell's plum and apple jam and canned fruit. At the top of the list were cigarettes and tobacco. The men were malnourished, because they lacked a balanced fresh food diet but they did not rely on inadequate rations provided by the Germans.

The authorities now wanted contented rather than rebellious prisoners. They encouraged the establishment of an artists' studio, a library and classrooms, a theatre, band room, metal and wood workshops and even rudimentary sporting facilities for football, cricket and athletics. The camp now manufactured its own low quality bread, wooden furniture and metal fittings for buildings. The tedium and boredom of 1914 and 1915 were a thing of the past. All prisoners were kept busy.

The exception to this sense of wellbeing was the pitiful ongoing starvation of the Russian prisoners who received no support from the Red Cross because of the turmoil going on in their own country. They had no choice but to try to survive on the inadequate rations supplied by the German military authorities.

The Germans cared not for the Russians because of their own state of hunger and misery. Gradually a situation had developed where the elderly guards—and the civilian population of nearby Paderborn—were living on a less sustainable diet than the Allied prisoners, whose rations were being supplemented by the Red Cross.

Now, instead of civilians turning up at the compound on Sundays to leer at the starving British prisoners as they had done in 1915, they did so to beg for food or in the hope of doing deals by providing items in exchange for tinned food and butter.

The new situation meant that both guards and civilians were easier to bribe. It led him to the conclusion that escape had become a possibility because items could be obtained from the civilian German population that might help in the planning of breakouts.

The rags he had worn during solitary confinement had been taken from him when he was forced to appear before the Irish prisoners in a new uniform. He had not been allowed to keep it and was now issued with a black single-breasted navy blue wool jacket with two skirt pockets and flaps. It had a stand and fall collar and five brass buttons. Around the collar was a strip of yellow cloth piping and on the cuffs an inverted chevron of yellow cloth piping. The lining was dark grey blue serge cloth.

It was now standard issue to thousands of British prisoners of war and one camp tailor confided in him that the yellow piping could be removed and the buttons replaced to resemble a civilian suit. It could, said the tailor, be worn in an escape attempt.

Anna had also been sending out clothes which he kept under his mattress in the NCO block so theft was not a problem. He intended to get a new British army uniform sent out in due course.

She also sent out £30 in sterling concealed in boxes of tea which he wanted for the purpose of bribing people and paying for services needed in his escape plans. Frank had become a figure of respect at Sennelager Camp and was accepted into the inner sanctum of the NCO's committee.

He had lost nearly three stone in weight but had so far managed to avoid dysentery. Unlike many of the others he continued to dream of escape. Then at last he received a letter from Emily and his spirits soared. She said she had been deeply depressed not to get any replies to her letters and now she at last understood from Anna that all their correspondence must have been destroyed by Major Bach.

He felt he was lucky Emily had not given up on him—but her adoration and love was quite explicit in the succession of letters that followed.

The Mary Borden Red Cross Field Hospital

Flanders,

April 10th 1916

My darling Frank,

Oh my dear boy how I have missed you all these months. One moment we were together and looking forward to a life of shared bliss and then we were torn apart. I know it may be difficult for you to tell me in a letter but I am desperately curious to know how it was that you were captured. The Edith Cavell network had been pretty watertight for several months before we ventured down it. I assume that somehow the plan went wrong near the Dutch border and that you had the misfortune to be taken by the Germans. As you know poor Edith was executed and her entire network of people imprisoned. It is whispered here that the ghastly Gaston Quien was implicated in her betrayal. Her death was so cruel and caused outrage not only in England but in the USA and all over the world. I worried for months that you would be tortured and indeed for all I know you may have been.

My own escape from Belgium went through without a hitch. The guards only glanced in a cursory fashion at the papers presented by the head of the American delegation as we changed trains at the border and I was in England within days. The Germans did not seem to want any trouble. It was then I wondered whether I had made a huge mistake in not asking the Minister whether we could have included you in the American party with false papers. Perhaps it would not have been allowed.

I went to see your dear mother shortly after arrival, as you may now have heard and Anna was most kind a few weeks later in telling me where you were. Now I can see that your evil commandant may have blocked all my letters so I will not scold you my darling—for weeks I imagined you no longer loved me!. My darling Frank the war will not go on forever and sometimes I think that you are safer where you are than being in the trenches at the Front.

I am now with Mary Borden's Red Cross hospital and ambulance unit and serving in Flanders. I see terrible things every day my darling and sometimes I imagine that a soldier brought in to me with terrible wounds is you—and it makes me cry. We work for many hours a day and the fatigue is terrible.

Our time off is spent catching up on sleep rather than recreation—there is none anyway for women. We cannot go to Paris for a night out!! My Australian chum Jackie Pretz is like a rock and cheers me up when I sink into the trough of despond because I am so far away from you. It is as if you are somewhere on another planet but then I picture you safe at Sennelager Camp and understand you are only two or three hundred miles away. I pray for you every night my dearest boy and that you will soon come back to me. I have passionate thoughts too my darling and remember all those wonderful nights we spent cuddled up in the deep of the night.

I used to stroke your body while you dreamed and I would feel your lean strength—then sometimes you would wake up and possess me. Now there are only dreams of such nights for me, and I expect for you too. I have promised myself that when we are re-united we will never again be parted for one day. In the meantime I will write each week and see that you are sent everything you need. Anna and I will make sure that you go short of nothing.

All my love, forever

Emily

During the time of torture he had dreamed of her, and had made up his mind that she was still waiting for him despite his nagging anxieties, but writing letters in vain to nowhere. Now all this was confirmed and their relationship was back on its strongest and most affectionate footing. He knew she would wait for him till the end of time.

He decided he could not wait until the end of the War, which might be many years away. He must go to her. Now it was time to make plans. In the meantime, over the coming months, he built up a collection of her passionate letters and would read them at night over and over again to ensure that every dream was of his beloved Emily.

He had been sitting on a hot afternoon for two hours listening to members of the NCO's Committee droning on about mundane aspects of camp life. The chairman of the library sub-committee had presented an interminably hour-long annual report on the condition of existing library books and the efforts being made to get more from England.

This had followed a dull monologue from the chairman of the education committee about the camp curriculum. Still to come was a boring diatribe from a dullard who spoke with a flat Midland accent about setting up sporting competitions between the British, French, and Belgians. By 4pm he had had enough.

The meeting halted briefly for a brew and scoff and before it reconvened he stood up and made it clear he wanted to speak. Percy, who was chairman, nodded for him to go ahead. He suspected he was heading for trouble but was determined to speak his mind. This committee business had become too remote from the War.

"I know this is not on the agenda gentlemen but can we add it to our list? I want to talk about escape and our duty as soldiers not only to try to do so, but also as a committee to foster and support any groups of servicemen who are planning to do so in the future.

"This camp can now harness the many workshop skills of the men imprisoned within Sennelager. We can sub-contract them to work for an escape organization using the equipment that has been made available . . . . . ."

Frank had already noticed the frowning faces around him and it was clear that he was not speaking with the support of the NCO's Committee. Several people were bursting to intervene and silence him.

"We've fucking been through all this," a Warrant Officer interjected. "It has taken us a year to get this camp working so everyone in it has a decent chance of survival with enough to eat—and something worthwhile to do to kill the time we have on our hands.

"Now, Nobby here wants us to stir up Fritz with bloody silly and futile escape attempts. What you're saying is straight from the boy scouts manual. Give it up mate—we're stuck in the middle of Germany's principal army training area.

"It's bigger than Salisbury Plain and there are several regiments here at any one time. Getting out is one thing mate—but the Russians and the

French have shown that you can't get away. It is just not practicable."

They took a vote and the show of hands demonstrated that the overwhelming majority of senior NCOs in the camp were against forming a sub committee to oversee escape attempts and to put a support structure in place for clothing and forging ID cards. There was no appetite for escape by the senior men in the camp and this indifference would filter down to the ranks without a doubt.

He continued despite the prevailing mood: "Very well then, but please can we vote on whether the committee will allow genuine escape projects to receive the support of skilled men in the camp for the purpose of forgery and clothing? Escapers will want the unofficial nod from the NCOs Committee to commission work by the tailors, printers, carpenters and metal-workers."

The meeting continued to buzz having been well stirred up. He thought he had definitely improved it after all the boring rubbish being talked about curriculum and library books. His view was not shared by many others who enjoyed the business of governing. They thought he was being entirely subversive and during the course of the rest of the meeting he was on the receiving end of several lingering stares which conveyed nothing but hatred and contempt. He had become yesterday's hero.

At Percy's bidding the committee agreed with some reluctance not to ban escape attempts altogether and to give tacit approval to those that looked as if they may at least have a chance of being successful. Some of the NCOs were extremely angry at what they saw as an inevitable disturbance of the peace by an escape hothead.

One stood up and said: "For every successful escape attempt there will be 10 or more attempts that end in failure and recapture. For the sake of one successful escapee, hundreds of men in this camp may have to face the reality of reprisals and a loss of their quality of life, perhaps even the withdrawal of food parcels and possible starvation. We are living on the edge. It just doesn't make sense to sanction escapes when we have at last created a system at Sennelager that enables all of us to survive."

Another NCO shouted: "Men like fucking Nobby are just being bloody selfish."

Frank butted in: "Men like me are thinking about the hundreds of poor devils on the Western Front dying every day in a filthy trench on the Somme having been blown to pieces by shellfire or suffering terrible injuries through gas poisoning. They have no choice but to do what is seen as their duty. Here we have a choice, and only one of them is honourable."

Another came up after the meeting and asked sarcastically: "So when are you going to escape Nobby and how are you going to do it?"

He replied: "Look mate, you're a weasel and I wouldn't tell you even if I knew, which I don't—but believe me I will find a way out of this bloody camp somehow.

"Hundreds of thousands of our chaps are fighting to win a war and dying in the process. What makes you think that you're so bloody special that you can sit it out here in safety behind barbed wire bleating about losing your Red Cross parcels? Just piss off. Go and audition for a part in the next camp musical. I'm sure you'd make a lovely lead soprano."

33
COME FLY WITH ME

The idea came to him when he was digging potatoes with a working party that included Mick O'Connor. A biplane marked with black crosses took off laboriously from a field less than two miles away, climbed to 1,200 feet and then turned towards them before flying directly overhead. There was a training airfield nearby and he remembered he could probably still fly a plane.

"Hey Mick see that?"

"It's just a fucking aeroplane Nobby."

"I know it's a ruddy aeroplane Mick but can you see how many men there are inside it?"

"Yeah, there are two."

"It could be the two of us."

The Australian laughed loudly. "You're not getting me inside one of those fuckers—especially with you driving. Forget it mate."

"Look Mick, if I can come up with a way of getting us both out of here, up to the aerodrome and nicking one of those planes—are you really saying you wouldn't be up for it?"

"I'll think about it Nobby but don't count on me."

As he worked in the potato field that afternoon he came gradually to the conclusion that the idea was not as preposterous as Mick thought. In the summer 1912, while on leave from the army, he had been invited to stay for a week on the Bandon Estate in County Cork by Walter Hill, its head gamekeeper.

One morning he thought Walter was going to take him fishing but he was diverted to join a group of land agents watching a two-seat Bleriot monoplane take-off and land in a meadow close to the castle. It was flown by an American called Jet Peters. The American ran a flying circus in the States which entertained townspeople in the mid-West.

Peters was also trying to sell the agents aeroplanes. He lectured the assembled group that aerial crop-spraying was the way of the future for the big estates and he asked for volunteers to take a trip beside him and have a go at the controls.

"Count me in on that Jet," he was the first to get inside the aeroplane alongside the American. Jet instructed the onlookers to turn the machine into the wind, wound up the engine and they began rumbling at increasing speed down the meadow. He experienced the sensation of leaving the ground for the first time and enjoyed a stunning view of the rolling Irish countryside. He had never witnessed anything so incredible before—more awesome even than standing on the summit of a mountain.

They flew over the river, circled the town, followed the railway line for a few miles and then returned towards the castle. He was hooked on flying.

He'd been saving up for a trip to Norfolk later in the year but decided instead to pay Jet for six flying lessons on the spot.

By the end of the week he knew enough about being a pilot to get an aircraft in trim ready for take-off and get airborne safely. Landing without damaging the aircraft or himself was more difficult but eventually he mastered it. Jet taught him to navigate and better still seek out railway lines and roads to get from point A to B.

He'd vowed then to become a properly qualified pilot one day, perhaps even to volunteer for the Royal Flying Corps, but the war had come too soon for that.

"It's all very well you saying you can fly mate—but how the fuck do we get out of the camp and get our hands on a bloody aeroplane?" asked Mick emphatically. He was terrified of putting his life in the hands of someone as inherently insane as Nobby. He loved the man, but there were limits to what you'd do for your mate.

Mick was no coward but he always hated the idea of losing control of any situation. Sitting in the observer cockpit of a German kite at an altitude of 2,000 feet with a novice pilot like Nobby at the controls was really asking for it.

"Mick let's take the other end of the proposition first and then work back. You are the king thief in this camp and if I was going to nick anything I'd do it with you OK?"

"Yeah, but. . . ."

"No buts mate. If we can get our hands on one of those training aircraft at the aerodrome with sufficient fuel in it we can fly due west of Paderborn along the Lippe River all the way to the Rhine. We'd pass over Lippstadt and Hamm and if we still kept flying on a due westerly bearing for 60 miles we'd reach Wesel where the Lippe joins the Rhine.

"Then hey presto it's only thirty miles flying north to the Dutch border at Spijk. So there's bugger all navigation involved and even you can read a compass Mick. We'll follow the Rhine from Wesel up to the Dutch border at Spijk and look for a landing ground somewhere in the Arnhem area."

"Look, even if we manage to nick one of the kites and get it airborne, how do we know how much fuel it is carrying? What if it's empty?"

"I know this is risky Mick and I don't know the answer to that right now—but I guess we'd have to steal some fuel somehow."

"You're fucking crazy Nobby—do you realise that?"

As they marched back from the potato fields in a column they came to a small village where they crossed a bridge over the River Thune. This was a fast flowing river with clear water descending from the Teutoburg Forest. He had always been fascinated by the Thune because it reminded him of so many similar small rivers in Ireland.

Every time he crossed that bridge he wanted to scrutinise the pools and look for signs of trout—but the guards never allowed him to delay the column. The other prisoners were not keen either because they always wanted to get back for food. He marched alongside Manfred the friendly guard. He was on good terms with Manfred—and put it straight to him.

"How would you and Hugo like some fresh fish out of that river?"

"Why, how you catch them then?"

"I'm going to buy some fishing tackle in exchange for tinned food off one of the Paderborn locals who come to the camp every Sunday to do deals. With your help during the field working parties I can catch enough fish in the river for you and Hugo and maybe the other guards."

"Mmm I'll talk to Hugo about it. Maybe it would be a risk for us eh? What's in it for you?"

"The chance to eat fresh food regularly, Manfred. OK, don't make any decision until I've found out a bit more about it. I reckon we could all be winners on this one," he added untruthfully.

That night he asked around the NCO block if anyone knew anything about the aerodrome and what was going on up there. He told them that he and Private O'Connor were considering stealing a plane and flying it to Holland. There was loud laughter all round the block because Nobby had come up with a number of madcap schemes—and in the end they never amounted to anything.

On this occasion there was someone to help him in the shape of Sergeant Ron Middleton of the Royal Engineers. Ron was a typical engineer and assumed that Frank would understand everything he said, which he didn't. He told him that a squadron of Albatross C III were based up at the airfield to train cavalry officers who wanted to fly in combat.

The C III was a two-seat general-purpose biplane that were easy to handle and much loved by pilots. He added: "They are powered by the Mercedes D.III inline engine so the cylinder head and exhaust manifold protrude above the front fuselage. So you'll curse it as soon as you sit down in it. By the way Private O'Connor will have a Maxim machine gun mounted in his cockpit which you might need if you're being chased at take-off."

The next day Manfred came up to him in a state of some excitement having spoken to his mate Hugo about the possibility of getting fresh fish.

"I think maybe we find a way for you to catch fish for us," he said.

The two Germans had decided not to supply the guards in the camp with the trout because it would be too dangerous.

They'd sell the fish he could catch on the black market via a contact in Paderborn. Manfred explained that the Feldwebel in charge of prison working parties had been ordered to restore and maintain an overgrown garden at one of the barracks which contained a small lake fed by the River Thune. The unit quartered there had been sent as reinforcements to the Front following the Battle of the Somme the previous month in July.

For the next few weeks the barracks would be unoccupied. The German explained it had been built by the Kaiser for his cavalry officers as a swimming lake just after the turn of the century but had never been used for that purpose during the war.

Someone had put netting and trout in there for breeding to supply the kitchens with a regular supply of fish—but the netting had fallen into disuse and the trout forgotten when new units arrived for short-term training.

"OK Manfred I'll do it. And I'll bring Private O'Connor along with me to do the gardening work while I catch the fish. It'll be our secret OK?"

That evening as they strolled round the recreation field inside the wire at the camp, they hatched their plan.

"So what will we do then mate?"

"We'll need two sets of clothes Mick."

"Why?"

"We'll take our normal camp outfits and something resembling a German uniform to wear over our clothes when we cycle up to the aerodrome dressed as two private soldiers. There are going to be soldiers cycling around in the middle of the day.

"When we get to the aerodrome we won't attract attention if we look like soldiers—and it will buy us time to get our hands on some fuel and find the right kite to nick.

"Once we get airborne we'll throw our German uniforms out of the plane so that if we are captured they won't shoot us for being dressed up like Boche soldiers."

"Neat thinking mate, but how are we going to get our hands on their uniforms? Do you want me to kill a couple of the bastards?"

"No I'm going to call in a favour with Albert, one of the tailors in the clothing workshop. They'll have dyes that can do the job and I'm going to get my mother to send over some light blue blankets in her next parcel so Albert can cut them up into uniforms.

As far as the boots are concerned I'll do a deal with the Paderborn Germans. It'll take a few weeks but we need first to gain the confidence of Manfred and Hugo by keeping up a regular supply of fish—and not escaping. I'm quite worried about being able to catch the fish.

"Why?"

"Well what if hungry German soldiers have been throwing hand grenades into all the pools on the Thune? Maybe there are no fish left—after all the town is reported to be going hungry and the way the locals moon around Sennelager on Sundays looking for any deal that will give them food, it's hard to believe someone hasn't already thought of nicking the fish out of the river."

"Don't worry Nobby, you always catch—you said that yourself. How are we going to get hold of the bikes?"

"That's your job and I don't want to have to worry about it. You are the best damned thief in camp.

"I don't think you'll have too much trouble nicking a couple of bikes over the next few weeks from the village when you are out with the working party."

"I'll do it."

The German woman from Paderborn called Ellie had been introduced to him by Hugo, one of the friendly guards on the working party. She said she had no money to buy food but wanted to exchange tinned scoff and butter for either fresh vegetables—or for items belonging to her husband. She had come inside the camp to meet him and stood outside the NCO's block in a shabby long sleeved summer dress and red waistcoat.

It was not a warm day and she shivered when she spoke to him. She told him, using Hugo as an interpreter, that her husband was at the Front and he could no longer provide for her or their four children. He guessed immediately that she was exchanging sex for favours with Hugo and he felt sorry for her.

Ellie was blonde, slim and of medium height. She would have been a Teutonic beauty before the War, perhaps the belle of the town in years when everyone had so much hope. The years of conflict had hardened her face, created lines under her resigned blue eyes and coarsened her hair which had been washed in nothing but water for a year. She hardly looked at him as she spoke to him in a soft voice.

"What food do you have?"

Mick had agreed to go halves on his Red Cross parcels for a month and he spoke with confidence: "I can supply you with tinned milk, meat, sardines, chocolate, jam and fruit to last your family for a month Ellie. I'll throw in butter and dripping too, and as a special treat some soap—if you can supply me with what I need."

"What is it you need Sergeant?" she asked looking alarmed into his eyes. One man was enough for sex and she now wondered whether the Tommy was being suggestive to her. She found this tall dark man attractive but sex made her even more exhausted and was unwelcome in these hard times. She need not have worried—the Sergeant had other things on his mind—and deep within her she felt a spasm of rejection because he had not noticed the double meaning of his words or looked into her eyes to see the hunger there for love.

"Well if your husband was a fisherman he'll have owned a fishing rod and reel and tackle. Can you get me these things?"

"My husband was always too busy for things like fishing but I think I can supply you with what you want."

"If you can I should be grateful—and even more so if it is a fly-rod suitable for fishing small rivers like the Thune and the Upper Lippe.

"I'm also looking for two pairs of German Army boots. I don't care what condition they are in but they have to be large size."

She thought for a moment and then replied: "I will return next Sunday with these items and you will need to box your food up and give them to Hugo to bring to me, otherwise I will be arrested. They will throw me in prison if I am caught with your food and my children will starve—so I take a terrible risk in even coming here to do business with you.

"I wouldn't want you to get into any trouble Ellie. I admire you and if there wasn't a war on would want to be your friend," he said, looking this time into her eyes.

She blushed, looked to the ground and walked away, then waved him farewell and was gone. He liked her and wanted to help her. He wondered how many poverty-stricken young mothers there were in Germany like Ellie.

How odd that people who were so alike were going to hell in fighting one another, when most people didn't want to be at war at all.

34
THE PLAN DEVELOPS

The next month the light blue-grey cloth for the uniforms arrived by post from Anna in Norfolk. He took the bundle over to the workshops so the tailoring could get started. Albert the cutter was delighted when he saw what Anna had sent because he did not think he would need to dye it.

"I want two pairs of trousers and two tunics with authentic pockets and pleats. Do you want us to do drawings?" he asked.

"No need Nobby," said Albert. "By now I ought to know what a bloody German uniform looks like. Leave the buttons to me as well. Give me two weeks and they'll be ready for you."

The following Sunday Ellie returned to the camp with a fishing rod, reel, silk line and hooks which were given afterwards to Hugo for safe-keeping. The split cane rod had three sections and when these were joined it was about 10 feet in length—which was long but usable.

It was not a fly-rod but had sufficient whip for him to get a cast out of it. Ellie also brought two pairs of dilapidated jackboots that would need hours of spit and polish to get them back into military condition. He didn't mind that at all. He handed three parcels of canned food to Hugo who slunk off with them towards the guard-room looking like a fugitive. He came back a few minutes later for the fishing tackle and took Ellie with him.

He had inspected the kit while Ellie waited with him and he was pleased with the deal. The steel centre pin reel was oiled and in good working order but the silk line was too light to cast an artificial fly without a small lead weight. He had an idea where he could get those and sat down that evening to write to Anna and ask for two boxes of lead weights from the chest of drawers at the farm where he kept his Norfolk fishing tackle.

Feather boas collected by the camp's amateur drama group were ravaged by Mick that night for strands of fluffy down. He broke into the props' room at the back of the theatre and helped himself. Mick also procured some glue and the next evening they pasted particles of feather onto silver tobacco paper that he had been wrapped around the hooks earlier. The result of their work was primitive but they made a dozen acceptable multi-coloured lures.

Some days later the two men were escorted by Manfred to the over-grown barrack garden for the first time. The lawns needed cutting back and the places where the flower beds should have been were overgrown with nettles and dock weed. No one had put a spade on them for two years. Perennials had been choked out by weeds and many of the shrubs and bushes needed pruning—if not digging out altogether.

Overhanging branches from the trees denuded the light. They looked

307

around in horror at the amount of work required and then it dawned on them that they wouldn't actually be completing it. They had been issued with garden implements and told to get on with the job.

They toiled for an hour before stopping for a brew on a nod from Manfred. They lit a bonfire from the branches they had cleared and the German rigged a stove over the fire to boil the water. Manfred watched nervously as Frank crept over to the water and disappeared out of sight in the thick foliage on the bank of the lake. He looked visibly relieved when Frank reappeared a few minutes later.

He knew they would have to go through a routine of behaving well for a week or two before Manfred and Hugo were relaxed about them being out of sight. There was no point in trying to rush things. When the time came to bunk off they would need every second of start that they could get—which was why the bicycles were so important and needed to be close.

He gazed at the lake and noticed the slow current running through it from the River Thune. It had been widened and dug out to provide a leisure facility for swimming of about an acre. An old wooden diving board was rotting on pillars under an oak tree and a pontoon that had presumably accommodated a punt or skiff in the old days was in a state of near collapse.

He noticed with interest there was a shed under a second tree at the end of the lake and made a mental note to check if it was locked and might make a good hiding place for the bikes. The garden must have been a refreshing place to relax in when it was built.

The water was as clear as gin. He could see weeds several feet below the surface and estimated the depth in the middle to be around six and a half feet. No fish were rising but he thought he detected movement well below the surface near the middle. This was going to be a challenge and he knew he would have to catch fish quickly before the guards got impatient. He handed the German a cup of tea.

"OK Manfred, when are we going to start fishing for you? We're ready when you are and if we're coming here every day then we might as well get started eh?"

"Manfred said quietly: "We wait a bit till everyone in my chain of command is used to you guys being here. Do plenty work first—make it look good, perhaps they relax."

The lead shot arrived from Norfolk thanks to the quick work of Anna. Now they really were ready to get the plan into action. The work on the garden continued for another week—Hugo guarded the working party in the fields while Manfred brought them to the gardens. Gradually it began to look cared for again—although they had no plants to replace those that had been choked out by the weeds. One morning Manfred suddenly produced the fishing tackle like a magician.

He had obviously been hiding it somewhere in the garden and had no intention of showing them where it was kept.

"You catch me fish today Sergeant," he ordered in his quiet voice, winking at Mick who grinned in delight.

"OK Manfred I'll have a go. Luckily I've brought my lures with me and some casts so we can start going for those trout. Now there's one thing you have got to understand and that is that I won't be able to catch fish while you are standing near to me. I have got to be completely alone. The shadow of a man's figure across the water frightens the fish. You stay around here and I'll keep reporting back to you every 15 minutes—and Mick can do that too when he's working down the end of the garden."

"I don't want to have to shoot you—so don't play any tricks OK?" said Manfred.

"I trust you, but not the Australian."

Mick feigned a look of being hurt. Frank assembled the rod and tied the feather lure onto the silk cast with a tiny lead weight mounted at its eye. He had been observing the pool closely for a number of days and by now had seen several fish, most of which were between one and two lbs. If they were wild brown trout from the River Thune, then fish of that size would fight hard and pose a serious threat to the light tackle. He'd have to be careful.

From his observation during morning and afternoon tea breaks from the gardening, most of the fish he'd seen were feeding on the nymph and would roll slowly over on their side, just breaking surface to catch the larvae. He hadn't been around in the late afternoon but guessed there would be an evening rise as the shadows lengthened in the receding sun of the summer sky.

As he approached the bank light of foot—and moving slowly—he felt the surreal nature of this strange episode. Here he was in a war deep in enemy territory with German soldiers all around him poaching on a lake where he had no right to be. He had to chuckle and did so loudly.

War or not, he began to treat it like any other fishing expedition, with an intense sense of concentration and anticipation, common to all successful fishermen. It was like switching on an electric current inside him. He came alive to the call of the wild, with new senses of sight and smell that were borne of years of experience at the water's edge. Birds called from the trees and insects buzzed around him.

He reached the water, crouched behind a bush and saw a long grass snake swimming ashore a few feet away. These were shy creatures and it was a sure sign not many humans ventured there. He looked into the depths for signs of movement. There was a living world beneath the surface but he could not see it yet. He moved from the cover of a Rhododendron bush and cast in his slow, unhurried and rhythmic style, elbow tucked into his side, looking like the ultimate expert.

The oiled silk line eased through the rod ringlets on the back cast and flew horizontally behind him before the pause. He confidently executed the wrist-driven follow-through giving him the distance and the light landing on the water.

The lure landed without great disturbance on the surface 30 feet away and sank quickly into the depths of the lake—he was able to watch its rate of descent in the gin clear water and began the retrieval when he judged it was over the weed bed that lined the bottom.

He cast three times but there was no response and he felt a tinge of disappointment. He knew he must report back to Manfred every 15 minutes. He managed to cover nearly 40 yards of bank in that time. The lure had evoked no response and he began to feel a sense of frustration because he was not in a position to vary his approach.

He had no fly box—only a small set of similar lures. The German was preparing a brew when he got back to him and Mick was waiting there too with a look of anticipation on his face.

"Where the fish?" asked a grinning Manfred.

"Didn't have any luck this time old chap, but it is early days yet," he replied.

He fished on through the morning and early afternoon and covered the entire lake but failed to move a trout, which made him mad with disappointment. Manfred was beginning to wear a resigned expression on his face.

"Perhaps there no fish in lake at all," he suggested.

"Yes there bloody are Manfred because I've seen them," he replied.

Mick opened up his huge hands and showed the contents to Frank and the German.

"How about using these mate?" he suggested.

The grubs were twice the length and circumference of maggots, pure white, and wriggling with activity.

"Christ where did you get those Mick?"

"I was digging up the docks with my fork when I came across dozens of the little beggars. I thought I'd catch a few and show you just in case. I know fuck all about fishing but they look good to me mate."

He returned to the lake with a sardine tin full of the white grubs and threaded one onto a lure. It was a technique called the flying maggot—and provided the grub didn't fly off the hook on the forward cast it might just present an irresistible morsel to a trout.

The flying maggot was a method used by unscrupulous anglers pretending to fish with just an artificial fly on posh English rivers—so they could fool a water bailiff looking through his binoculars. He had used it more than once in Ireland—but nobody really minded there. Everyone was a poacher in Ireland.

He cast 40 feet out into the lake and watched the grub sink. He saw the sudden movement under the water and watched in excitement as the line raced off his reel noisily. He counted three and struck gently—the rod dipped into a bend sharply and he knew he had hooked the fish. It had gorged the grub.

This wasn't scientific fishing but it was effective. The trout raced across the lake, shot into the air and then bored deep into the weeds. It came to the bank within five minutes and he stepped deftly into the shallows, lifted his rod and hooked his right index finger under its left gill before bringing it slowly onto the grass.

It was a brown trout of around two lbs and in magnificent condition, covered in red and black spots with a yellow back and white belly. It had sharp teeth and its fins were undamaged. He killed the fish and walked back to Manfred whose face lit up when he saw what the Sergeant had caught. He caught a further six fish in the next two 15 minute sessions and had no doubt he would clear the entire lake within a week at that rate. If he ran out of fish to catch the escape plan would be ruined.

"What are we going to do Nobby if you catch every fucking fish in the lake before we're ready?" asked Mick as they took their evening walk around the perimeter of the compound.

"I've been thinking and I reckon it could help us make our getaway more effective Mick."

"How come mate?"

"I reckon Manfred and Hugo are selling the fish down in Paderborn and they've got a nice little business going.

"They think we're in it only because they allow us to cook a fish every day on the fire. Manfred keeps the fishing tackle which never comes near the camp so none of the other guards have a clue what's going on. So, when we hop it next week the Commandant is going to conclude we were just two silly buggers who ran off from a working party."

"So?"

"Well they aren't going to know anything about our German uniforms, or that I can fly a plane, or that Manfred and Hugo unknowingly helped us."

"I still don't follow you mate."

"OK. I'm going to suggest to Manfred and Hugo that if they want to keep this fish business going for a few weeks into the autumn they are going to have to allow me to fish on the River Thune upstream and downstream of the lake. I'll tell them that I probably won't catch as much in the river but that I might get them a couple of trout a day. They're going to be too greedy to say no.

"On the day we go for it I'll meet you in the village at a pre-arranged spot. We'll grab the bicycles and go like hell for the aerodrome.

"I reckon you can sprint from that garden to the village within 15 minutes keeping out of sight by the hedgerows. You tell Manfred you want to go for a shit—hop round the back of the hedge, put your German uniform on over your prison clothes and start running.

"I know Manfred. He won't sound the alarm for 15 minutes after you've gone—he'll be too confused. He'll hope you are coming back, then he'll go looking for you, then he's got to get back to the camp to give the alarm. Meantime, he won't know whether I've hopped it as well. It also means we haven't got to get out of the garden at the same time. So really it's much neater.

"There's only one hitch."

"What's that?"

"Mate, I haven't nicked the fucking bicycles yet."

"Look Mick, you are the best thief I've ever met. You're going to have to do it over the two days before we break out. There are dozens of bikes in the village—you can't fail."

"Yeah—but when do I nick them? How do I leave the garden?"

"OK. I reckon Manfred and Hugo would cut us out of their fish business if they could because it would reduce their risk. So I'll start taking Manfred with me when I fish the lake. I'll offer to teach him how to do it himself.

"He's a dumb fool and he'll get so absorbed in learning to cast, strike and play a fish that he'll forget about you probably for at least 45 minutes. You'll have that time to put on your uniform, get into the village, look around and perhaps pinch one bike.

"The next day I'll give Manfred another lesson and you do the same thing. If you take my advice you'll head for the churchyard—every time we marched past it on the working party there were bikes there."

"Where do I leave them mate?"

"Leave the bikes under the bridge over the River Thune on the edge of the village. The place is inhabited these days only by old people, women and children. The chances are they won't have the energy to go searching for them—the local soldiers probably nick everything anyway, so the owners might not even bother to report to the military authorities that their property has been stolen."

"OK Nobby it sounds good."

"I know we are taking a lot on supposition with this plan but the beauty of it is its simplicity.

"We won't be travelling through enemy territory as fugitives with contrived identities. It will succeed or fail on our ability to get to that aerodrome and find a plane. By the way, I've had another conversation with Ron. I got him to explain to me how to start up the Albatross and check how much petrol there is in the tank. He told me you can't start them on your own so you will have to know exactly what to do. I've got it written down for you."

"No worries, I'm good with engines," said Mick.

"The last time I spoke to Middleton he wasn't sure about the range of that particular plane but he reckoned it might be as much as 150 miles on a full tank—which would get us to the Dutch border. If not, it may mean we have to land somewhere to refuel."

"How the fuck are we going to do that Nobby?"

"I don't know Mick—but somehow we're going to have to nick some fuel from the aerodrome and take it with us."

"You are fucking mad you know that don't you," laughed Mick.

"Yeah—well I've got a date with a girl called Emily and I intend to keep it. I admit I am mad—mad about her!"

35
READY TO GO

The next week the German uniforms and two military caps were completed and he paid Albert £10 out of the money that Anna had sent him concealed in a box of tea. It bought Albert's total silence. At that moment no one in the Sergeant's block knew anything about the advanced stage of the escape plan; only that some time ago he'd expressed a vague notion about stealing a plane from the aerodrome—which for a day or two had been a source of great amusement among the NCOs.

They were ready to go and now needed more unwitting compliance from Manfred to put their plan into action. The two Germans wanted stocks in the lake to last as long as possible and agreed that he could fish on the Thune—but instead of killing the trout he caught they wanted him to re-stock the lake. This seemed a shrewd plan to the two Germans because it meant that he would have to keep on returning to the lake with the fish while they were alive.

They were so pleased with the profits from their business that they now almost saw him as some kind of a partner and the fact he might escape when out fishing receded from their mind. When he suggested he should teach Manfred to fish they agreed immediately. Meanwhile, the two uniforms had been successfully smuggled out of the camp under their prison clothes and were neatly folded into a sack that had been buried at the furthest end of the garden from the entrance.

Frank had also put into the sack some tinned food and a small stove in case they had to make their way on foot across the Dutch border after ditching the Albatross. He exchanged his remaining sterling in a number of small deals around the camp with German Marks.

The fact neither of them could speak any German—or had any ID papers—meant they would probably never be able to spend the money. However, he thought it better to have some cash in case it could be used for bribes. If they did have to leg it across enemy territory they would be more likely to be dependent upon Mick's thieving skills.

Manfred took 25 minutes before he could cast the flying maggot even 20 feet and seemed to have no sense of timing or rhythm. There was a spot on the lake where it had narrowed to 15 yards across in a deep channel that led to the river. It was also well away from where Mick would dig up his German uniform and put it on. He took Manfred there so his casting would have more chance of getting a successful result. On the third cast the German hit a fish.

"I got one, I got one," he shouted gleefully but then made the classic mistake of many novices. He tried to yank the trout ashore without playing it. The delicate silk cast was smashed and the empty line flew up behind him.

"Ah I lose him," he sighed.

"Don't worry Manfred. You got excited and tried to bring the fish ashore too soon. Have another go."

In the next half hour Manfred caught two fish and was so excited by what he had done that he did not even mention Mick who had been left to his own devices for nearly an hour. When Frank and Manfred returned to the camp fire with his two fish, Mick was back in his prison clothes and brewing up.

He winked at Frank. Later that day on their evening stroll he said to him: "Tomorrow morning I'll give Manfred another lesson to give you the chance of nicking the second bike. After you get back I'll suggest that I go and fish the upper Thune in the afternoon. I'll make for the bridge over the Thune and go into concealment there until you arrive. At 2.30pm you tell him you are going for a shit, run to where our stuff is buried, whip on your German uniform over your prison clothes, bring the sack with my uniform, the boots and the food—and leg it to me as quickly as you can.

"I reckon we've got an hour before he'll raise the alarm. You'll need 15 minutes to get to me, which gives us 45 minutes to cover the two or three miles to the aerodrome on our bikes.

"We can do that easily. If there are no planes available we'll have to go into concealment and wait for our chance. I don't think they'll come looking for us at the aerodrome. They'll rush off in the direction of Paderborn. We've got enough food and water to last out for several days in concealment if we have to."

The next day Manfred had his fishing lesson, caught a further three fish and was relaxed about Frank going up the Thune to see if he could catch some fish to re-stock the lake. He told the Sergeant he would only allow him to be away for an hour and to go no further than the village.

Frank waded downstream wading with a growing sense of euphoria. He was free and he felt good but he did not allow the elation to overrule his good sense. Wherever he could he stayed at river level to keep out of sight. He was not too concerned about being seen by civilians but did not want to be spotted by German soldiers who would blow the whistle on a man dressed in dark blue prison clothes.

He succeeded in reaching the bridge within half an hour, found some bushes and lay down in them to wait out of sight about 30 yards from the bridge. He discovered the bicycles had also been left concealed in the bushes which meant they could get started as soon as Mick arrived.

Half an hour later Mick arrived beneath the bridge panting heavily. He was dressed in his German uniform and it was the first time Frank had seen him wearing it.

He thought for a moment Mick was a German and ducked down out of sight. Within a couple of minutes they were cycling like mad up the road—both dressed as soldiers. Miraculously they did not encounter anyone at all on the short ride to the aerodrome, except for a passing lorry which ignored them.

They left the bikes on the edge of a small pine wood at the edge of the aerodrome and set up an observation post less than 100 yards from one of several hangars. The aerodrome appeared to have a control tower 300 yards from where they lay concealed—and several Albatross training planes were parked up outside it.

The field was lined with large tents which had been turned into make-shift workshops and a forge where fitters, smithies and carpenters worked side by side. Frank estimated that there were about 40 people working there. Periodically two mechanics and an instructor and a trainee would step outside the control tower, the trainee would turn over the propeller blade to start the engine and the two flyers would taxi down the runway before turning into the wind and taking off.

"How the fuck are we going to get our hands on a bloody plane with them parked over there?" asked Mick, who was clearly disappointed that they had come so far only to be thwarted at this last stage. They spent the entire afternoon in concealment watching the goings-on at the aerodrome with planes taking off every few minutes.

"We're buggered Nobby," said Mick. "Let's hop it on those bikes and see how far we can get."

Frank replied sharply. "No sod that. We have just got to be patient Mick. What do you think those hangars are for? I can tell you what they are used for—they are bloody garages and workshops for the planes. If they park one in our hangar tonight it'll mean we can nick it shortly after dawn before all the activity starts tomorrow."

"Yeah—but we could be caught by then. It's nearly two and a half hours since we hopped it and even that bloody fool Manfred must have come to the conclusion by now that we've buggered off," said Mick pessimistically.

"I don't think they'll come looking here. They'll rush down to Paderborn and check the station first—then they'll start searching the woods and hedgerows in that direction.

"They'll expect us to put as many miles between ourselves and Sennelager as we can. They won't expect us to go two or three miles up here and then stop. We'll just have to hope they don't bring dogs in yet. We need to be patient and watch and wait."

He was right. As the evening began to set in the aircraft were dispersed to the various hangars around the aerodrome.

A silver Albatross with a red propeller and its customary black crosses was pulled by a tractor to the hanger which they had under observation.

"Christ—just look at that," said Frank jubilantly.

"What mate?" asked Mick.

"They are going to re-fuel her. There's a fuel truck coming across the field. That is fantastic—they are doing our job for us. It means that we won't have to look for any petrol to take any with us, unless there are cans in the hangar.

"At first light tomorrow we'll break in there and push her out. In fact with a bit of luck they won't even put her inside on a fine dry night."

"I bet they'll leave a fucking guard by that hanger though," whispered Mick.

"So what, we'll take him out at dawn. It won't be a problem with the two of us—especially as we're dressed as Germans."

Darkness fell and a sentry had been left on guard at the hangar—but the mechanics did not put the Albatross inside it. She was parked outside and she was full of fuel.

"We'll just do it the brazen way Mick. No creeping up on him—we might get shot. We'll wait till just before dawn then we'll walk over—looking like we're laughing and talking together.

He'll be surprised and bothered—but because we're wearing German uniforms he won't shoot, even if he challenges us. We'll just go on walking right up to him smiling and laughing.

"When we get there you chin him and knock him unconscious. We'll disarm him—the rifle will come in useful—and we'll dump him inside the hangar tied up with one of his socks in his mouth."

That was exactly what they did, but the hours leading up to dawn seemed to last longer than any he had known in his life. They opened two cans of baked beans and ate them cold. It did little to satisfy them in their interminable wait.

The first signs of daylight eventually came with a spectacular dawn chorus from the woodland. They communicated in sign language knowing how easily sound would travel towards the German sentry at night.

He thought of Emily for the first time since their escape and there was a stirring desire within him at the thought of seeing her again. All he had to do was get through the next 24 hours according to the plan and then the prospect of meeting her and loving her again could become a reality.

He was getting close to achieving his dream and he told himself that nothing bar an accident would stop him now from being with her again for the first time in more than a year.

36
TAKE OFF TO HOLLAND

Having squared the Albatross into the wind the two men were ready to start the pre-take-off routine. The German sentry had been slugged by Mick's huge right fist and they stripped him, tied him up and removed his rifle and ammunition. Mick now stood on the lower wing and helped to push Frank—with the full petrol can they'd found in the hangar—onto the lower wing and into the cockpit so he could do an instrument rating.

He sat on the fuel can because there was no other space for it. The can gave him a bit of elevation over the engine cowling but he could not see ahead clearly. He remembered what Ron had said . . . the forward visibility for the pilot in an Albatross was crap.

He remembered how to adjust the elevator trim using the small wheel inside the cockpit. He would need to maintain it by screwing down the length of elastic bungee attached to the rudder bar.

To keep the Albatross in trim during flight, he would be constantly adjusting the rudder at his feet. Jet had told him some pilots preferred to fly without the bungee setting and thus endure a rudder bias on the right foot—the disadvantage of this was that on long flights it meant the pilot had to watch out for cramp in his calf muscles.

He pushed the rudder bar on each side, to make sure it was free from any impediment. He waggled the joystick with his right hand pulling it backwards and forwards. It moved the flaps (elevators) up and down, which in flight governed climb and descent. Pulling the joystick sideways—to left and right—controlled the aileron that turned the biplane left or right into a dive. He could not help admiring the efficiency of the latest German technology.

He signalled to Mick—who was at the front of the plane. Mick pulled the propeller through its arc twice. He primed the engine with the small pump in the cockpit to gravity feed sufficient fuel through the carburettors, then activated the inertia starter.

Mick pulled heavily on the propeller and the engine roared to life. He pulled away the "chocs" and raced round to the side of the plane, jumped on the wing and into the observer seat. Then they saw that a motorcycle had left the control tower and was speeding towards them. Mick yelled.

"For fuck's sake don't hang about Nobby!"

There were things that had to be done and he didn't intend to bugger up the take-off by forgetting something important. He screwed down the primer but knew he must allow more precious seconds to elapse for the engine to warm up. It was now running smoothly and the instrument panel was fully active.

He checked the gauges; oil pressure, oil temperature, fuel and once again the brake pressure—and then ran up the engine to full revs. Everything was OK. He switched over to the main fuel tank and took a last glimpse at the trims. He held the kite steady on the brakes, continued to rev up and then released them.

The machine shot forward like an impatient racehorse but the motor-cycle was now less than 100 yards away and a soldier in the sidecar waved his rifle at them frantically.

"Shall I shoot the fuckers Nobby?" screamed Mick. "There's a belt of ammo in this gun."

"Try to disable the motorbike—don't kill them," he ordered as Mick took aim and fired off a short burst from the machine gun destabilizing the Albatross and making it skid sideways violently.

"For Christ's sake don't do that again until we're airborne," he shouted.

He regained control of the aeroplane and the Albatross sprang forward again gathering speed over the grass meadow. Mick had miraculously missed both machine and men but the burst of fire had terrified the two guards who lost control and jumped off the bike as it overturned.

They ran frantically across in front of the moving plane and aimed their rifles at the fuselage. This time Mick used the rifle he'd taken from the sentry and put in four shots at the Germans who dived to the ground for cover.

Frank took no notice of what was happening around him and the machine sped past the crouching soldiers gathering more speed. He heard or felt a bullet ricochet near him as it pinged off the cylinder head. He had never come so close to getting a bullet through the brain.

The Germans had rolled out of the way at the last moment to save themselves from being chopped up in the propeller as the Albatross raced down the landing strip away from them.

They continued to fire at the plane and one or two bullets ripped into the canvass fuselage but the trainer continued to bump along down the landing strip; its engine roaring louder every moment.

He eased back the joystick at 60 knots and they were airborne, climb-ing into the early morning sky. He banked to port at 2,000 feet and gave them a full view of the ground below—including Sennelager prison camp which they flew over directly.

Mick had noticed a convoy of horse-drawn military vehicles on the road approaching the camp from Paderborn and was tempted to give them some.

"Shall I spray those German bastards on the ground and give the boys down there something to laugh about?" he asked.

"No don't make it personal Mick. Save your ammo in case another kite attacks us."

He was feeling a mixture of terror and exultation.

Here he was struggling with the controls of a violent mechanical beast 2,000 feet above the ground unable to avoid a disaster if things went wrong. He remembered clearly the instructions that Jet had given him during the lessons in Ireland but realised modern warplanes were now much more sophisticated than the primitive Bleriot he had flown several years ago.

So far she was flying smoothly and the engine sounded sweet but he felt the surging power of the Albatross and it sickened him with fear. They flew over Paderborn and he followed the curving line of the Lippe for several miles. It began to change its course so often that after 10 minutes he decided to ignore the river and follow the compass on a course due West.

The gamble seemed to pay off and over the next 25 minutes they passed over Lippstadt and Hamm and crossed the green undulating country-side, woodland and valleys of Westphalia cruising at 90 knots. Half an hour into the flight they remembered they were still wearing German uniforms.

These—apart from Frank's trousers which he had to keep on because he couldn't take his foot off the rudder bar—were ditched over the rim of the two cockpits. There was little sign of life below and the roads appeared empty. Behind him in the observer cockpit Mick scanned the skies constantly through an arc of 360 degrees searching for signs of hostile aircraft.

There were aircraft flying in the vicinity at a much higher altitude but the lone Albatross was ignored. The white arrow on the fuel gauge gradually sank to half level by the time they reached what he believed was Wesel and he looked anxiously for the Lippe again so that he could follow it to its confluence with the Rhine.

They passed over Wesel and he began to worry that he had got his calculations wrong. Two minutes went by but there was no sign of the mighty river—and he began to question his own judgment. He descended to 1,000 feet. Where were they? The river was not where he thought he would find it. Just as his self-doubt began to develop into a feeling of panic they saw the Rhine ahead and he immediately experienced a surge of optimism.

"We're on the bloody way now—Holland here we come!" he shouted to himself.

He banked to the right to turn due north. The Rhine was nearly 200 yards wide here and it was heavy with barge traffic going both up and down river. He spoke down the tube triumphantly to Mick who had been strangely quiet for the past half an hour weighing up the chances of German fighters diving upon them out of the sun.

Mick, who rated himself a first-class machine gunner, felt almost disappointed that his marksmanship was not going to be tested. Frank was now flying low and many people on the ground waved at them in a friendly fashion. He spoke down the tube to Mick.

"We're now heading due north we should cross the Dutch border at Spiik Keep your eyes open for the border crossing points and barbed wire fences.

"No worries Nobby."

He looked at the fuel gauge again and saw with alarm that it now read only one quarter full. It was going to be touch and go. Could they reach Spiik? He knew he'd have to come to a decision soon whether to find a field large enough to land to re-fuel the plane from the five gallon tank he had lugged on board and upon which he was now sitting.

The Albatross droned on at 90 knots flying into a strengthening head-wind but following the course of the mighty river—they covered 10, then 15, and then 20 miles but there was no sign of any large town or of any border posts and barbed wire fences which would mark the end of enemy territory.

He worried he'd read the compass wrongly, or perhaps under-estimated the distance to Spiik from Wesel. The map he'd got his hands on in the camp library had indicated that only thirty miles of flying would be nec-essary by travelling north down the Rhine to the Dutch border at Spijk. Maybe his calculations had been wildly inaccurate. He looked at the fuel gauge again and it was now dropping to almost zero.

"That's it Mick. We're practically out of fuel. I'm going to look for a field to put down in. I shall keep the engine running and pour the contents of the can straight into the tank from here in my cockpit.

"I shall need you to hop out and keep hold of the tail while I do it— then turn her straight into the wind. When we are on the ground keep your eyes open for unwelcome guests—and this time shoot to kill with your rifle. We're bloody nearly there now and I'm not too worried about topping people who want to stop us."

"I'm a marksman—remember?"

He kept to the left bank of the river flying downstream and looked across to select a flat meadow in the undulating countryside. In the dis-tance he saw one and began to descend until he was flying at 300 feet. Lanes, hedges, and small copses of tall poplar trees flashed below and he noticed the meadow for which they were heading was almost alongside a village. That meant curious people and was not good news.

It was too late now—they were almost upon it and down to 100 feet and the engine had begun to splutter for lack of fuel. As they came in he realized the field was full of cattle most of which had been lying down.

"Oh shit, we don't want to hit one of those," he said to himself.

He throttled back sharply and the Albatross literally sank onto the field, narrowly missing a telegraph pole on the road as it came down. The machine hit the ground too hard and far too fast but the meadow was a long one and he was not unduly worried unless the under-carriage had been severely damaged—preventing a subsequent take-off. They bumped noisily at over 60 miles an hour across the rough grass surface scattering the herd of cattle that ran amok in terror at the approach of the roaring machine.

It was Mick who noticed it first. He wasn't strapped in and had peered over the side of the cockpit to look ahead as the aircraft careered down the meadow.

"For fuck's sake Nobby—you've dropped us right in the shit here mate!"

He had no view ahead of him because of the engine mounting and did not see the deep open ditch that bisected the meadow, until they were only a few yards from it. The Albatross plunged down into the deep dip with a sharp sheering noise of tearing metal as the propeller bit deep into the soil and was dislodged from the front of the fuselage, cutting out the engine.

The effect of the collision in gravitational terms was to cause the entire aircraft to do a forward somersault before landing on its back across the far side of the ditch. Fortunately the two occupants were thrown out of the fuselage as the Albatross turned over on itself.

"Oh shit, what rotten bloody luck," he murmured to himself on the moment of impact before the world went black. Both men lay unconscious in the field unaware of their broken bones as the plane burst into the flames due to the ignition of the fuel in the five gallon tank upon which Frank had been sitting only moments before.

Sennelager prisoner graveyard

Memorial stone to prisoners

Fishing on the lake 2007

*Captain Mark Harrison of the British Army fishes the lake at Sennelager
in 2007 that Frank W Clarke fished in 1916*

River Thune

Frank W Clarke and his Australian companion Mick O'Connor made their escape from Sennelager along the banks of the River Thune.

Another view of the lake at Sennelager

37
EMILY AND THE BATTLE OF THE SOMME

Nurses like Sister Emily Horstmann serving on the Western Front knew it was a disaster long before the Generals had grasped the scale of the slaughter. On July 1st, the opening day of the battle, the British suffered 57,470 casualties, including 19,240 dead. A total of 35,493 men were wounded, 2,152 missing and 585 had been taken prisoner. The field hospitals and casualty clearing stations were overwhelmed in a tidal wave of maimed humanity whose frail bodies had succumbed to the red-hot shards of metal from bursting shells or German bullets from machine guns.

"The men were laid out in three rows on either side of the central alley way. It was a big hut and there were about 60 stretchers in each row. There was a space between the heads of one row and the feet of another row, but no space to pass between the stretchers of the same row; they touched.

"The old Territorials who worked with me passed up and down between the head and feet. I had a squad of 30 of these old orderlies and two sergeants and two priests, who were expert dressers. Wooden screens screened off the end of the hut opposite the entrance.

"Behind these were the two dressing tables where the priest dressed the wounds of the new arrivals and got them ready for the surgeons, after the old men had undressed them and washed their feet. In one corner was my kitchen where I kept all my syringes and hypodermic needles and stimulants." (Mary Borden, The Forbidden Zone)

Emily could not forget the horror of that first afternoon. Nothing had ever happened at Bellignies Hospital that could be compared to it. The Red Cross hospital was only three miles behind the reserve lines not far from the Albert-Bapaume Road. Some of the worst cases were brought to Mary Borden's hospital where Emily and her Australian friend Jackie Pretz.were put in charge of sorting out the wounded as they were brought in from the ambulances.

Outside there was another harrowing spectacle that cried out military disaster. The less seriously wounded men, some swathed in bandages, were walking or hobbling back in a state of shock from the scene of battle, some hardly able to stay upright, in columns that seemed to stretch for miles.

They were dazed, mud-fouled and bloodstained, faces blackened with cordite fumes. In the opposite direction and somehow finding space on the highway, horse-drawn artillery was being conveyed forward often at a desperate gallop to put pressure on the Germans and prevent counter-attacks. It was a chaotic scene.

Shell bursts from German artillery continued to land in the fields around the wounded men and sometimes they found human targets—compounding the misery of what was already a living hell.

Black fountains of earth were coughed up as shells burst at random on the nightmarish scene and men were lifted from their feet by the explosions in thick choking clouds of yellow smoke.

Miraculously, some walked through it unscathed and continued on their way—but the terrible din never ceased from the allied and German guns. Emily and Jackie had to grade the men from the dying to those who might possibly survive surgery. These critically wounded men, from several different regiments and of all ranks including officers, lay on the floor on the blood-stained stretchers that had brought them there.

The British class system of the old Edwardian era met its nadir here. Gentlemen and servants lay together. The sickly stench of body odour, sweat, blood, mud and dirt pervaded the air—overpowering the presence of chloroform, ether and disinfectant.

"My God, we've got to keep them alive long enough to have a chance. It seems so unfair, we hold the power of life and death," she whispered to Jackie—but loud enough to be heard above the din of moaning and crying. "We must give them all morphine, the poor loves. You take that row Jackie, I'll take this. Orderly bring morphine now—lots of it!"

Several young men died in front of them on the floor moments after being brought in—their lives ebbed away too soon. Those she felt still had a few minutes left to live became the urgent priority and she sent runners to the six operating rooms to plead for their lives to the surgeons. Emily graded the wounded from what was written on their ticket, from the way they looked and the coldness of the body she touched with her hand.

A dying man, soon to be a corpse, carried the encroaching freeze of death—and by now she knew it well. The surgeons, some stripped to the waist, worked like butchers on scores of wrecked bodies; the sweat shining on their shoulders as they leaned across the operating table and sawed and hacked at limbs that had to be amputated. The debris of limbs—arms, legs, hands, fingers and feet—were tossed into bins for the orderlies to clear away.

Emily wanted to turn her eyes away from these body parts but somehow she could not do so. Hours before they had been living limbs on men but were now just carcass remains. Mary Borden had warned her that a third of the men brought in would die after surgery—and a quarter would not make it to the operating rooms.

The overwhelming majority of casualties were shrapnel cases. The extent and gravity of the wounds on each man was dictated by his proximity to the shell burst in the air. A few feet could mean the difference between life and death.

The men lay in their filthy uniforms; many caked in mud and dried blood, mostly on their back and staring patiently at the steep iron roof of the hospital. The initial terror of being wounded—and of not knowing how seriously—abated as they grew weaker.

Those whose pain had been dulled by the morphine occupied a twilight world between consciousness and a timeless private and inward sense of drifting.

In some cases a trouser leg or a sleeve had been cut off by orderlies in the trenches or in no man's land. For most of the victims the terrible ordeal of having the shreds of a stiff uniform removed from an open wound was the first act of hospitalization and the men cried out in agony as it was done.

It was a job that fell to the elderly hospital orderlies—for the most part old territorial soldiers—who carried out their unenviable task with gentleness and sympathy, some with tears in their eyes at the plight of the young men. Many of the wounded soldiers, having cried out in pain, apologized to the old men for putting them to such trouble. Occasionally Mary Borden herself would come to comfort them.

Mary, an unconventional woman whose radical views were untypical of her generation, was born into a wealthy Chicago family and was living in England in 1914 at the outbreak of war. She used her own money to equip and staff a hospital at the Front in which she served as a nurse and recruited other young women who had the stomach to witness the ghastly harvest of trench warfare. She was later to become a significant early 20th century novelist. For now Mary Borden was much loved and respected by her nursing and orderly staff.

That first day had turned out to be the bloodiest day in the history of the British Army. Overall the Somme Offensive, fought from July to November 1916, incurred more than 1.5 million casualties as Allied forces attempted to break through the German lines along a 20-mile front north and south of the Somme.

The Germans held the high ground and had been more or less unmolested since October 1914, with time to construct extensive trench lines and deep shellproof bunkers in the chalky soil. The attack also lacked surprise and the Germans were waiting for the Tommies right along the length of the attacking line—waiting for the assault by young men who had never been under fire before.

The attacking infantrymen were burdened with a monstrous load of equipment and in some cases were ordered to form up into uniform waves and advance at a walking pace, like sheep to slaughter.

British artillery gunners lacked the accuracy to bring their fire onto the German trenches. North of the Albert-Bapaume road, the advance was a failure from the outset. In a few places, the attackers got into the German front-line trench system or even the support line, but invariably, their numbers were too few to withstand the German counter-attacks.

In a few places there were units with more enlightened officers. They ordered the men to crawl out into no man's land early and dumped much of their heavy kit—so they could rush the front German trench as soon as the barrage lifted.

"The leading battalions of the 36th Ulster Division had been ordered out from Thiepval wood just before 7.30 A.M. and laid down near the German trenches . . . At zero hour the British barrage lifted. Bugles blew the "Advance." Up sprang the Ulstermen and, without forming up in the waves adopted by other divisions, they rushed the German front line.

"By a combination of sensible tactics and Ulster dash, the prize that eluded so many, the capture of a long section of the German front line had been accomplished.

"At Gommecourt . . . attacking from the south, the 56th (London) Division had performed brilliantly. Making use of the new trench they had dug in No Man's Land and a smoke-screen, four battalions captured the whole of the German front-line system." (Martin Middlebrook—The First Day on the Somme.)

Overall there was little to celebrate apart from limited success in the French sector of the line. Communications were inadequate, and many commanders were largely ignorant of the progress of the battle. To make matters worse, initial casualties were especially heavy among officers, who still dressed differently from NCOs and other ranks, and whose uniforms the Germans had been trained to target.

In five months of attrition fighting that started in July 1916 the British and French captured little more than five miles at the deepest point of penetration—well short of original objectives. The British had gained approximately two miles and lost more than 420,000 soldiers. It was also a slaughterhouse for the Germans who had entered the war with a trained force of regulars and reservists.

The German Army Group Commander stated: "What remained of the old first-class peace-trained German infantry had been expended on the battlefield."

The Battle of the Somme was now more than two months old. Emily looked at herself in a mirror in the women's room of the Red Cross hospital before she came off duty. She sighed deeply at what she saw. There were lines around her eyes which were sunken deep into the sockets and ringed in a dark hue.

She looked thinner than she could remember and there was no longer the gaiety of expression in her face that had so enchanted Frank at Bellignies a year earlier. She rarely wore any make-up and was sad to see that the freshness in her face had been replaced by weariness from witnessing the death of so many young men at every turn. It had been the worst year of her life. First her brother Pete had been killed in a military accident in February while training with his regiment in Virginia.

A few weeks later in April her father Heinrich had died of a stroke, overcome with grief at the loss of his son. There was now pressure upon Emily to return to the United States and take up responsibility for running the apple farm.

She knew that she would eventually have to succumb to her mother's pleas for help and go back to the USA. Before she did that she wanted to make contact with the man she loved who was the focus of her life.

Above her bed she had hung the framed oil painting of Frank fishing on the lake in the early summer of 1915. His mother Anna had reluctantly parted with it. Apart from a few snapshots it was all the record she had of him. She had to rely on her daydreams for memories of her Englishman and his mellifluous voice.

"I have never seen such mutilation," Jackie said to Emily that night as she lay in bed.

"I thought the sight of inner guts dropping out of a man's body would make me want to vomit—but I feel only a kind of numbness. I can't cry either—there are no tears within me. I've just tended to one man who appears to have lost his arm and most of his right shoulder—yet he smiled at me.

"All I could do was smile back and tell him not to worry. In reality he's now just a collection of body parts and will die during the night. I'm not sure I can stand much more of this. Tomorrow I have been detailed to check the identities of the remains of the men in the bags and I know I won't be able to do that."

She turned over to go to sleep having turned out the bedside light. A crucifix had been hung on the wall above her bed and she said her prayers quietly—even though she felt inwardly she was even losing her faith. Jackie decided to speak to one of the priests about her spiritual dilemma.

Her Christian faith, her values and sense of duty as a nurse were so intertwined that to lose one aspect seemed to seriously damage the integrity of the others. She also missed her family in Woy Woy.

As Jackie slept, Emily read four or five of Frank's collection of romantic letters and then wrote a letter to Anna asking if she had received any further information about his whereabouts.

She had been sick with worry that she had heard nothing from Frank for a month. One day he was at Sennelager and the next he seemed to have gone. Had he somehow escaped, was it successful, or was he in trouble again?

When Anna received her worried letter, she wrote back immediately saying that she had received a report via the Sergeant's Committee at Sennelager explaining what had happened.

He had been involved in an escape attempt by stealing an aircraft and had been recaptured in Germany—but his whereabouts were unknown.

Emily had still not received Anna's letter the following week when she volunteered to accompany an ambulance team of four vehicles, its drivers and two orderlies in each, to the field hospital at the front nearly two miles away to pick up wounded men. She was instructed by Mary Borden to take a message to the senior surgeon asking for additional supplies of chloroform and ether.

It was expected to be a routine trip that would not take more than two hours but would expose all in the party to more intensive shellfire from German artillery than they had been used to. Coming so close to the Front Line would put the convoy at considerable risk but by now Emily had seen so much death and mutilation she felt no fear for her own life.

She was indifferent to danger—in fact she welcomed it out of a feeling deep within her that perhaps she needed to experience the trauma of being wounded to better understand her patients. It was called the guilt of survival.

They arrived at the field hospital.

"We'll take the convoy to the back of the field hospital Sister and I'll send the orderlies inside with stretchers to fetch out the ones that are to come back with us," the driver at the head of the ambulance convoy told her.

"Just as you wish Jacob—but do tell the men not to rush things. I am sure these patients are in great pain despite the morphine so let's be gentle with them even if it takes longer to load up the ambulances. We'll just have to put up with being shelled."

The convoy approached the ruined village which had been demolished by gunfire the previous year and followed a winding track through an orchard of tree stumps where three large tents had been erected. A further tent set back from the others served as the hospital's morgue.

There was intermittent shellfire coming from behind the German lines a mile and a half to the east and every few minutes a salvo landed less than 100 yards away from the ruined village. A recent artillery attack had devastated a battalion field kitchen pulled by several teams of horses and the mutilated animals were still lying on the side of the road as the ambulances came past.

Emily delivered the written message from Mary Borden to the chief surgeon, helped herself to a cup of coffee from the field hospital canteen and walked outside into the orchard to light a cigarette. She had found it impossible not to smoke in recent months despite everything she had said in the past to Frank about the evils of the tobacco habit. She took a long drag on the cigarette, sipped her coffee from a mug and looked by chance into the sky.

She was thinking of Frank as she watched a silver grey biplane approaching west in a steep descent and then it banked to port and appeared to make directly towards the ruined village. She saw the black cross on the fuselage as it turned and she recognized the plane as an Albatross.

Moments later she saw that a second German plane was following the first one and heading on the same course. For a moment she was puzzled about the sudden appearance of the two aircraft but assumed they were a reconnaissance mission. A small voice within Emily pleaded with her to take cover but the late September sun was still warm and she lingered for the next 10 seconds as the planes came in.

She continued to smoke her cigarette and watch their approach in fascination. Her stomach churned when the first plane flew over at less than 200 feet and dropped what looked like a small black object on a trajectory directly headed to where she stood. Still she did not turn to seek shelter even though it was too late. Emily's last thought three seconds later was an image of Frank smiling at her. . . . after that there was only darkness preceded by what seemed like a huge banging noise.

"There are no men here; so why should I be a woman? There are heads and knees and mangled testicles. There are chests with holes in as big as your fist, and pulpy thighs, shapeless; and stumps where legs were once fastened.

"There are eyes—eyes of sick dogs, sick cats, blind eyes, eyes of delirium; and mouths that cannot articulate; and parts of faces—the nose gone, or the jaw. There are these things, but no men; so how could I be a woman here and not die of it?" (Mary Borden, *The Forbidden Zone*)

38
WESEL MILITARY PRISON

Both men regained consciousness at the point of a bayonet. Two elderly members of the Landsturm insisted on poking them aggressively with the tip of their bayonet while fuming and spitting with rage in German invective. Their captives were in such pain from broken limbs that the minor cuts sustained by the bayonets seemed of little importance—and in Frank's case the frustration of being caught again was so great that he did not care whether he was shot.

He was struck down with a sense of hopelessness and tears of rage—rather than pain—filled his eyes. Mick saw the lighter side of things and kept a smile on his face which intensified the anger around him. The two old soldiers had been driven to further heights of indignation and apoplectic reaction because of the baying of a large crowd of local civilians from the village who had gathered in the field after the Albatross exploded in a sheet of flame ignited by the fuel can.

Among them was the enraged farmer who believed at least six of his cows that were in calf would abort as a result of the sudden descent upon his herd of a raging mechanical beast. He wielded a pitchfork with which he threatened both Frank and Mick before being pushed back by one of the soldiers. They kept the lynch mob at bay successfully after the pitchfork incident but remained angry because they could not work out how or why two men, dressed in prisoner-of-war uniforms, had managed to steal a German military aircraft and fly it to within a few miles of the Dutch border. They demanded answers to questions that neither man could understand.

"Englander?" screamed one of the Germans at Mick while prodding him roughly in the ribs again. Mick laughed despite his agony.

"Fuck off mate I'm a bloody Aussie."

He had a broken arm, broken ribs and a serious spinal injury. Frank had broken his left leg as he hit the ground, having been tipped out of the fuselage as it somersaulted out of the ditch.

He was too pissed off to see the funny side of it like Mick—who revelled in the furious attention he was attracting. The pandemonium continued for a further 25 minutes until a horse-drawn ambulance and fire crew arrived and the two men were put onto stretchers and taken to the military hospital at Wesel.

They had several visits from intelligence officers during their confinement in hospital demanding to know exactly how they had escaped from Sennelager. They stuck to their story of running away from a field working party and no mention was made of fish or fishing.

After three visits the intelligence officers stopped coming to the hospital and they imagined wrongly that they were in the clear.

Wesel Prison, a mediaeval castle, was run by the military and some of the inmates were German and Austrian servicemen who had committed a range of offences and were serving sentences.

There were also some hardened civilian prisoners believed to be gangsters and a greater number of what were regarded as especially troublesome Allied prisoners. The latter were in the main habitual escapers, mainly officers and serving sentences for "crimes" committed while on the run. Frank accepted that the Germans would probably regard him as an ideal candidate for long term confinement at Wesel.

The Commandant was tall, thin, blonde haired and wore a monocle.

"You are both criminals and will be charged with two counts of attempted murder, assault and stealing and damaging German state property. The lesser charges of stealing and damaging the property of German civilians will not be proceeded with because of the serious nature of the primary charges—some of which can carry the death sentence.

"You will have separate hearings and you will each be required to appear at your own preliminary hearing—to be held in this prison. You will not be in court for sentencing in the law courts. The charges against you both are criminal and for that reason you are deemed to be outside the protection of the terms of the Geneva Treaty and the auspices of the Red Cross.

"I hope that you understand the serious trouble you are both in. You are at liberty to speak for yourself at the preliminary hearings or a German officer with legal training can be instructed to act on your behalf. Which is it to be?"

Frank said: "We demand to be treated as prisoners of war who were attempting to carry out our duty to escape from captivity in enemy territory. Any damage to property incurred in the execution of our duty is incidental and cannot be the subject of a separate criminal charge. You know all that as well as I do."

The major's face creased in anger and flushed crimson. His mouth quivered as he struggled to control himself.

"How dare you address an officer in such an impertinent manner? Remember you are an NCO. In camps all over Germany there are respectable British officers who accept their confinement and in some cases even sign parole. They set an example which you—a mere sergeant—have chosen to ignore."

The cells were nine feet in length and four and a half feet in width with a 10 foot ceiling. High up in the wall was a window two feet square but admitting only a tiny shaft of daylight.

It was heavily barred, while outside was a sloping hood which descended to below the sill, so all the light which penetrated into the cell was reflected from below against the black interior of the hood.

The window was glazed but filthy and the tiny quantity of light remaining was obstructed further by small-mesh wire netting.

Consequently the interior was wrapped in a dismal gloom throughout the greater part of the day, through which one could scarcely discern the floor when standing upright. After daylight waned the cell was enveloped in blackness until daybreak.

The bed comprised three rough wooden planks and a mattress. There was a small jug and a sanitary pan. High on the wall was a shelf. The stone wall itself was about two feet thick and covered with gloomy inscriptions by past prisoners.

Frank was still in plaster and could only hobble with a walking stick. He eased himself down on the wooden bed. He heard the turning of the key. The jailer entered with a bowl containing soup and black bread. The former did not smell good but he drank it.

As the night wore on he began to shiver with the cold. How he passed that first night he could not recall the next day, but he was certain that a greater part of the time was passed in delirium and he almost cried with delight when he saw the first rays of the breaking day.

In the weeks that followed, he realized that whether by sheer indifference or deliberate policy he was now the victim of a far more deadly regime than the one orchestrated in Sennelager by Major Bach in 1915.

He would not be badgered, coaxed, or threatened in the hope of extorting a signed confession, but condemned to a regime of loneliness, silence and solitude. The gloom could be felt and within a short time would eat into his soul. The sense of hopelessness and the indifference of the guards to his plight were deepened by deprivation of exercise and insufficient food. His previous incarceration at Sennelager told him that his brain would be the first to succumb to the utter loneliness. Somehow he needed to dream well again.

DREAMS OF THE NAR 1895—DIARY ENTRY 1916

In the last trout season of his life—and in my 12th year—George Printer purchases a 10-foot split cane fly rod and presents it to me together with a steel fly-reel to which he adds a braided silk line that is ideal for short casting on a small river.

'May and June—my favourite months old chap—provided it is warm with a few heavy showers to put a spate on the brooks and streams. When it comes to trout fishing in Norfolk everyone talks about the Wensum—and that is certainly a wonderful chalk river with prolific fly life—but few speak of the native brown trout in the Nar, the Glaven, the upper reaches of the Heacham, the Babingley and the upper Gaywood.

'The Nar also supports a run of sea trout and even a few salmon. A good flow of water on the Nar is needed to ensure that gravel beds, used for spawning by trout and migratory fish, are kept free from silting.

'Fortunately most of the farmers around here support the argument in favour of a clean river and carry out the necessary maintenance work using their own labour force.

'One thing you will always have to remember Frank is that nature only thrives when mankind cares about keeping a delicate balance between his needs and the requirements of the wild creatures around us.

'There are other rivers in Norfolk whose upper stretches have been abused by bad farming, but I think many of these are still worth exploring for trout. They include the Tud and the Mun, plus a score more brooks, some less than 12 feet wide, that don't even have a name.

'I want you to promise me Frank that after I'm gone you'll go on fishing these little streams for me and champion their cause—because I shall leave all my tackle to you. Fred, John and Thomas have their own equipment and your brothers are not so interested in angling. So you will inherit. This rod I have given you is really designed for the Wensum because of its length, but it will be good practice for you to use on the smaller rivers.

'Oh don't talk about inheritance grandfather—there's plenty of life left in the old dog yet,' I tell him.

"Yes Grandad, don't talk about that please!" pipes up Emily who has joined us on our way along the road and is pushing a small pram with a small black china doll in it.

"Well, we shall see."

I take Emily by the hand and continue: 'Anyway these small rivers you talk of are just names to me at the moment. You will have to take me with you, show me where they are—and how to fish them with my new rod.'

We climb aboard the trap and start off on a journey through the flat lanes to the picturesque village of Castle Acre. The three of us stay overnight at the Ostrich Inn so that we can be up at dawn for the morning rise. The village is dominated by the ruins of an early Norman castle and priory—and flowing through its centre is the River Nar.

It is a clear and gentle stream with shallow glides and deeper pools that hold abundant numbers of small wild trout up to 16 ounces or more. They rise enthusiastically to a dry fly in the evening and early mornings—and grab any wet fly presented under the surface during spate conditions.

As we walk across the fields to explore downstream from Castle Acre, I notice the grasslands are carpeted with blood red poppies and other wild plants including wild orchid and cowslips.

The air is thick with the flight of butterflies, dragon and damsel flies, and the banks of the river are busy with darting Kingfisher, industrious Grey Wagtails rooting out worms—and moorhens slipping in and out of the indigenous aquatic bushes, reeds and exotic plant life lining the river.

Grandfather tells me about the world of the River Nar and its valley—a favourite with game anglers.

'This is a unique part of Norfolk because the river is flanked by floating water meadows which were put here by man a hundred years ago to provide a natural run-off from the marshland parts of the surrounding farmland. The floating water meadows round here were in continuous use until quite recently.

'The abundance of wet conditions supports rich flora and fauna and means that the river is a spectacular place to observe bird life and the insect life—both of which I know interest you.

'Long after my lifetime I am sure you will come here with young Emily and enjoy, like I do, the extraordinary variety of the

337

plants in this valley.

'What do you mean by floating water meadows?' asks Emily.

'Bed work or floated water-meadows were built on almost-level fields along broad river valleys in many parts of the country but they are rare in Norfolk. They require careful construction to ensure correct operation and were used to divert water from the river and keep it at a higher level, often along the edge of the valley.

'This water was then used to supply many smaller carriers on the crests of ridges built across the fields. Each small carrier would overflow slowly down the sides of its ridge and this seeping water would be collected in drains which return the water to the river.

'The complex mixture of wet and drier ground still gives derelict water-meadows superb fertility in the soil, which of course is exactly what the game angler wants—and as an example the River Nar is literally full of well fed trout because of the diversity of insect food.'

He points to the flying insects all around us and I recognise several species which are not common such as the Small Red-eyed Damselfly, the Four-spotted Chaser and the Norfolk Hawker. Emily chases them but after a few moments gives up laughing.

We come to a gentle gliding run not far below a wooden bridge which a farmer has put there so that his collies can drive the sheep across it to the pens by the farm. George opens his fly box and shows it to me.

'Most keen anglers will have different fly boxes to suit different rivers. Below Litcham the Nar is a Chalk river which means that my box here is full of gnats, midges, olives, duns, spinners, caddis and sedges—and of course the mayfly. To have success on this river we need to fish with tiny flies and light delicate gut leaders of no more than 2lbs breaking strain. We have to learn to cast lightly upon the water—no more than three casts onto one spot or the trout will go down.

'Remember always that they are wild trout, not stupid stocked fish. Wading is OK where the banks are steep, but better avoided if possible by the more skilful angler. Keep well behind the fish in the pool you intend to try to bring on to your fly—and don't pile up on top of those that are swimming in midstream between

338

you and your quarry.

'The other secret is to come to the pool and stay still for at least five minutes before even thinking of drawing line off your reel. The best friend of the Nar fisherman, apart from skill, is patience.'

'Oh I'm so excited I can't keep still,' laughs Emily.

In time, these parcels of advice from George Printer all become familiar aspects of my skill range, but this first expedition to the little river turns into something of a disaster.

I have not used a fly rod before, even in less demanding reservoir or lake fishing, and am entirely unable to deploy sufficient skill to outwit a wild fish.

First my timing on the cast is errant because I have not developed any familiar rhythm, especially on the back swing, and I try to thrust the line out towards the pool with my elbows too far wide of my waist.

By the time I master the timing of the backswing, I still have to master the art of allowing the fly to sink gracefully and slowly through the air to the surface of the water in imitation of a dying insect. By the time I master the cast, I find I cannot control the flow and the pull of the current upon the fly line—which means that I will not be able to strike effectively on a rising fish.

Eventually I catch a small trout which hurls itself at my black gnat with such ferocity and enthusiasm that the tiny hook gets embedded in its lip—and even though I am late on the strike, the fish is still captive. Emily claps her hands in excitement and kisses me on the cheek.

'Don't worry too much Frank at this early stage. Many anglers never enjoy much success on a small chalk stream because they lack the skills to make it work for them. You already have the rhythm, now you have to learn more about what is happening in terms of fly life upon the river and how to be more cunning.

'Small stream fishing with the dry fly in clear water is as exciting as any type of angling and demands keener skills than any other. Your cast has to have the accurate flight of the most skilled archer.'

The old man then demonstrates his sublime skill by casting under a tree—without wading into the water—to the head of a pool where a trout has been swirling continuously for the 15 minutes in which the three of us have observed its feeding activity.

He perches himself midway down a steep bank strewn with small bushes, disturbing a Bank Vole, systematically draws off exactly the right length of line and with an unhurried action sends the dun skyward but directly under the branches of the obstructing tree. It hovers momentarily at the head of the pool before dropping with delicacy onto the surface.

A second later there is a flurry on the water, the hook set, and the trout is on. George, aware of the lightness of his tackle, plays the darting fish with great skill, and backs off gradually downstream to a point where he can net it.

The trout weighs slightly over 20 ounces and is released to live another day. He catches four more like this in the session. My initiation to dry fly fishing on chalk streams has started on a brilliant note by observing the technique of a master angler.

They were sentenced to nine months imprisonment for criminal damage of German state property and assault but the court found them not guilty of attempted murder—which was by far the most serious of the charges.

It meant they would both be confined in Wesel Prison until October 1917—that's if they managed to stay alive and he rated their chances at less than fifty-fifty with the diet regime imposed upon them.

The men were getting two bowls of vegetable soup with black bread each day and ersatz coffee twice a day. Once a week the soup the Germans served would have some kind of meat in it.

There was no sign of sustenance from Red Cross parcels for any of the men—or of food sent from their families in England, or of letters from loved ones. Both men were out of the punishment block and now joined other British and allied 'troublemakers' who were confined in the prison. He found it just about tolerable although his frequent bouts of claustrophobic despair and panic when confined to his tiny cell in the daylight hours began to trouble him deeply. He did not seem any longer to possess the inner strength to control the panic attacks by remaining detached or by focusing on events or memories of his earlier life.

In an act of considerable compassion—and entirely it may be said out of character—the Commandant decided that his Category A prisoners would go insane if they were not allowed access to one another in some kind of common room. He introduced a rota system which gave four men at a time two hours each day in the library common room.

It meant all 20 men would get out of their solitary confinement for a short period of time every day when they would also be allowed to shower or bath. The Commandant then permitted the prisoners to have two evening sessions a week of social intercourse when they would all gather in the one large room.

These took place in a long annexe that must have been intended originally as the prison library. Each wall was lined with empty bookshelves, but they were gradually filled by battered publications in several languages. Cards, dominoes and a darts board were also provided and the evening leisure periods of two hours from 7pm till 9pm were eagerly awaited by the men.

An elderly Scottish major of about 50 who introduced himself as Alan and who Frank had not seen before, told the first meeting that as the senior officer present he would decide what form these twice weekly meetings would take. The first thing they were going to do, said Alan, was elect a committee to make all the decisions on behalf of the group and these would be on a democratic basis. He would be chairman of the committee and it would be his task as the senior officer to represent it at all meetings with the Governor.

"We must have the confidence of knowing that we act with the moral authority dictated by civilised and Christian democratic rules—if you like as a fundamental act of defiance against an evil regime."

Frank held his tongue but thought to himself: "What a pompous fart. How bloody English—and coming from a Scotsman! Here we are in hell and we're going to deal with it by forming a committee. I can see everything's going to be on the committee's agenda except for bloody escaping. He wants us to become model citizens instead of soldiers."

Alan, who appeared to have the confidence and backing of several junior British officers in Wesel, liked to give what sounded like a sermon at each meeting before they relaxed with games and informal discussions.

He told the assembled group: "A free democratic moral society has the right as well as the obligation to resist the incursions of those perversions which would lead to its destruction. A free society requires order, discipline and moderation. Man is an imperfect creature living in an imperfect world but he should always strive to be better than he is. In this struggle we should never, never, never, give up."

He told them that those who functioned best in captivity were strong in three areas of belief: God, country, and family. While the enemy, he found, could repeatedly attack one's country, and might attempt to manipulate one's behaviour regarding God and family, there was nothing the Germans could do to change one's faith if one truly believed. God's enemies had no way of disproving belief.

The capability to make morally correct decisions derived from a code of conduct, a reminder of moral values; a sense of duty to one's country; one's Christian upbringing; military training and respect for rank.

He held up several pieces of paper with his code of conduct upon it and passed it around. Frank read it and was not in the slightest surprised that nowhere within the pious tome from Alan's pen was written the word escape.

Alan had been a regimental chaplain and in this mission—his walk with God—he had volunteered to work in the toughest German prisoner-of-war camps to help those allied soldiers who had to deal with living in the cruellest prison regimes.

When he had heard of the civilian jail at Wesel incarcerating soldiers deemed to have committed criminal offences while on the run, Alan had volunteered immediately to work there. The Germans appeared to trust him and thought he would be a calming influence upon the prisoners.

Frank agreed that it was a virtuous act of self-sacrifice on Alan' part to have done what he did and conceded that in the end it might result in the arrival of Red Cross food parcels and the introduction of privileges.

It would do nothing, however, to aid and abet those who nurtured plans to escape from Wesel Prison. His weight had already fallen to below nine stones and if it continued to drop much further he knew he would be too weak and debilitated to find the physical reserves of strength to make another escape attempt to get to Emily.

He would have to act quickly. There were no outside working parties at Wesel, so there was no realistic opportunity for escape while outside—and in the prison yard walking sessions they were kept under constant scrutiny. There were only two options.

Any escaper would need either to get hold of a disguise that would get him through the doors to the outside world—or obtain a copy of the relevant keys to doors that led to freedom. This would be difficult but surely not impossible. The first aim he now realised was to help Alan get Red Cross parcels restored because this would give prospective escapers a tool with which to work.

The food shortages in Germany meant that the guards could possibly be bribed with offers of scoff from the parcels in exchange for access to clothing, ID cards and duplicate keys.

The first blow came three months after the sentencing when Mick and six other private soldiers were called into the Commandant's office and told they would be transferred to labour parties repairing roads behind the German lines on the Western Front.

They were given less than 12 hours notice and to Frank's dismay he was not even able to exchange a few words with his old Australian friend. He caught a glimpse of him in the prison yard and they were able to manage a salutary wave. Frank was never to see Mick again.

39
THE TERRIBLE LETTER

He was fortunate not to have been shot summarily and he would have been had it not been for another prisoner's intervention. Instead, the guards put him in a straitjacket for 24 hours while he raged totally out of control. It was a paradox because all the other special category prisoners in Wesel Prison were celebrating.

The commandant had released a huge backlog of letters and agreed to allow the distribution of Red Cross parcels following the visit to the prison of a delegation from the Switzerland who had reminded him of the terms of the Geneva Treaty. Surely, they hinted, he would not want to be tried as a war criminal after the war.

A room was set up on the same floor of the cells for the storage of the parcels which the commandant said could be shared out on a weekly basis. Alan, as senior officer, had recommended strongly that the committee should pass a resolution making it compulsory that every prisoner would receive a weekly parcel, regardless of whether or not it was addressed to the prisoner. The food contents of each parcel would be shared out equally if there were insufficient parcels to go round the 20 inmates.

He said during the weekly meeting, at which Frank was not present: "This concession by the commandant will save our lives because it will stave off the likelihood of gradual starvation by the time the war ends. We know of course that we were entitled under international law to receive these gifts and the letters from our loved ones, but Germany is not a democracy as we understand the word and we can count ourselves lucky to have been the beneficiary of one man's humanitarian gesture.

"I should like you now to join me in saying a prayer for Sergeant Frank Clarke so that the Lord will bring him through his terrible ordeal in which he attacked a guard. We must pray that his sanity will be restored.

"It appears he received a letter from his mother in England telling him that his fiancée had been killed during the course of her nursing duties on the Western Front. He has been a prisoner-of-war since 1915, was a regular soldier in August 1914 and has been under extreme stress for all of these long months. I understand that having disarmed the guard he attempted to use the weapon to end his own life—and this was only prevented by the courageous intervention of another prisoner.

"That prisoner is here tonight and I should like to thank him personally on behalf of us all for the great risk that he took in saving the life of a brother prisoner."

Frank did not hear the long applause following Alan's short speech. He was asleep dreaming fitfully of Emily again.

They were together in the forest at Bellignies walking hand in hand.

Emily was at the centre of all his dreams now. At last all their troubles and frustration separations were over and they could look forward to a life of sublime content, make a family, even start a dynasty and live to grow old together untroubled by the haunting nightmare of a world war which just seemed to kill young people.

"After the war we'll get married in Norfolk and then I want you to come to America with me and make a new life there. You say you are a country boy and so you will find the life in Virginia exactly to your liking. You will be my equal partner in the ranch—and we'll build a cattle business together."

He smiled: "Emily you've given me a vision of heaven. There's nothing really to keep me in England except for Anna and she will have her family to look after her in Norfolk. Meanwhile, we'll have lots of babies and bring them up as healthy outdoor kids and come back to England when we can. I tell you what else—you'll have to give me plenty of time off to go trout fishing in the Blue Ridge Mountains. I've read stories about how the rivers are choc-a-bloc with good fish."

She hugged him: "You'll be too busy for that—remember you promised me you'll be my manager in building my political career and my run for the Senate. I'm afraid you are going to have to accept that your fishing days as a loner are over Sergeant. When we have time you're going to take me with you whenever you go fishing—and I bet I'll catch more than you. Suddenly she was gone."

He woke up in the darkness and looked around for Emily. For a few moments he could not understand where he was or why he had lost all freedom of movement. Then he remembered. It had been two days since they placed him in the straitjacket. He had read the letter from Anna while he was in the reading room with four other prisoners and it was as physically painful as any bullet.

It was a short letter because Anna felt she could say nothing else in it that did not involve Emily—but in truth she really had no inkling of how much they meant to one another. Emily had not told her that they were officially engaged and neither had he. She knew they were lovers and had spent months together hidden in a French chateau but the war had thrown up thousands of intense relationships like that.

They were often love affairs that would go nowhere after the War but were vested in the nature of the times—where so very little could be judged as normal. She hoped that was the case with Emily and her youngest son—and that the words she used in the letter would not break his heart.

The Farm

Colby

Norfolk

November 4th 1916

My dearest boy,

I do not know how many letters before this one that you will have received from me during your incarceration in Wesel Prison. I do hope that this is not the first letter you read because I have to inform you of tragic news and I do so wish I could be there to comfort you my son in your confinement.

I must tell you that your dear friend and sweetheart Emily Horstmann was killed a few weeks ago while working in a Red Cross hospital near Bapaume for an American lady called Mary Borden, whom I'm sure she told you about.

Apparently poor Sister Horstmann had accompanied a small fleet of ambulances to collect wounded soldiers from a field hospital just a mile or two from the front line. In the short time she was there she was unlucky enough to lose her life in an unexpected air attack upon the hospital by German planes.

It certainly was an act of great barbarity but it seems the airmen thought they were attacking an important military headquarters—and they pointed out later in a communiqué through Switzerland that no signs or symbols in the form of a red cross had been posted to indicate it was a hospital containing both allied and German soldiers.

There was terrible loss of life and the atrocity was widely reported in the newspapers here in England. My poor Frank, I am so sorry to have to give you this news but I felt it was better that you should know of her tragic death rather than face the frustration and disappointment of receiving no further letters from Emily. If it is any consolation her death would have been instant and she would not have suffered any pain.

I received the terrible news by letter from her Australian friend Jackie Pretz who is absolutely devastated at the disastrous turn of events. The only comfort my dear Frank that I can offer you is that Emily died serving us all in doing her duty in a brave and courageous manner and she always had strong faith in God.

Have strength my dear boy and remember that you will be reunited in heaven—from where now Emily looks down on you in love and tenderness forever. Perhaps she will act as your divine guardian here on earth.

Your loving mother,

Anna.

He had read the letter over and over again choking back his sobs which soon caught the attention of the other prisoners using the room at the same time. It was only when he looked more closely at the batch of letters and found one from Emily that had been written a few days before her death—expressing hope and excitement for the future—that he suddenly lost it. His mind raced and became a confusion of images with echoing voices calling from all directions.

He seemed to hear her voice above the others. . . . she was repeating his name asking him to go to her, over and over again, until it drove him into total confusion. There could be no escape for him now; there was no purpose to it.

He no longer cared about anything or anyone. The only meaningful thing to do was to die and be reunited with his love.

He felt the rage within him again that she was gone, but he was detached from himself as he strode across the room bellowing and crying out. He snatched the rifle from the elderly guard who was totally unprepared and terrified by the sudden attack, hitting the German hard across the skull with the butt and knocking him unconscious. Quickly inspecting the magazine, he saw it was full of bullets and he turned the rifle upon himself.

His right thumb now held the trigger with the muzzle of the gun at his heart—but then all went dark as he was knocked conscious from behind. Frank lay still in his cell and knew that all his strength was spent. He felt no pain, no hunger, just apathy and a sense of total exhaustion that no amount of sleep could supplant.

He could not fight the enemy and he could no longer fight to survive. He could not bring himself to eat. The next day he was released from the straitjacket but was still delirious and did not notice it had gone.

He declined to get up to use his recreation time during the day and did not make any effort to participate in the social evenings that week. He drank water but the food left by the guards was ignored and by the fourth day he lacked even the strength to turn over on his side. He wept constantly.

Alan sat opposite the Commandant in his office and waited patiently for him to complete writing on the buff file in front of him. At length he looked up.

"How can I help you Major McCrae?" he asked impatiently.

"Thank you for taking the trouble to see me Major. I have come to talk to you about the prisoner Sergeant Clarke. His deteriorating condition is causing concern among the other prisoners."

The Commandant interrupted: "If the damn fool wants to starve himself to death Major then it is not the responsibility of the German military authorities. He is given food and water in his cell and declines to eat. He also refuses his Red Cross parcels."

"I understand your point Major. I am sure you would agree with me that his actions indicate that the Sergeant is in a mentally unbalanced condition. His physical health is now a cause for serious concern which is having an effect upon the morale of my men."

The Commandant began to look impatient. He replied: "What would you have me do about this—we are soldiers not doctors Major."

"I would ask you to consider transferring Sergeant Clarke to a hospital where he can be looked after by doctors, perhaps benefit from the company of others on the same ward and regain his physical wellbeing through good nursing. In the meantime I should like you to give me permission to visit him in his cell alone to counsel him. I do have considerable experience in mentoring."

The Commandant screwed up his face in disapproval. "I think you know as well as I do Major McCrae that prisoners are strictly forbidden to visit one another in their own cells for moral reasons. To allow this request would be against military regulations, even for a prisoner like you who is trusted by the authorities. As for a transfer from Wesel Prison, I can only say it would be highly irregular because this is where Sergeant Clarke has been sentenced by the court to serve his term for criminal activities."

The following week Alan was allowed into Frank's cell during the day. He was told he had half an hour and the meeting would be monitored through the aperture in the cell door and the conversation noted.

Only a few shafts of daylight permeated the cell and in the gloom Alan could see that he was lying motionless and facing upwards with his eyes open. A tray of food was lying on the floor by the cell door and had not been touched.

"What do you want Alan? Why are you here?" He asked quietly.

"Sergeant I have not come here to commiserate with you, or to plead with you. I come as an officer to inform you—and you are a regular soldier not an enlisted man—that in allowing yourself to starve and to deliberately neglect your physical health, your conduct is contrary to His Majesty's military regulations. Your conduct is having a serious effect upon the morale of your fellow prisoners and therefore cannot be tolerated."

For the first time in over a week Frank smiled.

"Really? So, what are you going to do about it Alan? Are you going to court martial me? I don't think so. I have fought as hard as any man in this war—both as a soldier and an escaper. I have resisted the Germans in torture and they did not break me. Now I cannot go on. I will not go on. So leave me alone to die in peace."

He had never heard Alan raise his voice. Now the chaplain shouted so loudly that it brought the guard to the door of the cell and he found himself sitting bolt upright as Alan's voice thundered in his ears.

"You will do as you are ordered Sergeant and you will start taking food immediately.

"You will report to the evening meeting tonight and you will receive your Red Cross parcel, take it back to the cell and start eating properly. Do you understand?" screamed Alan.

He then left the cell wondering to himself how his performance—an act entirely out of character with his personality—had been received. Frank continued to stare at the ceiling and felt an attack of claustrophobia encroaching upon him. He prayed for sleep and gradually it came upon him. That night he did not show up at the evening meeting.

The following morning in daylight when he was in his cell, Alan looked at the letter he had surreptitiously tucked in his tunic pocket after picking it up from the bench beside Frank's bed. The letter was from Anna and her address in Norfolk was written at the top of it. That is what he had been after and it was the true purpose of his visit to the cell. It was time for Alan to get help for Frank Clarke from a wider source than the German Military authorities.

He wrote a letter to Anna alerting her to the situation and advising her to intervene by putting in a request to the Red Cross in Switzerland to have her son repatriated to Holland as soon as possible. He explained that he was a sick man both mentally and physically and that his original wound from 1914 was still troubling him.

He appealed to her to write to Frank and to get his friends and loved ones to write too, to persuade him to change his mind about committing suicide through starving himself.

40
ANNA GETS TO WORK

They were seated in his office at the House of Commons. Noel Buxton, Harrovian and graduate of Trinity College Cambridge, was a slim-faced man with a grey beard and moustache. His large dark eyes seemed to express compassion.

He had been North Norfolk's Liberal MP since 1910 and because he came from the Aylsham district knew Anna's family well. Buxton's wife Lucy, a well known campaigner for women's political rights, was an acquaintance of Anna.

He listened to Anna's story about Frank with patience and sympathy.

"My dear Anna I am so sorry to hear this sad story about your youngest son and of course as a father myself I can quite understand your anguish. I do have strong connections at the War Office and with Sergeant Clarke's regiment. I will start moving on this immediately. As far as I can see there is a strong case for the Red Cross in Switzerland to submit an appeal on behalf of your family for his early repatriation to Holland.

"I will speak to their London headquarters this week. Priority is being given to men who were seriously wounded at the start of the War and I see no reason why the Germans would want to continue holding your son in view of his state of health; for them he is now harmless and just another mouth to feed.

"I am sure you understand that bureaucracy dictates that these things do not happen quickly, especially as we are dealing with a country we have been at war with for more than three years. But let us have hope and leave it now in my hands."

Anna flushed with pleasure and smiled and Noel Buxton continued talking.

"I read in the London Gazette your older son James is serving with the Army Service Corps in Mesopotamia fighting the Turks—and has been promoted to Captain. Is he in good health?"

"The last we heard he was in a place called Basra with responsibility for the supply of several regiments fighting in the desert. He wrote last month to say he was sick and off work but we have not heard from him since. I should imagine it's a dreadful place and far too hot for Europeans.

"It is another great worry for me. As you know I have already lost two of my four children."

Noel Buxton paused and then continued. "How many people are writing to your son at the moment to lift his spirits?"

"Members of the family write but most of the letters come from me now that Emily Horstmann is dead. Why did you ask?"

"It occurs to me Anna that it might be useful if we could introduce another correspondent into your son's miserable existence—perhaps a young woman who would lift his spirits and give him a fresh perspective on life.

"I am not suggesting of course that it would serve to divert his abject misery about Emily's untimely death but a letter from a woman of his own age might help.

"Given time, the regular receipt of letters from someone outside the family might help to revive his spirits—especially if they are from an attractive and unattached young woman.

I have to say that tragically there are thousands of spinsters in England who have had to face the trauma of loss. Not all are sitting at home in their grief—some are taking an active role in building a future."

"That's a wonderful idea Noel—but how do I find a young lady willing to take this on? It means writing to a complete stranger and might be considered rather improper."

"I remember attending a wedding at St George's Chapel in Hanover Square a few weeks before the War started. The Buxtons and the Worths of Sutton Bridge in Lincolnshire have been close friends for generations. Lucy and I attended the wedding of their daughter Edith to a retired colonel from Ireland called James Lepper Alison. He was a widower and one of the bridesmaids at his second marriage was his oldest daughter Maud, a most attractive woman in her mid-20s.

They are one of Ireland's top industrial families, having pioneered linen milling in Belfast and been major investors in the shipping industry including Harland and Wolff.

"I haven't seen Maud since her father's wedding but Lucy told me she met her again only last month at a meeting in Maddox Street of the Society for the Advancement of Women in Politics."

He smiled at the anxious expression on Anna's face. "Don't worry they have nothing to do with the Suffragette movement!"

"So how could Maud Lepper Alison help us?"

"It seems that Maud and a number of other young women from good families in England and Ireland have taken it upon themselves to start writing to long-term and unmarried prisoners of war in Germany. Many of the recipients have sweethearts of course and so they do not reply to the letters, but there are a considerable number whose loneliness and misery is assuaged by correspondence from well educated young ladies. I should add that romance is not their purpose—but a sense of duty and wanting to help our men."

"If you could obtain Maud's address from Lucy and send it to me I should be pleased to write to her and ask her to find us a young lady who could write to Frank. Perhaps she has a list of names and I could tell her about my son."

"I can do better than that Anna. She lives in 16 Maddox Street, her father and step-mother's London home and Lucy, whose idea this was I might say, has been presumptuous enough to warn Maud that you might be in contact with her. So it saves you the bother of having to explain who you are and all that.

"She already knows about the case of Sergeant Clarke and will be most happy to have a discussion with you. Here is the address and telephone number. I think it is quite a busy household—Maud's sisters are also living there at the moment although the Colonel has moved to Bournemouth with his wife Edith."

The following morning Anna and Maud met for the first time and they liked one another. Maud was a slim woman of medium height with long fair hair that curled down her back. She had the brightest blue eyes Anna had ever seen.

Anna found her quite beautiful and was impressed by her graceful manners and soft voice. Maud said she would correspond personally with Frank and send off a letter that week. It was a decision that may have been influenced by Anna's decision to hand her a photograph of Sergeant Clarke in 1914 outside the farm in Norfolk, looking very handsome and wearing the Harris Tweed fishing suit of a typical English country gentlemen.

41
MAUD LEPPER ALISON

He was lying in bed and read the letter several times in astonishment. The high quality paper was perfumed and each time he read the letter he held it close to his nose to try to remove from his nostrils the stink of shit, sick and stale body odour that permeated the hospital ward.

He did not understand how a total stranger could have known so much about him, where he was imprisoned and so much about his personal circumstances. Initially, he felt a sense of indignation and much intruded upon. The letter, he decided, was an impertinent imposition.

He read it dozens more times, however and at length detected a sense of compassion and warmth in the writing that stirred him. His astonishment was exacerbated when, in the course of the next week, he received two more letters from Maud Lepper Alison—and almost got to the point of feeling some disappointment when he did not receive one from the postal orderly each evening.

The tone of the perfumed letters soon became personal and familiar and in the third letter she sent him a photograph of herself that revealed she was a beauty. He continued to tell himself that he cared not if he lived or died—although his mother's anguished pleas had persuaded him to come off his death fast.

Emily had dominated his inner self and psyche to such an extent during their brief relationship of just a few months that he felt no joy could be derived from his future existence.

There seemed to be nothing to look forward to; no dreams to be fulfilled. Even his passion for fishing had been dulled and he no longer returned in his sleep to his many adventures and fishing expeditions of the pre-war years.

Alan McCrae had been in no doubt that the Wesel commandant's decision to get rid of the troublesome sergeant and assign him to Dulmen Camp was based on a determination to keep the death list at Wesel as low as possible. Situated in a desolate area of the Rhineland, to the north of Essen and 25 kilometres south-west of Munster, in Westphalia, Dulmen was a small town close to the frontier between Germany and Holland. The climate was similar to England; quite damp and misty and unsuitable for a sick man who was receiving no medication. Frank was down to six and a half stones in weight when he arrived by ambulance at the camp hospital late in 1917.

The hospital was almost 50 yards long with dozens of hard military beds in a row on each side—and the moaning and the crying continued without respite 24 hours a day. Sanitation and hygiene was at such a low level that the camp hospital did not resemble a place where sick men would be expected to recover but was more a hell on Earth. Blood-stained bandages littered the floor. Pools of blood, excreta and urine were cleared by the Russian ward orderlies only once every two days. There were no sheets on the beds and the mattresses were ridden with bedbugs.

The doctors dispensed some morphine to those in severe pain or who were dying from Septicaemia, Dysentery, or Tuberculosis. Apart from that, there were only bandages and supplies of cheap French brandy to swab wounds and neutralize infection. The Russian orderlies stole the brandy and were often drunk on the ward—much to the amusement of the German guards who stood at the entrance with their bayonets fixed. All prisoners were mixed up, men suffering from all kinds of complaints, which meant that those in a very bad state of health tended to infect those who would otherwise soon recover.

He was in a bed next to a Russian prisoner who was dying of TB. On the other side a Frenchman suffered from chronic dysentery and within a week he had contracted it. So, despite the arrival of the Red Cross parcels he continued to lose weight, was in a permanent state of dehydration and often delirious.

He was not making a fight of it and allowed his critical predicament to continue. This situation had arisen in the days before the letters from Maud began to arrive. He found that he no longer possessed the strength to get out of the bed and use the pan beneath it in which to squirt out the obnoxious greenish liquid excreta that is the hallmark of dysentery. A stern middle-aged German doctor examined him again at the start of his fourth week in the camp hospital and decreed that he would not be allowed to die there. The doctor pronounced him fit and well for release.

"I have read your papers from Wesel and as far as I am concerned you are a malingerer and I do not want you in my hospital. There are hundreds of men out there in the camp with a stomach bug just as serious as yours. You will either have the strength to recover from it by natural means—or you won't.

You can stay here for this night only—then you will be sent into the main camp. There are no residential privileges for non commissioned officers here and so you will work outside Dulmen like every other man, although I shall sign a certificate giving you rest from work for two weeks, so that you can make an honest attempt to rebuild yourself.

"I am confident you will make up your weight with the assistance of food from the Red Cross and it is entirely your responsibility that you do so.

"We do not care whether you live or die—as I have said I shall write in my records that you are a malingerer."

This vitriolic personal attack so infuriated Frank that it had a refreshing effect upon his psyche. He had someone to hate again and it revived him. He was thrown out of the hospital the next day and carried by stretcher into one of the huts having been issued with two blankets. They left him on the floor alone to acclimatize to the conditions.

Soon after his arrival other fitter prisoners took pity on him. They gave him food, hot drinks, and helped him to stagger to the latrines. It was taboo to shit in the hut. He responded to the kind way in which he was treated and his spirits began to be further revived by the constant supply of letters from Maud who always found something pleasant to say—and expressed her goodwill in such personal terms that he found her increasingly endearing.

He gained the strength to walk with a stick and started to look around the camp. He was appalled by what he saw. All the huts had electric lights and a stove but each one was accommodating up to 250 men. The interior of these huts resembled a bee-hive because there were so many men living there and they were constantly moving about by day, stepping over the sick lying on the floor. It was primitive, degrading and totally lacking in privacy.

The single stove burning in the centre gave off smoke but was quite useless in winter because fuel had become so scarce. Being winter time, the camp was practically under water, drainage being non-existent, the rain collecting in large ponds, but gutters had been dug around the huts. Altogether the prisoners were living in the most dismal and depressing surroundings.

Built on sandy ground, the camp was enclosed by an electrified barbed-wire fence 10 feet high that could be easily cut when the power was off— were it not for the sustained vigilance of the guards. The outer perimeter comprised a four square barbed wire fence of about 12 feet high. The barbed wire was so thick that a man could only just put his arm through it and 10 feet outside this fence was a new brick wall 15 feet in height with four feet of barbed wire on the top leaning inwards.

Every 50 yards or so inside the inner fence was a German sentry with a loaded rifle and bayonet fixed and outside each of the outer walls was one or more similar sentries pacing up and down.

These guards were on duty night and day. Along the fence and at intervals on the barrack square were huge electric arc lamps switched on all night which made the whole place, especially the ground all round the outside walls, as light as day.

Roll calls were held twice a day on the barrack square which was about 110 yards by 80 yards. It formed the only ground for sport and exercise to take place.

He found the conditions much worse than Sennelager and to make matters more serious he was fighting a losing battle with Dysentery. It seemed to come and go but the bug was in his system permanently.

Maud had somehow regenerated the feeling within him of wanting to live and he began to ache physically in anxiety if her letters did not arrive several times a week.

He could still not keep any solid food down and the doctor had refused to supply him with any medication—saying there was nothing available. He would have to wait to see what Anna could send from England.

EMILY'S FAREWELL—DIARY JUNE 1917

I always meet Emily in my dreams by the lake at Bellignies. It is our special place and she is waiting for me on the bank seated at an easel upon which is mounted a half-finished landscape.

I notice that I am in it, as always. It is high summer now and the air is alive with the buzzing sounds of nature in the afternoon sun. Emily has been watching a pair of dragonflies dancing around the white flowers of the lily bed when I walk up and kiss her gently on the cheek.

'I am so happy for you,' she says smiling at me.

'What do you mean?' I say, taking her in my arms and pulling her gently to the ground.

'I mean Maud. You were so depressed my darling and needed a woman in your life. I like her sincerity. I want you to know that I approve of her. She writes you beautiful letters and is deeply caring.

'It will be a good relationship and you will soon love her dearly. You must remember you are still a mortal being and I am no longer.'

Her last words overwhelm me so much that I begin to weep, tears stream down my face. I kiss her passionately and grip her hard in my arms pleading for her love.

'It's you I love my darling. No other woman can take your place ever.'

She holds my hand tightly as we lie on the ground locked in an embrace.

'No it cannot be darling. I am at peace now. You know I love you—but my darling you must move on with your time on earth. You will live for many years and experience old age.

'My masters have instructed me that my soul must soon inhabit other worlds. I shall be reborn but energy from my earlier life will remain to watch over you.'

We kiss passionately and soon we are making love—reaching such heights of passion that we both cry out. Afterwards she presses her face against mine. She is crying now.

'You must have the strength to go from here my darling. Maud is a beautiful woman and she is already falling in love with you. You will have three beautiful children with her that I cannot give you and they will be very special. I can no longer be there for you as a mortal.

'Our shared memories will live on in your mind forever even after you started your new life with Maud—but take care in sharing those memories with your living descendants for fear of being misunderstood.

'Maud and I will always share the bond of loving you and my darling you are fortunate to be the object of such love from both a living woman and a spirit. God bless you. We will not meet again my love, I am drawing back now. Farewell.'

42

LIFE IN DULMEN CAMP

Frank's sobbing became the focus of attention of the other prisoners lying on mattresses on the floor in the hut—and one of them prodded him gently until he was awake.

"Steady on old chap," he said kindly.

"I am sorry John, please forgive me. I was having a dream and it was a bit sad," said Frank and the tears still ran down his face.

It was the last time he dreamed of Emily. He still thought of her constantly but she did not come to him in his dreams and he gradually came to terms with it. Soon after he arrived in the main camp, Anna had sent a letter saying that she was taking steps through official channels to get his case considered for repatriation to Holland.

She did not want to say anything more than this in case his letters were intercepted and read by hostile eyes (they were) and steps were taken to destroy the foundations of his case. In the time that he spent recuperating in the camp, he approached as many senior NCOs as he could find to discover if there was any sort of regimental system within Dulmen, as there was in Sennelager, that could be used as a way of communicating with the Commandant. He now wanted to help create a better existence for all the prisoners.

He was introduced to RSM Hughie Jones from the Welsh Guards and a Warrant Officer Ian Parker from the Royal Engineers who told him a written approach calling for the establishment of a committee had been made after the influx of men from the Battle of the Somme. It was still under consideration.

He felt a sense of déjà vu when they told him that the Prussian commandant who had been on station for two years had just been transferred and replaced by a much older man who seemed to be less rigid in his approach.

He told the senior NCOs that he felt he was too weak to do physical labour after such a long imprisonment and wanted to find a way of doing clerical work that would not involve going outside the camp.

"Christ Nobby you don't have to tell us. You're a bloody skeleton already," laughed WO Parker, who remained quite a stout man despite his imprisonment. The Warrant Officer agreed that when the committee was formed, Frank's name would go to near the top of the list for special treatment. The 1914 soldiers had been dying in significant numbers at Dulmen in the past few months and nobody resented the efforts of the survivors to get special treatment.

RSM Jones said in his Welsh lilt: "Most of the men who arrived here last year are standing up well under the strain, relying on the care and humour of their friends for strength.

"The work consists of farm labouring, roads maintenance and some factory work in nearby Dulmen. We feel there is a lot we can do for the men if we can get this committee going. We can make sure only the strong have to work, that they get paid for what they do and are not exploited by the Germans who employ them. We want to siphon off a percentage of the men to set up skilled workshops within the camp.

Frank laughed. "There was a time when I ridiculed committees that did not deal with escapers—then I met this officer called Alan McCrae in Wesel Prison, a devout Christian, who saved my life.

"He was a committee man and I think that what it achieved for the inmates probably stopped them from going insane. I'm too weak to even think about escape now."

The RSM said: "No don't get the wrong idea Nobby. We are positive about escapes. We are close to the Dutch border, we think many of the guards are going to be willing to accept bribes for food and hundreds of men are out in the fields and on the roads every day—which makes hopping it quite feasible.

"It's all part of the committee's plans for the future. We want clothing workshops, printers and a shoe factory—all operated by the prisoners. That way we can offer a support structure to potential escapers."

Warrant Officer Parker added: "Yeah well, recreation is practically non-existent and that sort of thing has to have priority at the moment rather than escaping. We need to use our own initiative. A lot of men have lost their self-respect having lived under a harsh regime for so long.

"They have given us one hut as a library and concert room which doubles up as our chapel. There is now a good supply of books and for those with the stamina football is played once a week.

"The Germans don't like large gatherings and so no spectators are officially allowed. So far the prisoners have just ignored the rules. At the moment football is played during the mornings and afternoons, with as many as 200 spectators. But we want to get all this on a properly organized basis."

Frank discovered there was also a walk within the perimeters of Dulmen Camp during the same hours as the football with as many as 400 men taking advantage of the exercise. The privileges were regarded as being of great value and much appreciated.

He was beginning to hope that work was going on behind the scenes to get him repatriated to Holland. Anna had taken his case to the local MP who had passed it on to the War Office with the support of the Norfolks. He had to believe in miracles. The senior NCOs had told him that several of the 1914 men in the camp had already been sent to Holland.

Sometimes he would lie on his mattress and dream of unlimited supplies of fresh meat, milk and vegetables—and the medication to rid him of Dysentery which still plagued him and stopped him from putting on any weight. He had to hold on somehow and survive this last terrible period of his captivity.

Emily would no longer be at the end of his rainbow when the War ended and this still made him weep a lot—but there would be the opportunity to meet Maud. Her constant letters, all of which were deeply caring, began to make him feel he knew her well already and he felt growing affection for this Irishwoman who had come into his life without any warning. The prisoners were allowed to write four post-cards, and two letters a month, which was fair and he was now receiving far more than that from Maud.

He began to find out more about her family and learned that her parents had been living in India for much of her childhood and her siblings had remained in Antrim before the brothers were sent away to school at Mostyn House School in Cheshire and then Shrewsbury. She and her two sisters found themselves in a boarding school at an exclusive ladies college in Salisbury.

Frank soon gathered she was a member of the privileged industrial upper middle class in County Antrim and probably had a substantial private income. The Lepper family he learned had built the first linen mills in Belfast and had been substantial shareholders in the Inman Shipping Line and Harland and Wolff.

Maud told him her sister Mabel was supposed to have travelled first-class on *Titanic* on her maiden voyage but a warning from her psychic maid at the last moment had persuaded her to cancel it. Maud was wealthy and an heiress—but far too well brought up to mention anything as vulgar as money.

She certainly did not enquire about his rather humble means, or why he was an NCO rather than an officer. In many ways she seemed to be classless and he gained the impression from her writing that she was highly intelligent, perceptive and a practicing Christian. She told him her grandfather James Alison had been a Presbyterian Minister and an MA from Cambridge University.

He remembered Emily's words and continued to be deeply influenced by the dream when she left his conscious world forever. He knew she would never return in the real way she had come to him for the last time when they had seemed to experience an actual sexual union that was far too vivid just to be a dream. There was no point in denying his grief for Emily but now he felt no guilt for beginning to want to move on.

He had started to hope for a long lasting friendship with Maud, even possibly something leading to romance, but feared a mere sergeant might not be deemed suitable for a senior officer's daughter who rode side-saddle to hounds with the upper crust Mid-Antrim Hunt.

He knew he was not quite a gentleman and perhaps this would make a relationship impossible—perhaps her father would veto a mere sergeant becoming his son-in-law. He decided that was extremely likely. In the end he decided all these things were for the future and he should not try to influence or push their friendship in any specific direction for the moment.

Women were deep and strange creatures, more subtle than men and he remembered how Emily had not revealed her feelings for him until he was nearly beside himself with frustration at her seeming indifference to his unrequited love. Maud sent several more photographs of herself and her family and he began to think he was extremely lucky just to know her.

23 Maddox Street

London W1

6pm Thursday October 29th 1917

My Dearest Frank,

I enjoyed reading your last letter about your family and the people that mean so much to you. I am glad, too, that you told me about Emily and how your deep love for her kept you alive during those dark, dark days. It is good that you now feel robust enough to write about her and the extraordinary devotion of her service as a Red Cross nurse. She will be remembered as a heroine of the United States of America.

Emily will always be in your heart and her loss must be a terrible thing for you to bear. No words from another person, especially one who did not know her, can convey meaningful consolation but in my experience grief has to run its course. Emily would want you to have a happy and successful future when you feel you are ready.

These are indeed testing times for our generation my dear. My own close friend Hugo was killed during the Battle of Paschendale in 1915 while he was serving with the Dragoon Guards, then last year my youngest sister Dorothy was widowed when her husband Victor Robb died of his wounds on the third day of the Battle of the Somme fighting for the 14th Battalion Royal Irish Rifles in the 26th Ulster Division. They had been married for only two years.

In the past few weeks my middle sister Mabel has heard that her long-standing friend Richard, a pilot with the Royal Flying Corps, was shot down and killed in an air battle over the Western Front.

We three sisters have had to bear this grief with many of our girl friends who have also lost their husband or fiancée in this terrible conflict.

I think many women of our generation are now condemned to be spinsters or widows for the rest of their life for there will not be enough men left by the end of the War if the killing goes on at this appalling rate.

My brother Charles is a Latin master at a public school and won't be called up because of his health.

Poor Arthur, known as A.J. is the youngest of us and has been trying to cope with an alcohol-related problem for the past three years.

He was asked to resign his commission in the Royal Field Artillery as a result of his problem and now suffers the guilt of being at home when others of his generation are serving their King and country and giving their lives.

Arthur was a talented athlete when he was at Shrewsbury School and one of the most complete horsemen I have ever met. After leaving school in 1910 he decided to go to Canada where he took a job breaking horses on a cattle ranch in British Columbia, 500 mles north of Vancouver on the edge of the world.

He stayed for nearly four years and never once wrote back to his family—during which time my mother Ellen died. He came back to England during the summer of 1914 with the intention of joining the army and was able to obtain a temporary commission in the artillery with the help of my dear Papa.

We did not understand that he had developed this problem while in Canada and when he joined the army in Ireland he found he was unable to learn to abstain, and it seems he found the arduous problem of learning mathematics in a technical service like the artillery too tiresome.

It all broke my dear Papa's heart and the scandal of A.J. having to resign his commission was why he moved with my step-mother Edith from County Antrim to Bournemouth. We do not know what will happen to A.J. but he says he will re-enlist as a private soldier under a false name.

What do you think Frank? I shall value your advice and want you to know that I am keeping all your letters and read each one many times. I am knitting you socks and a pullover.

Your affectionate friend
Maud Lepper Alison

43
MARMITE—THE LIFE-SAVER

He read the letter, sniffed its scent, and put it under his mattress. Maud's letters had now rekindled his desire for life. The question was would he live to meet her? Diarrhoea was not so much a disease in itself but a symptom of other infections.

He was dying gradually from **Dysentery and his weight continued to fall rapidly despite his improved spirits. Periodically he was sent back to the hospital despite the objections of the stern German doctor who continued to regard him as a malingerer.**

The stools were now tinged with blood and mucus and the attacks were characterised by colicky pains as frequently as 30 times a day. He knew from what the trained British medical orderlies at Dulmen had told him that the danger of amoebic dysentery lay in the deterioration of the liver which might lead to hepatitis, cysts and abscesses. Liver problems, they warned, could remain dormant for many years.

The onset of the attacks was sudden, perhaps with only a few moments notice, often accompanied by a high fever and thirst.

Anna's letter warned him Dysentery would cause rapid dehydration of the body and deplete the store of sodium in his body, which was essential for the body to function healthily.

She said that as a rule of thumb, if he lost 10 percent or more of his body fluid he might die.

"It's time for you to take whatever action you can because the German doctors do not seem prepared to do anything to give you effective medication," she told him by letter.

She had mentioned earlier that ginger and also coriander was an effective antidote to sick intestines and her parcels began to arrive with jars of pickled ginger sweetened with other fruits and herbs that spread well onto biscuits.

He found the urge to go to the toilet was gradually diminished but the strong discharge of gases from his intestine smelled very unpleasant and people began to avoid coming close to him.

He asked Anna and Maud for other remedies and the latter sent Isafgul husk—also known as spogel seeds—which had to be taken three times a day with curd/yoghurt which was obtainable from the guards in exchange for tinned meat.

The two women also sent jars of garlic and urged him to spread that on his biscuits. It was highly effective but again people tended to avoid him and he never got properly into the routine of incorporating it into his medication. Some days he felt better than others—on the bad days he could hardly crawl along the floor.

The newly-formed NCOs committee believed that the widespread use

by the Germans of human excrement as a fertilizer for crops was causing the outbreaks of dysentery among the farm labourers and appealed
for gloves for the men so that their hands would not become infected.
Unsurprisingly there was no response from the prison authorities.

The committee also blamed the poor quality of the water supplies at
Dulmen. To combat the effects of dehydration, oral salts could be taken
along with plenty of clean water. But where could they get that clean
water?

The men agreed to boil everything for him. Finally, Anna came up
with the solution that arrested the decline in his weight and began to stave
off the attacks of dysentery. On the face of it his fellow prisoners were
surprised it had taken Anna so long to come up with the answer. It came
in the form of a sticky dark brown paste with a distinctive and powerful
salty flavour—and was supplied in earthenware pots.

It always amused him after the War to remember that when he was so
close to death it was a German who prevented him from losing his life
through Dysentery.

Justus von Liebig developed a manufacturing process for beef extract.
In 1902 the Marmite Food Company was set up in Burton on Trent.

The by-product yeast for the paste came from Bass Brewery, the biggest
brewer at the time. The main ingredients of Marmite were yeast extract,
sodium chloride, vegetable extract, niacin, thiamine, spice extracts, ribo-
flavin, folic acid and celery extracts.

Thanks to its high B vitamin content, Marmite kept alive thousands of
Allied soldiers in the First World War including Sergeant Frank Clarke.
Later in the War it was included in soldiers ration packs and was introduced as a staple food in hospitals. B vitamins, he was told, helped regu-
late the kidneys, liver and the body's nervous system—as well as assisting
with skin disorders and boosting energy.

English scientists had proved that eating extracts of yeast could stave
off beri-beri and it worked at Dulmen to stop Frank's condition from
deteriorating any further from Dysentery. He began to get used to eating
up to 20 biscuits a day spread thickly with marmite. It burned the roof of
his mouth but, as a result, his weight stabilized at 84lbs (six stones)—a
shadow of the man who was 13 stones when he was captured in 1915, but
one who was going to survive the War.

He was elected to be the special escape advisor to the Sergeant's
Committee from that day and for his remaining weeks at Dulmen played
a key role in helping to organise escape attempts from the camp that took
place during 1917.

His letters from Maud—and the sense of gratitude for his wise advice
that he got from the men planning to break out gave him a sense of
fulfilment that he had not felt since the months with Emily in 1915 at
Bellignies.

He had been in hiding from the Germans or in captivity for three and a
half years and felt his life was now about to move on. He had mellowed to

such an extent that when he walked to the wire and looked out across the electrified fence to the countryside beyond he no longer felt any desperate urge to escape.

Now he felt he belonged to a community that he wished to support and from which he enjoyed considerable respect. He had become one of the camp elders; a wise old man. At Christmas 1917 he even allowed himself to be part of the chorus in a camp musical and he rediscovered his fine baritone voice.

The carols that he had last heard in Belgium in 1914 were sung to the accompaniment of the camp orchestra and as tears welled in his eyes he felt that real life, civilized humanity, was once again rising. Millions had died but for some reason he did not understand, he had been spared by the Lord and he would live his life to the full out of respect for all the men in the Regiment who he remembered would not come home to live out their lives in peacetime.

He would also live his life for Emily, even though her soul had moved on to other worlds as she had told him it would. Frank knew her love for him and for Maud from the other side would continue to be strong for as long as he lived.

44
REPATRIATION

Less than two months later in early 1918 he was in Holland.

One day, without warning he was escorted to a truck outside the commandant's office, given a bundle of papers signed by the German authorities and the Red Cross and driven to the railway station in the town.

The Red Cross papers explained in both English and German that he was being repatriated on the grounds of his serious wound, the length of time in captivity and his dramatic loss of weight and strength through Dysentery. It was a short railway journey to freedom and the moment he crossed the border was one he would never forget.

It was as if a great weight had been lifted from him. He thought endlessly of Emily and their frustrated dreams and he wept, feeling a tinge of guilt about Maud.

The Dutch authorities placed him in a special hostel on the outskirts of Rotterdam which he shared with 30 other former prisoners-of-war who were also medical cases. They had complete freedom of movement, provided they reported to the local police station twice a week and their army pay sent out on a weekly basis, which did not have to cover the cost of their meals in the hostel.

He grew to admire the orderly culture of the Dutch but found their language incomprehensible. Shortly after arrival he made several good friends among the British soldiers, who included some officers and during this period he took up reading seriously.

The weeks were spent scouring the newspapers and books from the library. He had not read British national newspaper for nearly four years and now he read every sentence on every page every day—including the advertisements.

The Dutch served large meals three times a day, eggs, cheese, meat, vegetables pasta and cream sauces were predominant. Through eating rich food he gradually reached just over 10 stones (140 lbs) but still looked emaciated.

He felt strong, however, and although his wound meant he would have a disability for the rest of his life he was active again—even finding time to play for 10 minutes in a game of football for the British army against the French. Most of the men were semi-invalids but it was amazing what they could do when fired up to play.

Several of the Frenchmen turned out to been former professionals players and they beat the British team by six goals to one despite his best efforts. He could still play in short bursts before coming to a heaving and wheezing halt.

He was able—with the goading and encouragement of the spectators—to use his lightning pace and acceleration on the right wing to fire in a stream of brilliant centres to the hapless British forwards who seemed to lack the vital skills to do anything useful with the ball.

It annoyed him so much that after a particularly robust tackle on a French full-back—the referee who did not speak any English—strode up to him, blew his whistle, and waggled a forefinger under his nose.

He bowed, smiled graciously and said "bollocks" which fortunately the referee mistook for an apology. Afterwards the French and British drank Dutch gin in a small bar near the docks and forgot about the game, enjoying long conversations about the world that they would inherit when Fritz had been sent packing back to Berlin.

They all knew the world would be a very different place after the conflict but now they seemed to possess the confidence of believing they would be part of it. These were happy days that seemed more in tune with the years of peacetime and military exercises, than what was for them the aftermath of a bloody conflict that had locked up the western world in savage butchery for four years—and set a stamp upon the 20th century.

He felt a sense of ease about his future with Maud but wondered what problems the transition to peacetime living would bring for him.

He would spend many hours in the city art gallery in Rotterdam which housed a collection spanning five centuries but was most famous for displaying the work of some of the leading Impressionists.

His skin looked healthy again and his black hair had developed a natural sheen that had been absent for nearly four years, although it was now thinning. He had always been a rather vain man and he worried when looking at himself in the mirror. He doubted that with such well worn wrinkles after years of confinement he would have a chance of romance with the well-bred Irishwoman. His hair had become thin prematurely.

He tried not to think of Emily too much because such thoughts continued to make him cry. Maud had continued to send an astonishing number of letters, far surpassing those from Anna. He was developing a deep affection for a woman he had never met—which was a curious feeling. Could he be falling in love with an idea, a person he had never laid eyes upon, never touched in the flesh, even in a handshake?

One day he found himself writing a letter that was more special than the others—thanks to his steady weight gain. Because of it he felt reassured that when he got back to England she would not be shocked and repulsed by his emaciated appearance.

He knew he would never get back his dashing looks of the pre-war years but he hoped that she would still desire him. He tried to avoid thinking of Maud in a strictly sexual sense and knew that the presence of Emily deep within in his psyche would need to fade away first before he could feel passionate about another woman.

He understood he could not hold forever onto her vision and memory—the problem was that Emily had been such a strong presence, such a commanding personality.

Her beauty of face, body and mind was such that she was etched like a portrait upon his immediate recall. The memories would come on him without warning and cause spasms of physical pain in his stomach. She no longer came to him in his dreams, but she lingered in the back of his mind—images of their time together, like snapshots, of the months when nothing else in the world seemed to matter but their time for one another.

The Chateau months had been the happiest and most contented period of his life and she was so perfect for him that sometimes in his darker pessimistic moments he could not envisage any really satisfying future without Emily. He was scared that Maud would realise the strength of these memories and become frustrated at his inability to leave them in the past.

He wondered what she had planned for them. Was she building a long term relationship for them as close friends in which she would help him rebuild his shattered life—or did she see them as a couple when he eventually reached England?

How would he feel about the freedom of expression and movement, would it be something from which he could not escape, forever a lone wolf? He had no idea of the future but developed a vague hope that they might plan a life and family together if they got married, indeed of being born again virtually.

He knew that many of the other former prisoners felt the same way as him despite the isolation of incarceration—yet many rejected the idea of going straight into a relationship when the War ended. Imprisonment and years of deprivation changed people into creatures of underlying self containment. Peacetime emotions were obscured by the brutalisation of the surroundings in a prison camp.

Perhaps those who hesitated were the more sensible men, mused Frank, but there again Maud had made such a strong impression upon him that he began to believe that he wanted her—and indeed he realised he would be a fortunate man if she accepted him.

A small voice within warned him to hold back from any commitment and to spend a few years after the War as a bachelor, getting back his life and having only himself to answer for, perhaps within the caring orbit of his mother Anna. There was still some money left from the inheritance his grandfather had left him.

He did not really have to hurry anything and maybe James his brother would come up with some scheme for a business if he survived the War. Frank knew he was not by nature impulsive emotionally but he overruled all the practical arguments and decided to take a gamble with his future.

He had always been a gambler with his money, which was a paradox to his cautious nature in relation to other matters. He wrote the letter to Maud on an impulse driven more by hope than in expectation, but felt that it came from deep within his heart. She seemed to express such care and devotion in her letters that he would be a fool to let her drop out of his life after the War.

He knew that being brought up in the genteel manner of her class she would probably be shocked and embarrassed when she read what he had to say and he would not have been surprised if he had never received a reply to it, or if she had just ignored its content.

He was not to know then that in fact the Irishwoman read the letter with great joy and excitement and regarded it as the most beautiful letter she had ever received. Her sisters Dorothy and Mabel disagreed strongly with what their older sibling was intending to do with her life, as did her older brother.

Dorothy told Maud she would be soft in the head to accept a proposal from a man she had never met, appeared to have few prospects, and wasn't even an officer. Sergeant Frank Clarke, she argued, might not—and probably wasn't—the man Maud had pictured in her mind. He might turn out to be feckless, selfish, without ambition and even lazy. Perhaps his intention was to spend her fortune and then leave her penniless.

Mable added that Maud could have no idea about what the effects of years of incarceration might have had upon the sergeant's mind. Maybe, when he said he was a Christian, he was just paying lip service to her because he knew that was what she wanted to hear. After nearly four years of incarceration he might have become slightly insane and certainly unbalanced—thus unable to rebuild his life in a normal manner.

Maud was unconvinced by the arguments of her sisters.

"Mabel, if I forsake this man now it would drive him back to the edge. He might even give up his struggle for life. No, the Lord has led me to this man and I will follow that guidance."

Her father, the Colonel, was also anxious that his oldest daughter was being unduly impulsive, but was such an indulgent man with his daughters that he did not interfere in the plans Maud was making. He had been deeply depressed by the War and the loss of so many fine young men in the family circle in Antrim, including the disgrace of his younger son AJ who had re-enlisted under a false name. The Colonel decided not to thwart the plans of the young couple.

Maud, who had always been gullible and impulsive, overruled her sisters and said she felt instinctively that she was doing the right thing. She was going to accept Frank's proposal and she wrote back a few days later to tell him so. A religious woman, but strictly non-denominational, she had prayed to God for guidance and felt strongly that he wanted her to marry this man.

Rotterdam

July 25th 1918

My dearest Maud,

I've done it! Just 28 weeks after arriving here I have overtaken the nine stones mark which I feel is an incredible gain of nearly 49lbs. I feel so well. Even the nagging pains from my wound which have plagued me for years have subsided. It may be the good weather and perhaps the aches in my shoulder will return to spoil my sleep.

Thank you my darling for the brown leather brogues and the twills which look as though you might have bought them from Knightsbridge. I hope they didn't cost you too much money my dear old girl. I shall try to keep them in topping condition here in Holland so that I can wear them on the day of my return to England.

The other men are extremely envious, especially when I wear my Harris Tweed sports jacket too. Please thank your father the Colonel for the camel coat and tell him I shall always treasure it. Anna has sent me a super trilby which absolutely completes the set. I tend to wear my best rig on either Friday or Saturday nights when we go out to eat in a city centre restaurant. To be honest it all looks a little baggy on me but I wear it with the greatest pride and in the knowledge that I shall soon fill out.

Rotterdam is a bustling city and this oasis of normality and pleasure is odd in the context of war torn Europe. It is hard to believe that the Western front is within a day's travelling. There are still many people enduring great misery and it is difficult for us not to feel guilt, even though we are wounded men and have earned our repatriation. We hear from the Dutch that the German offensive caused a scare in France and Belgium but I understand the enemy has now exhausted himself and a final counter-offensive is on the way—with the Americans to take the lead.

They have come so late into the war but thank God they are here. Our poor men are so exhausted and the Americans are so fresh. The Germans have had it—say the Dutch—even their men returning from the Russian front won't make any difference. We have read that in Germany there are threats of socialist revolution that could dethrone the Kaiser.

What all this means my dear Maud is that the War will be coming to an end and with the grace of God I will be able to return to England and start life afresh. Darling Maud I could not countenance my new life without you being at my side. You have brought me back to the world of living with your beautiful letters.

While I will always cherish the memory of my dear Emily I have come to terms with her death. Part of her will live on inside me and I know that you won't resent that—you have told me so. Emily is part of my past and I am now no longer a young man.

It is the future that matters to us and I want to settle down and start a family with the woman I regard so highly and believe I have come to love. I am being impulsive but I would ask you to consider this letter a formal proposal of marriage.

If you are gracious enough to accept me we can discuss the length of the engagement while we really get to know one another. I shall also be writing to the Colonel to seek his blessing and I shall inform Anna, ask her to talk to the Colonel and start making arrangements for a wedding sometime next year. I should like it to take place in the church at Felmingham where my father Henry Jocelyn is buried. However, if you would prefer the wedding to be in either Bournemouth or County Antrim in more familiar surroundings, I should not object.

I know there is a difference in social rank between us Maud, but I do come from a good family even though I am perhaps not quite the gentleman you would have wished

Your respectful loving friend and suitor,

Frank W Clarke

45
TOGETHER AT LAST

He stood on the quay by the troopship at Hull looking pale, thin and tired—a baggy figure in the jacket and trousers that Maud had sent to him. He was looking for a sight of Anna whose distinctive tall figure would be easily visible. Perhaps one of his cousins would be with his mother and also a slim fair-haired woman with curls that tumbled down her back. He knew her only by her photographs.

Maud had said she would be wearing a French blue dress and matching coat and a fur hat to stave off the bitter north winds that raced across the sea from Siberia. It was mid December 1918 and the First World War had been over for several weeks.

When the troopship came alongside the passenger quay he had been overpowered by the familiar smells of England—the sea-weed, the fish, the town gas and the horse manure. Of all the senses, he had always regarded that of smell as being the most vivid. Cars and trucks thronged the harbour in much greater numbers than he remembered and there were lines of taxis waiting for the disembarking men and their families.

Everyone seemed to be dashing about somewhere and at first all the activity confused him. He was not used to such freedom of movement. Where were they? He became anxious and his heart was beating fiercely for his first glimpse of Maud. Beads of perspiration ran down the back of his neck in nervous tension.

What would she be thinking when she saw him? Would she find him attractive—or the opposite? Would she be diffident and reserved? Would he know what to say to his fiancée—a woman he had never met? Would they live to regret this relationship which was founded entirely on correspondence?

He sensed she would be even more beautiful than her photographs conveyed and that he would be foolishly speechless when he first stood in front of her. He looked to the sky which was an icy blue. The winter sun shone in an empty azure due to a ridge of high pressure that set back the clouds. One large white cumulus moved slowly towards them from the far horizon.

Suddenly he thought he caught a glimpse of the smiling and beautiful face of Emily gazing down upon him from this cloud. Feeling guilty that he was there to meet not his beloved Emily but another woman, a tear formed in the corner of his eye and it began to drop slowly downwards across his cheekbone.

"You are there aren't you?" he heard himself asking aloud and his heart felt heavy as he remembered the woman he had loved so much.

He felt at that moment a new sensation and looked down to see that a small gloved hand had placed itself in his much larger one. It belonged to a young woman of such astonishing beauty that he could only gaze at her in awe. She was smiling at him in adoration and gazing directly into his eyes.

The power and radiance of her bright blue eyes was almost disturbing but it portrayed a sense of goodness and compassion directed at his inner being that was so earnest he began to lose control of his emotions. The tears flowed freely down his face now and his heart beat faster than it had for years. This big strong sergeant of the Norfolks, who had fought in a war, had led men into battle, suffered a terrible wound, endured imprisonment, torture, misery and terrible bereavement, began to sob like a young child. His mother Anna sobbed loudly too.

It was time to let go. He had bottled it all up for too long. He embraced his fiancée tightly and remembered her compassionate words forever.

"Don't cry my darling. I am here now. I am here for you always."

Back

They ask me where I've been
And what I've done and seen.
But what can I reply
Who know it wasn't I,
But someone just like me,
Who went across the sea
And with my head and hands
Killed men in foreign lands . . .
Though I must bear the blame
Because he bore my name.

Wilfred Gibson

Sergeant Frank Clarke and Maud Lepper Alison were married on 24th January 1919 (six weeks later) at Felmingham St Andrews Church, North Norfolk and lived happily ever after. They had three children, Phyllis, Arthur and George.

THE LAST DIARY ENTRY—JUNE 1953

Amori finem tempus non animus facit

The wind jostles the leaves in the majestic Elm trees bordering the country road ahead of me. I glance up at the darkening sky, the clouds sailing above me and everywhere across the horizon. The corn and wheat in the fields are still low, but move like waves in the growing wind. I quicken the pace; the purposeful stride of an old man used to walking briskly. The golden Labrador at my side responds. People say I carry myself like a soldier—chest out and shoulders high, which is hardly surprising.

I look like what I am—a solitary man of nearly 70 years, wearing a dark green trilby, tweed jacket and cavalry twills with brown brogues. All these garments have seen better days but together represent the impression that I might almost be a gentleman—which I find amusing.

Few would mistake me as anything but an ex-serviceman. Perhaps, though, my fastidious appearance is not strengthened by the battered leather travelling case and creased raincoat I carry in my right hand. In my left hand I hold a paper bag and a cloth rod holder tied up in a bow at one end.

I have never been a wealthy man. I have few material possessions and don't care about those things. One's true wealth in life lies in one's health and the breadth of one's mind, especially in being receptive to new ideas—Epictetus taught me that in Enchiridion. I still have the book.

The two mile walk is of no consequence to me, even though a storm threatens. I listen to the birdsong, breathe in the country air and my thoughts are occupied by the morning's events in which I have experienced the thrill familiar to any angler who has just caught a specimen fish.

It is a chance encounter with Mad Jack in the tap room at the Crab Mill Inn in South Warwickshire—run by my daughter Phyllis and her husband Jerry and where I work as a barman—that leads to the morning's fishing. Mad Jack is sober now, but his bloated face, high colour and crimson eyes, leave no doubt in the mind of anyone who meets him that he is a drunk. Apparently he is quite a wealthy farmer and owns a string of racehorses.

Other customers stand in groups talking, but Mad Jack is part of no circle, sitting upon a stool alone at the far end of the bar. I find myself unavoidably engaged in conversation by the drunk when I serve him.

He confirms he is a farmer at Blackford Mill in Henley-in-Arden.

I hope Jack might proffer a tip on one of his horses running at Warwick tomorrow, but the conversation turns to my military background. Jack points to the badge on the lapel of my jacket.

'The Old Contemptibles Association—so I'm talking to an old soldier then?'

'Yes,' I reply.

'I fought at Mons in 1914, 1st Battalion Norfolk Regiment, and was captured. I spent over three years in a Prisoner of War Camp in Germany.'

Jack eyes me more closely. 'It doesn't seem to have done you much harm. You're a big, strong, guy—and you look fit.'

'I keep myself in shape. Do a lot of walking,' I say and bend down to pat Bruce on his back. 'We enjoy a walk don't we Bruce,' I say quietly. Bruce licks me affectionately.

'So you're a fisherman then?' Mad Jack continues, pointing to the salmon fly embedded in the black ribbon around my trilby which is hanging from a peg behind the bar.

'Come and fish my stream any time you like. It's a tributary of the Alne. There's a weir and a few other holes. Years ago, before the war, they used to catch trout, but only a few people have fished it since the 1930s. Come and try your luck.'

I thank him and walk away to serve another customer. Mad Jack looks like a troublemaker and there is much gossip about his violent manner when he is in drink. I decide I will talk horses with the drunk some other time.

The following week I stroll unhurriedly along a public footpath across a meadow near where the Barons de Montfort had once built a mediaeval castle on a mount. I carry my travelling case, paper bag and fishing rod.

The overcast sky obscuring the sun and the mild summer breeze from the West is unlikely to shift the clouds. I feel a keen sense of anticipation like any angler about to explore new water.

The River Alne is one of Warwickshire's most prolific rivers for game and coarse fish. The field above the Mill is in a state of neglect, mostly horse pasture. A hare scampers away as I walk across the field. Gorse bushes and heather choke the river bank.

As I pick my way through the wild foliage, my footfall disturbs a colony of linnets, which are spooked by my approach. They fly low over the meadow in demented arcs. I walk half-a-mile upstream, near to the public footpath that takes me towards the Mill.

I take care to keep at least 20 feet from the banks of the meandering stream. The distinctive aroma of wild garlic permeates the warm air. Cowslips and delicate orchids populate the banks of the stream where they have not been choked by the heather. It reminds me of the countryside of my boyhood years in the late 19th century around Felmingham in North Norfolk.

There are spinners (flies) in the air that have come to lay their eggs and then die. Occasionally the surface of the stream is disturbed by the swirl of a larger fish following a nymph as it arises from the bed of the river to begin its short life.

The trout suck in the larvae at the instant before it reaches the surface and roll over exposing the side of their body. Then I hear the plop of a small brook trout snatching at a spinner—her wings spread-eagled lifelessly upon the surface of the water as she is carried downstream on the gentle current. Today I will not fly-fish for small trout.

I do not have game fishing equipment although I still love more than anything to explore a small Norfolk river populated by wild brown trout with a fly rod; something taught me by my grandfather in the previous century.

Today I seek a specimen fish—a cannibal, a monster of the small river that lives somewhere in a deep hole under concealment, breaking cover only to dart across the river in pursuit of fry.

I sense there will be a few fish of specimen size on this tributary of the Alne. I am intent on luring a specimen fish out of its hiding place. I pull out a packet of Players, light a cigarette with a silver liquid fuel lighter—given to me as a retirement present from colleagues at the Barracks in Norwich—and smoke it while I survey the river. I have come to catch just the one big fish and the most likely place is in the weir at the side of the mill.

I have not been here before but know that others talk of it as a place to catch a specimen. It is worth a try. Weirs have always been like a magnet to me whether in Ireland or Norfolk because of their sense of mystery.

There is something mystical about the power of water unleashed in a weir and I know from long experience that here I will find the kings of the river. The Alne is now diverted from the disused mill and it curves round to the right of the farmhouse to a man-made concrete slope. Its flow descends into a wide pool towards the right bank of the river where the tree roots stand fast against erosion of the bank.

The current veers away double-backing into the central flow where it later collides with the left bank bordered by more trees. Here the current double-backs again, flowing in reverse slowly, before rejoining the main current of the river.

It is an angler's paradise—so many flows and food channels for the fish to explore. I wash my hands to remove the reek of tobacco and walk back to the shelter of a tree above the left bank, spending a further five minutes observing the patterns of the swim.

I decide to plumb the depth of the river where the current plunges into the roots of the trees on the right bank. I thread on a lead plummet and the depth shows itself to be over five feet. I decide to use ledger tackle, to fish with a big worm and risk the distraction of an eel. Then the unexpected happens in the way it so often does for anglers when they are fishing on a small river.

A small shoal of minnows dashes across the river in the shallow water at the far end of the swim. Some break the surface on the right bank. Any pike angler knows that this kind of activity is a sure indication that a feeding predator is about. In June pike are still spawning, listless and weakened by the reproduction process. They are reluctant to expend energy in search of food.

It has to be a cannibal trout, or possibly a large chub. There is no time to change tackle and I cast the worm at a depth of five feet into the swim. The quill float swirls up and down the pool three or four times.

I give and collect line from the star-back as the float dances past me and then continues on its way again bobbing across the pool. I know that to draw the worm and tackle out of the water and repeatedly cast it back into the water will disturb the swim and diminish my chances of luring a large fish. So I leave the float and the bait in the water patiently.

On its third journey through the swim the float's progress is arrested and twitches. The worm is not on the bottom of the riverbed, so it will not be an eel, but more likely a small fish like a gudgeon or a dace. I flick the rod and feel the twitch in response.

The dace has gorged itself on the worm and will not survive the extrication of the hook. So I pull the hook from the mouth of the little creature and fasten it through the head.

I cast the small fish out into the main flow of the river and watch the float continue on its journey around the swim. The quill is by now at least 30 feet away and approaching the right bank.

I pull it back so it will catch the reverse current and watch the float sail past the root of a tree. Suddenly it veers across the surface and plunges out of sight.

I wait five seconds and then strike. Line comes cascading off the reel as the fish feels the incision of the hook. Instead of diving into the roots it dashes towards me and I have to hold the rod high and gather line with my hand to stay in touch with it.

The fish then changes direction; I feel the tension as its run is checked and it leaps a foot out of the water, revealing itself for the first time to me. It is a magnificent trout, perhaps 20 inches long with a deep belly. This old fish will fight until it is exhausted.

It leaps from the water twice more and tears around the weir pool in a frantic bid to free itself. My line is strong enough to take the tension but the fish is making its final run for freedom. I check the run of the trout when it is less than two feet from the far bank and the tree roots.

The struggle is now nearing its conclusion and I begin to reel in the trout, holding the rod high and bringing the nose of the trout to the surface where it glides across the mill pool under my control.

The fish is now directly beneath me and I descend to water level at the foot of the bank. I drop to my knees and stoop down so that I can dip my right hand into the water. Then I guide the exhausted fish to my hand and gently thrust my middle finger between the gills.

Carefully, I lift the specimen out of the water and bring it in my hand up the bank. It flaps in protest but its fight is spent. The lower jaw of the trout extends beyond the upper, and its teeth are sharp.

I estimate the trout to be about two and a half lbs. It has a large head, black and red spots down its back, silver flanks and a cream coloured belly. The fish is in good condition—without a blemish on its body and no sign of disease. I feel pity that I am going to end its long life. It is good for the table and at home there is someone who will want to see this magnificent creature.

I put the fish in the battered leather travelling case and I walk at a leisurely pace down the front drive of the farm.

It has been what fishing is all about and now I am looking forward to a well earned pint. Three quarters of an hour later I approach the end of the walk to Preston Bagot and descend the long hill to the Crab Mill looking across to the little church on the hill where Maud has been laid to rest only a few months before.

The old Inn is a landmark pub in South Warwickshire and the outside walls are still bedecked with Coronation bunting. I walk into the kitchen where a small boy of about seven—my grandson—is waiting with wide eyes.

'Have a look at this boy,' I say, opening the battered case. It is the lad's first glimpse of a trout.

'Wow," he exclaims. 'Will you take me fishing?'

The following day, when the small boy comes home from school, he finds two small roach, still alive, in a saucepan of cold water in the kitchen sink. I promise him as we put the two fish alive into the small stream next to the pub: 'We'll go to the canal on Saturday, and you will catch your first fish—like these.'

A few days later I deliver on my promise to take the boy fishing. He sits down on a wicker tackle box beside me in anticipation and we wait patiently as the minutes tick past. As we watch the float together, I remember the times with my own grandfather George Printer. Then I see the reflection of my two beautiful women gazing at me from just below the surface of the mirror smooth water.

I smile and mumble 'Hello.'

I am too old for passion now but their appearance quickens my pulse.

I have loved them both so much and I recall the deep bonds of love and romantic affection we shared nearly half a century before; in another lifetime it seems, when I was an athletic young man with most of life before me.

One is a strong-boned woman with long auburn hair; the other more delicately-built and fair with large blue eyes in an open innocent face. They both smile at me and I am still spellbound by their beauty.

The auburn haired girl says: "Hello Frank. It's been so many years has it not—but to me you will always be a young man. Maud and I are close now on the other side and we will always protect you and your family. Don't worry, we understand that you love both of us dearly and soon you will be with us—but not yet, perhaps another 15 years.'

'Good God—as long as that?' I ask.

The boy must think I am talking to myself, just as old men do. So for several minutes, while I smoke, I indulge in a conversation with these young women. At length I bid them farewell. I confide in them I sometimes feel weary of life.

Their image fades and my mind moves to other times in my life. I must tell the boy more of my stories—he seems to enjoy them, even though they are often repeated.

He looks at me patiently as I mutter one of my familiar phrases in Latin—Amori finem tempus, non animus facit. He will not have learned Latin yet and won't understand what it means.

One day perhaps he will experience a brief glimpse of paradise like I did—but hopefully never become a prisoner incarcerated in a cell like I was. This will be my last diary entry.

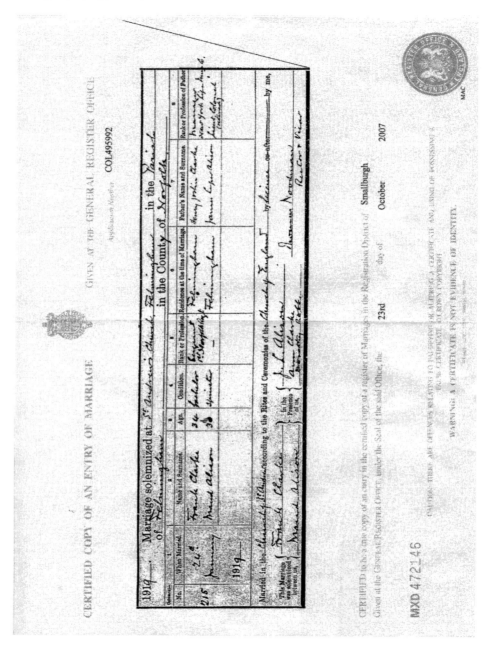

The marriage certificate recording the wedding of Frank W Clarke and Maud Lepper-Alison is all that remains of the day at Felmingham St Andrews Church. Photographic records were lost in a house flood on the Norfolk Broads in the 1930s.

Felmingham St Andrews Church
Picture by Elvin Derrick

Frank's boyhood home in Stavadore Road, Islington, North London
Picture by Victoria Parnall-Vaughan

Frank W Clarke in his 6th birthday sailor suit

The Lepper Alison mansion in Bournemouth

Maud Lepper-Alison who married Frank W Clarke in January 1919

Frank W Clarke with his daughter Dorothy Phylis Clarke on her wedding day in Norwich in September 1940.

Phylis Clarke

George Clarke,
younger son of Frank W Clarke

Arthur Clarke, older son of Frank W Clarke

Frank Clarke follows the hunt with a friend in 1953

When Frank W Clarke worked for his son-in-law and daughter Jerry and Phylis Le Vack as a barman at the Crab Mill Inn at Preston Bagot, Warwickshire, and later the Red Lion at Claverdon, in the early 1950s he made many friends. He was frequently invited to go shooting and fishing even though he was in his early 70s.

Frank W Clarke outside the tap room of the Crab Mill, Preston Bagot, Warwickshire (1953) where he worked as a barman for his son-in-law.

The author Dale le Vack as a child with his grandfather Frank W Clarke